Revit Architecture 2011 Basics: from the Ground Up

Elise Moss

ISBN: 978-1-58503-570-0

SDC
PUBLICATIONS

Schroff Development Corporation

www.SDCpublications.com

Schroff Development Corporation
P.O. Box 1334
Mission, KS 66222
(913) 262-2664
www.SDCpublications.com

Publisher: Stephen Schroff

Trademarks

The following are registered trademarks of Autodesk, Inc.: AutoCAD, AutoCAD Architectural Desktop, Revit, Autodesk, AutoCAD Design Center, Autodesk Device Interface, VizRender, and HEIDI
Microsoft, Windows, Word, and Excel are either registered trademarks or trademarks of Microsoft Corporation.
All other trademarks are trademarks of their respective holders.

Moss, Elise
    Revit Architecture 2011 Basics: From the Ground Up
    Elise Moss
ISBN: 978-1-58503-570-0

Examination Copies:
Books received as examination copies are for review purposes only and may not be made available for student use. Resale of examination copies is prohibited.

Electronic Files:
Any electronic files associated with this book are licensed to the original user only. These files may not be transferred to any other party.

The authors and publisher of this book have used their best efforts in preparing this book. These efforts include the development, research, and testing of material presented. The author and publisher shall not be held liable in any event for incidental or consequential damages with, or arising out of, the furnishing, performance, or use of the material herein.

Printed and bound in the United States of America.

Preface

Revit is a parametric 3D modeling software, used primarily for architectural work. Traditionally, architects have been very happy working in 2D, first on paper, and then in 2D CAD, usually in AutoCAD.

The advantages of working in 3D are not initially apparent to most architectural users. The benefits come when you start creating your documentation and you realize that your views are automatically defined for you with your 3D model. Your schedules and views automatically update when you change features. You can explore your conceptual designs faster and in more depth.

As more architects see and grasp the advantages of creating their building models in 3D, Revit will gain more loyal users.

Revit will not make you a better architect. However, it will allow you to communicate your ideas and designs faster, easier, and more beautifully.

The book is geared towards users who have no experience in 3D modeling and very little or no experience with AutoCAD. Some experience with a computer and using the Internet is assumed.

I have endeavored to make this text as easy to understand and as error-free as possible…however, errors may be present. Please feel free to email me if you have any problems with any of the exercises or questions about Revit in general.

Acknowledgements

A special thanks to Rick Rundell, Christie Landry, and Steve Burri, two Autodesk employees who are tasked with supporting and promoting Revit. Steve Burri suffered particularly from my pointed technical support questions. Additional thanks to Carl Bass for his support and encouragement.

Additional thanks to Scott Davis, James Balding, Rob Starz, and all the other Revit users out there who provided me with valuable insights into the way they use Revit.

Thanks to Stephen Schroff and Mary Schmidt, who work tirelessly to bring these manuscripts to you, the user, and provide the important moral support authors need.

My eternal gratitude to my life partner, Ari, my biggest cheerleader throughout our years together.

Elise Moss
Elise_moss@mossdesigns.com

TABLE OF CONTENTS

Lesson 1
The Revit Interface

Revit can be started from your Start menu or the desktop icon.

Go to Start→Programs→Autodesk →Revit Architecture 2011→Revit Architecture 2011.

When you first start Revit, you will see this screen.

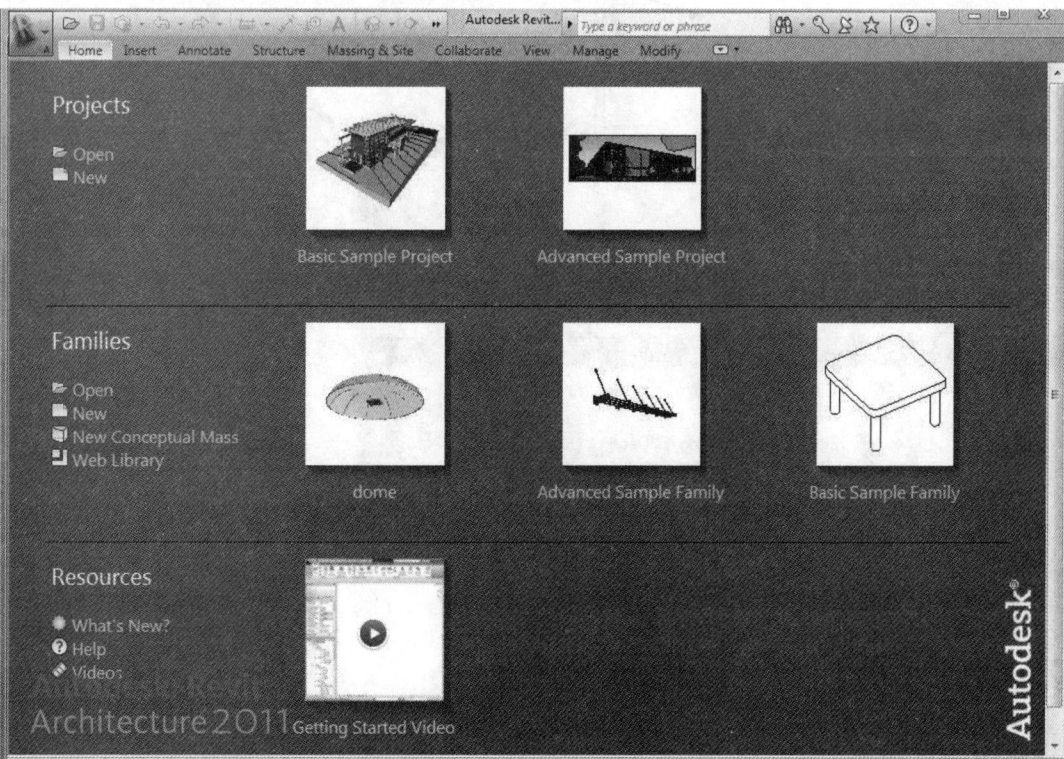

It is divided into three sections. The top section is to Open or Start a new project. Revit calls the 3D building model a project. Some students find this confusing.

The second section is used to open, create, or manage Revit families. Revit buildings are created using Revit families. Doors, windows, walls, floors, etc., are all families.

The third section, Resources, contains help, tutorials, and videos to help new users learn how to work in Revit.

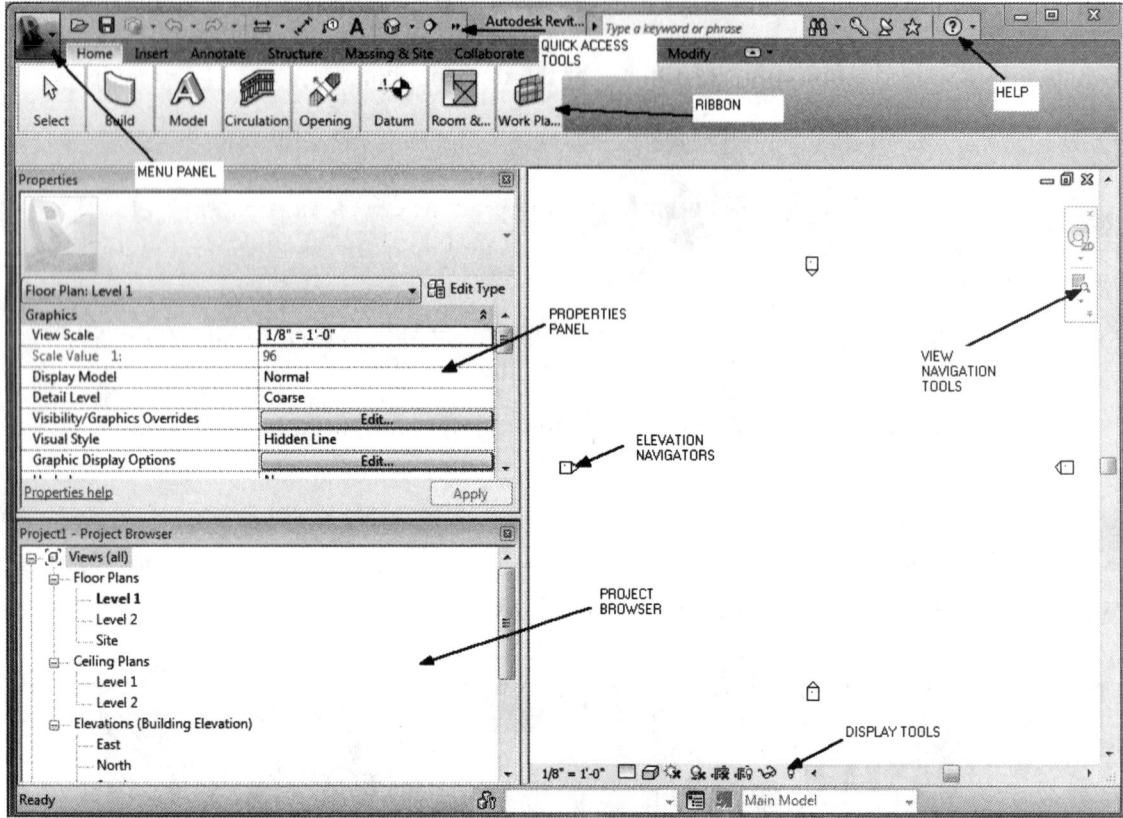

The Revit Ribbon

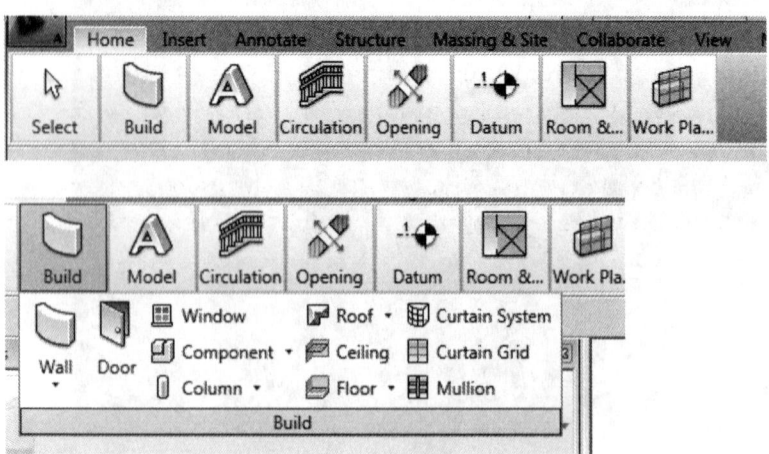

The Revit ribbon contains a list of panels containing tools. Each button, when pressed, reveals a set of related commands.

The Quick Tools Toolbar

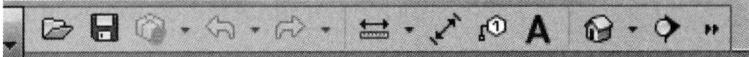

Most Windows users are familiar with the standard tools: New, Open, Save, Undo, and Redo.

	Save to Central is used in team environments where users check in and check out worksets on a shared project. The Central location should be a shared drive or server that all team members can access. The **Save to Central** tool is greyed out unless you have set up your project as a shared project with a central location.
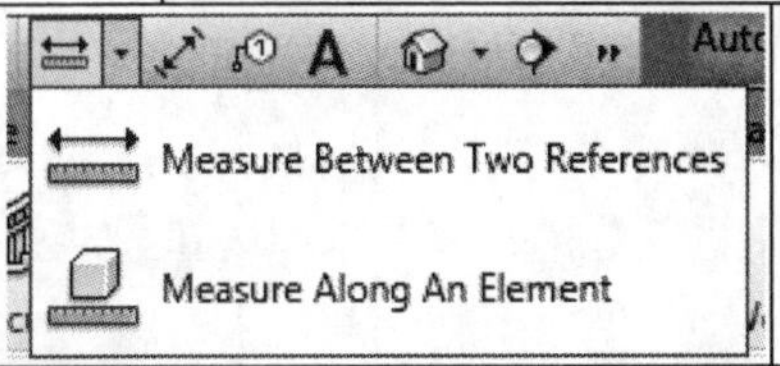	Measure is used to measure distances.
	Places a permanent linear dimension.
	Tag by Category adds a label or symbol on doors, windows, equipment, etc.
	Adds text to the current view.
 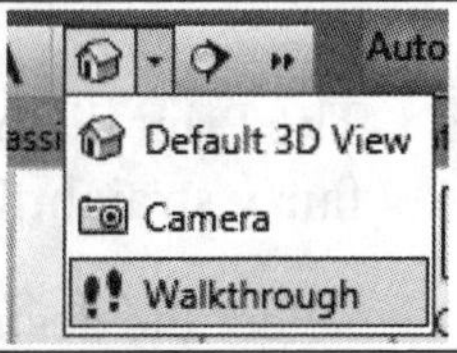	Allows the user to switch to a default 3D isometric view, place a camera or create a walkthrough.
	Create a section view.
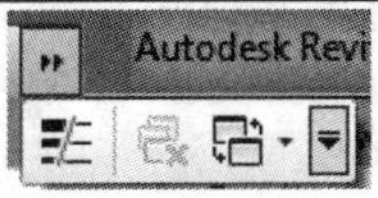	Additional tools are available on the flyout section. The first tool allows users to set lineweight. The second tool closes non-active windows. The third tool allows the user to select/switch to a different window. The down arrow allows users to customize which tools appear on the Quick Access toolbar.

Printing

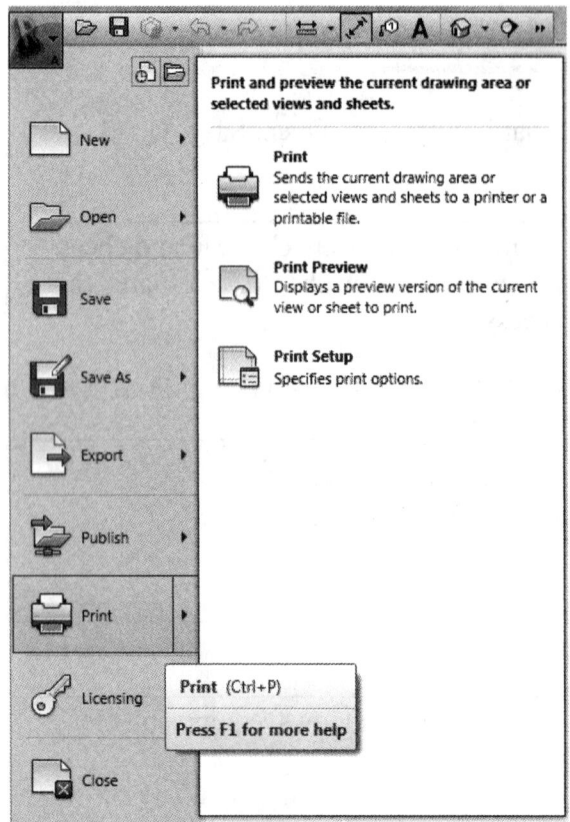

Print is located in the Application Menu.

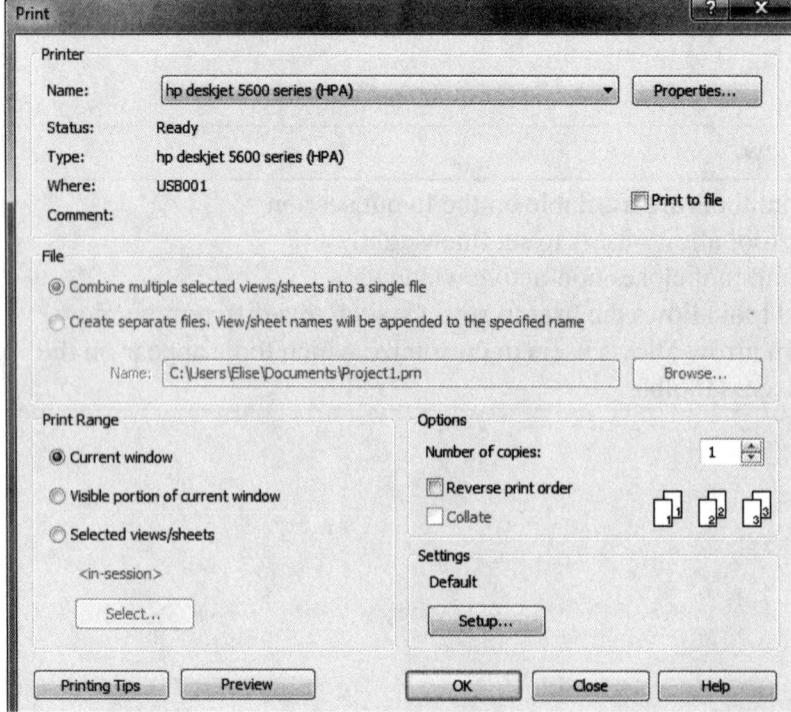

The Print dialog is fairly straightforward.

Select the desired printer from the drop-down list, which shows installed printers.

You can set to 'Print to File' by enabling the check box next to Print to File.

The Print Range area of the dialog allows you to print the current window, a zoomed in portion of the window, and selected views/ sheets.

Undo

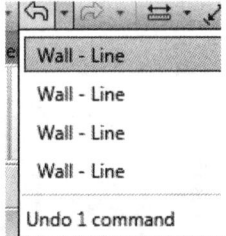 The Undo tool allows the user to select multiple actions to undo. To do this, use the drop down arrow next to the Undo button, you can select which recent action you want to undo. You cannot skip over actions (for example, you can't undo 'Note' without undoing the two walls on top of it.)

Ctl-Z also acts as UNDO.

Redo

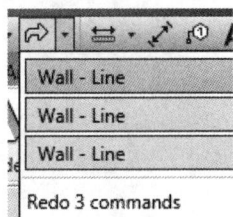 The Redo button also gives you a list of actions, which have recently been undone. Redo is only available immediately after an UNDO. For example, if you perform UNDO, then WALL, REDO will not be active.

Ctl-Y is the shortcut for REDO.

Viewing Tools

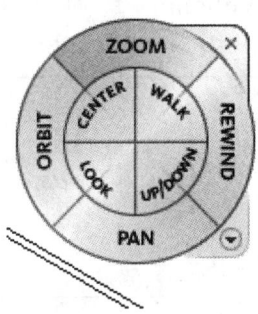 A scroll wheel mouse can replace the use of the steering wheel. Press down on the scroll wheel to pan. Rotate the scroll wheel to zoom in and out.

The Rewind button on the steering wheel takes the user back to the previous view.

Different steering wheels are available depending on whether or not you are working in a Plan or 3D view.

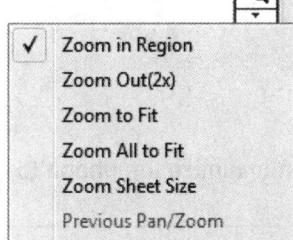 The second tool has a flyout menu that allows the user to zoom to a selected window/region or zoom to fit (extents).

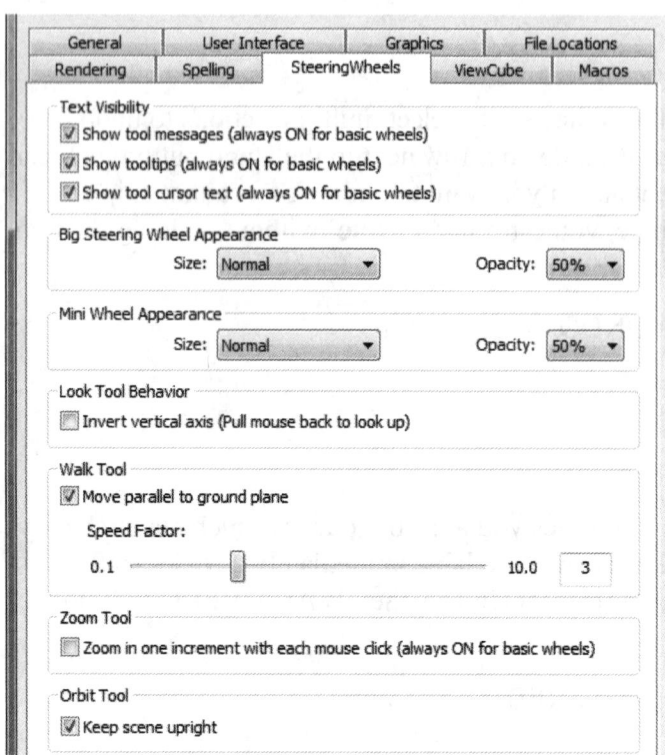

You can control the appearance of the steering wheels by right clicking on the steering wheel and selecting Options.

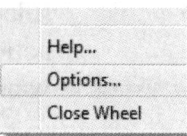

 TIP: Orient to a view allows one to render an elevation straight on without perspective. Orient to a plane allows user to create sweeps along non-orthogonal paths.

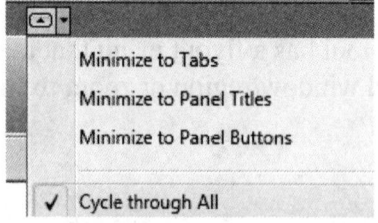

> If you right click on the Revit Ribbon, you can minimize the ribbon to gain a larger display window.

Exercise 1-1:
Using the Steering Wheel & ViewCube

Drawing Name: *i_Cohouse.rvt*
Estimated Time: 15 minutes

This exercise reinforces the following skills:

- ❑ ViewCube
- ❑ 2D Steering Wheel
- ❑ 3D Steering Wheel

1.   Go to **File→Open**.

2.   File name: i_Cohouse.rvt   Locate the file called *i_Cohouse.rvt*.

     This is located on the CD included with the text.

3.   In the upper right corner is a tool called the ViewCube.

4.      Click on the top of the cube as shown.

5.   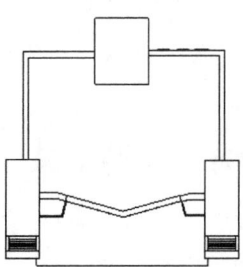   The display changes to a plan view.

6.

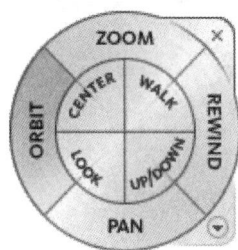

Select the Steering Wheel tool located on the View toolbar.

7. A steering wheel pops up.

Notice that as you mouse over sections of the steering wheel they highlight.

Mouse over the Zoom section and hold down the left mouse button. The display should zoom in and out.

Mouse over the Orbit section and hold down the left mouse button. The display should orbit.

Mouse over the Pan section and hold down the left mouse button. The display should pan.

8.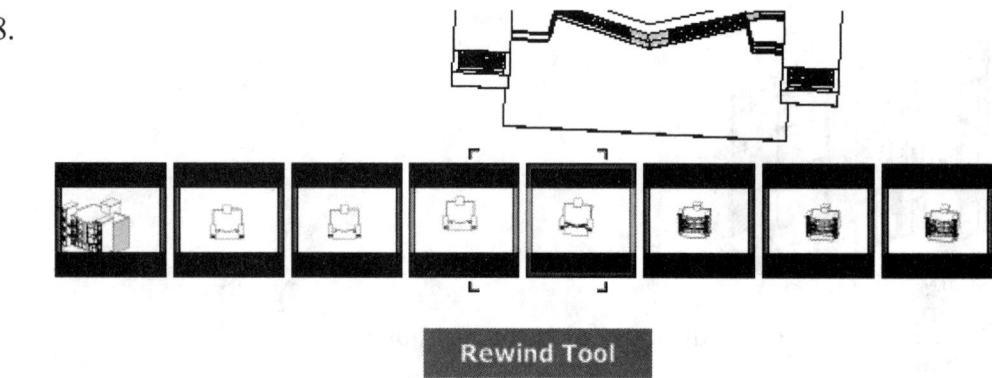

Select the Rewind tool.
A selection of previous views is displayed.
You no longer have to back through previous views. You can skip to the previous view you want.
Select a previous view to activate.

9.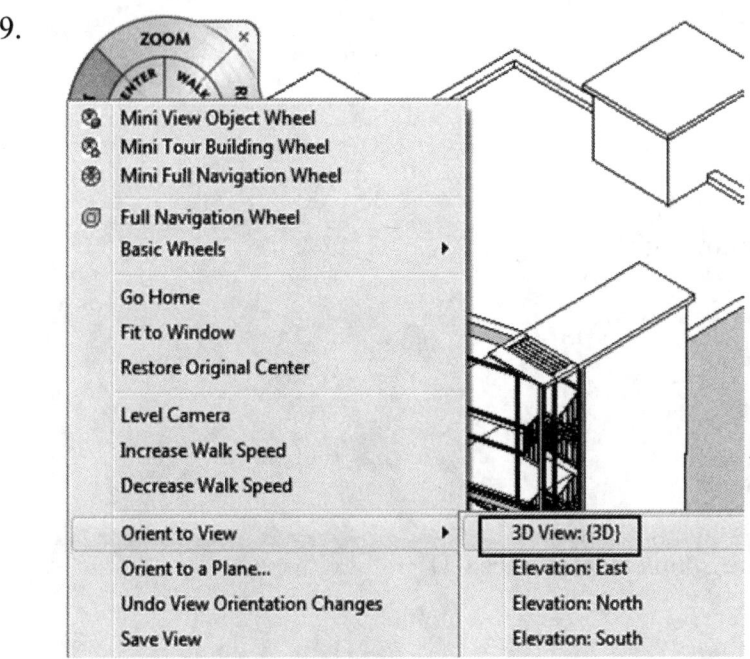

Place the mouse cursor over the steering wheel.

Right click and a shortcut menu appears.

Select **Orient to View→ 3D View {3D}**.

10. Close the file without saving.

The Modify Ribbon

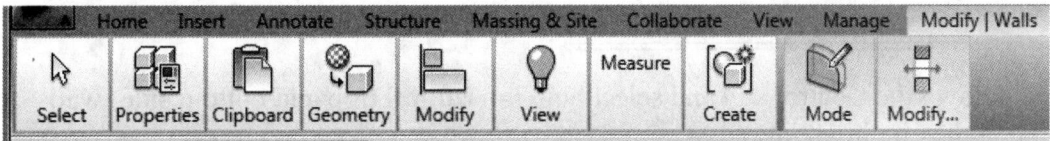

When you select an entity, you automatically switch to Modify mode. A Modify ribbon will appear with different options

Exercise 1-2
Using Scale

Drawing Name: ex1-2.rvt
Estimated Time: 15 minutes

This exercise reinforces the following skills:

- ❑ Scale
- ❑ Graphical Scale
- ❑ Numerical Scale

1.   Browse to *ex1-2.rvt* on the Supplemental Files CD.
Save the file to a folder.
Open the file.

The file has four walls.

The horizontal walls are 80′ in length.

The vertical walls are 52′ in length.

We want to change the vertical walls so that they are 60′ in length.

2.   Hold down the Control key and select both **horizontal** (top and bottom side) walls so that they highlight in red.

NOTE: *We select the horizontal walls to change the vertical wall length and we select the vertical walls to change the horizontal wall length.*

3.   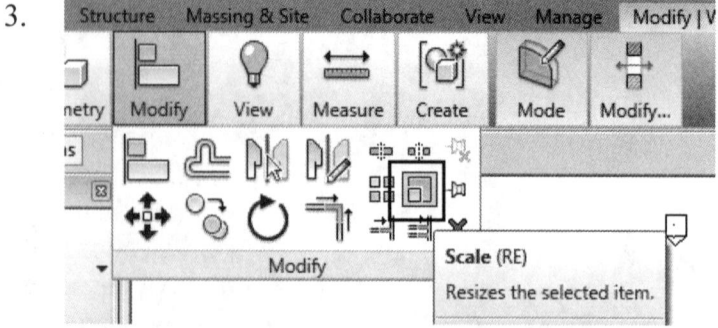   Select the **Scale** tool located on the Modify Walls ribbon.

4.

| Modify \| Walls | ● Graphical ○ Numerical | Scale: 2 |

In the Options bar, you may select Graphical or Numerical methods for resizing the selected objects.

5. Enable **Graphical**.

    The Graphical option requires three inputs.

    > Input 1: Origin or Base Point
    > Input 2: Original or Reference Length
    > Input 3: Desired Length

6. 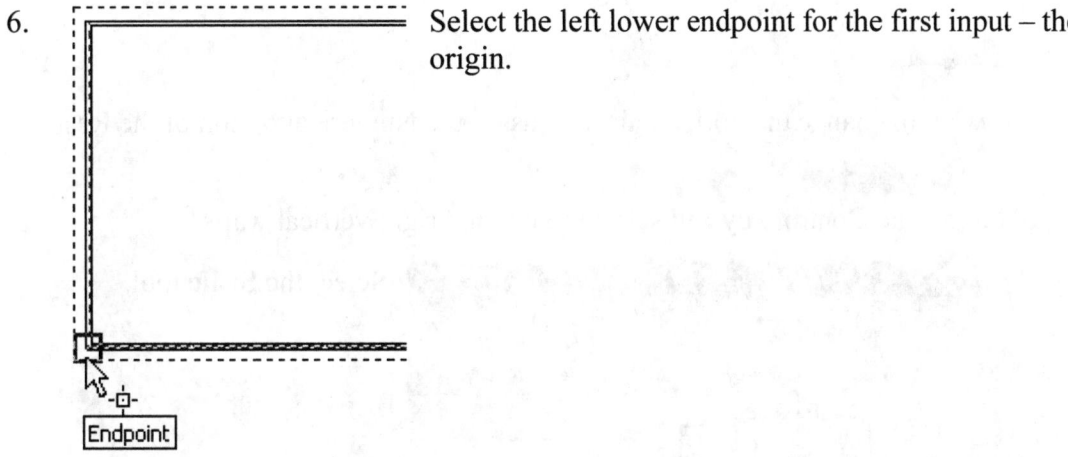 Select the left lower endpoint for the first input – the origin.

7. Select the left upper endpoint for the second input – the reference length.

8. Extend your cursor until you see a dimension of 60′.

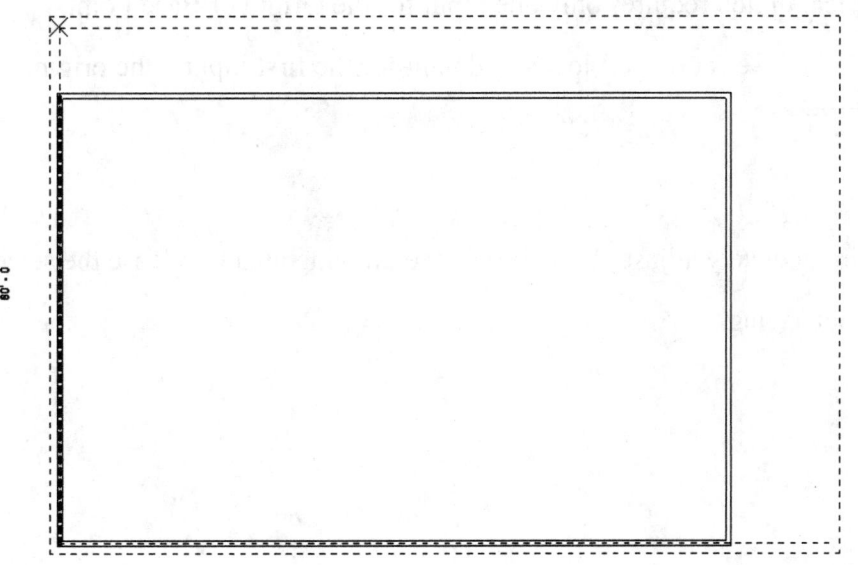

Then pick for the third input – the desired length.

Left click anywhere in the window to release the selection and exit the scale command.

9. Select either the top or bottom horizontal walls to verify that the new length is indeed 60'.

60' - 0"

10. Now, we will change the horizontal walls using the Numerical option of the Resize tool.

    Hold down the Control key and select the left and right vertical walls.

11. 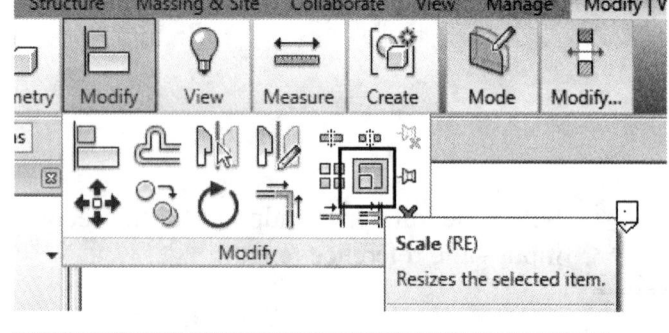 Select the **Scale** tool.

12. Enable **Numerical**.
    Set the Scale to **0.5**.

    This will change the wall length from **80'** to **40'**.

    The Numerical option requires only one input for the Origin or Base Point.

13. Select the left lower endpoint for the first input – the origin.

    Endpoint

14. The walls immediately adjust. Left click in the drawing area to release the selection.

15. Close without saving.

Model Group ▾

The Group tool works in a similar way as the AutoCAD GROUP. Basically, you are creating a selection set of similar or dissimilar objects, which can then be selected as a single unit. Once selected, you can move, copy, rotate, mirror, or delete them. Once you create a Group, you can add or remove members of that group. Existing groups are listed in your browser panel and can be dragged and dropped into views as required. Typical details, office layouts, bathroom layouts, etc. can be grouped, and then saved out of the project for use on other projects.

TIP: If you hold down the Control key as you drag a selected object or group, Revit will automatically create a copy of the selected object or group.

Exercise 1-3
Working with Groups

Drawing Name: ex1-3.rvt
Estimated Time: 20 minutes

This exercise reinforces the following skills:

- ❑ Groups
- ❑ Rename Group
- ❑ Select Group
- ❑ Copy Group
- ❑ Add to Group
- ❑ Remove from Group

1. Browse to *ex1-3.rvt* on the Supplemental Files CD.
   Save the file to a folder.
   Open the file.

2. 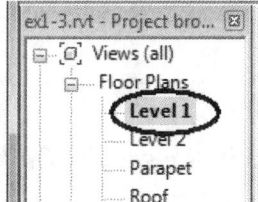 Activate the **Level 1** view in the browser.

3.

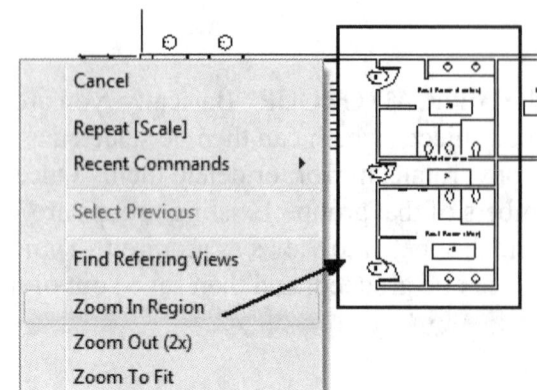

Zoom in to the area with restrooms as indicated by the rectangle.

Right click in the display window. Select **Zoom in Region**.

4.

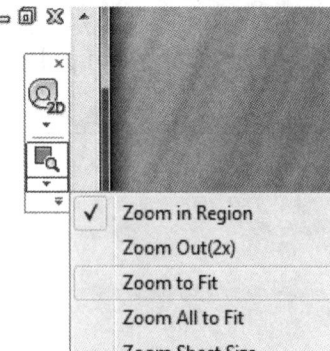

An alternative method to zoom in:

Use the Navigation toolbar located on the right of the display window.

Select Zoom In Region.

5.

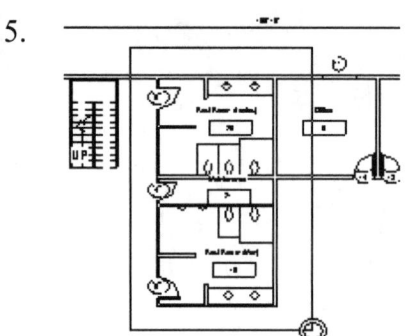

Pick a point to the left and above the restroom area.

Drag a window down towards the right to zoom into both restroom areas.

6.

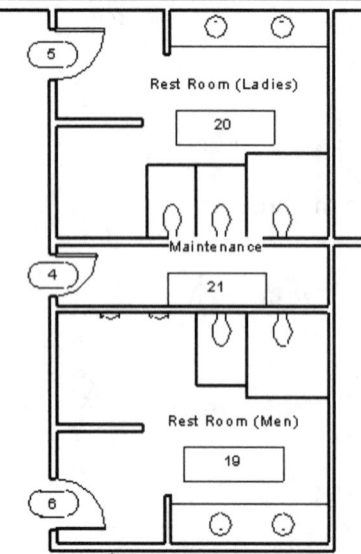

Hold down the Control key and select the two sinks and their casements and the toilets with dividers in both restrooms.

You can select by picking or windowing.

Selected objects will highlight in purple.

Do not include the urinals in the group. Do not select any of the walls.

Use the CONTROL key to add to the selection set and the SHIFT key to remove items from the selection set.

Alternative method:

Window around everything to select.

Use the Filter control to deselect the walls and to ensure only the lavatory items are selected.

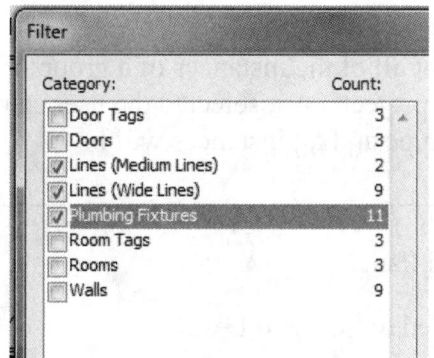

Check the lines and the Plumbing Fixtures. Press OK.

Then use the SHIFT key to deselect the urinals.

7. Select the **CREATE GROUP** tool.

8. A dialog will appear prompting for a Group Name.

    In the Name field, enter **Lavatory Layout**.

    Press **OK**.

9. In the browser, notice **Groups** are listed at the bottom of the tree.

10. Expand the Groups category until you see the group you just created listed.

11.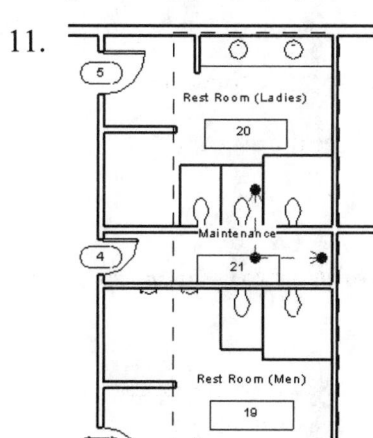

    Pick one of the sinks.

    The entire group should highlight to indicate the sink is part of a group.

12. 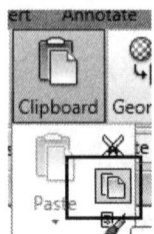 Select **Copy to Clipboard** from the ribbon.

We see the group automatically highlights in red in the graphics window.

TIP: 'Select All Instances' allows you to highlight all of the instances of a group or family(door type, window type, etc.) in the whole project, once selected the user can change the selected object or group to a different type and all instances will be updated.

---

13. 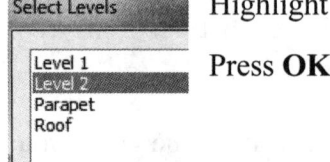 Under the Clipboard Panel:

Select Paste→Aligned to Selected Levels.

This allows you to copy the group to multiple levels.

14. 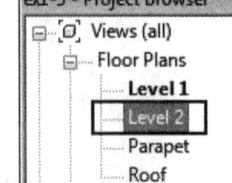 Highlight **Level 2**.

Press **OK**.

15. Activate **Level 2** in the Project Browser.

16. Your layout is pasted to the second level.

But we forgot to add the urinals to the group.

Activate **Level 1**.

17. Pick one of the group members to activate the group.

18. 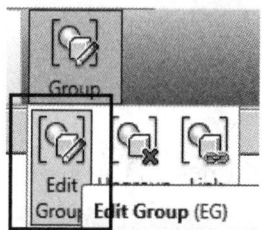 Select **Group→Edit Group** from the Ribbon.

19. 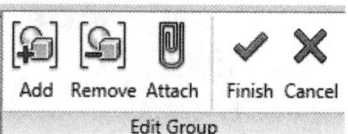 Look for an **Edit Group** toolbar. It should launch somewhere on the top of your screen.

20. 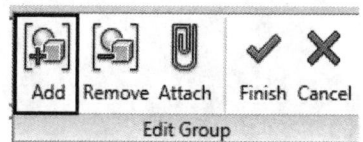 Select the **Add** tool.
Select the two urinals to add to the group.

21.  Select the **Finish** tool.

22. Switch to **Level 2**.

23. 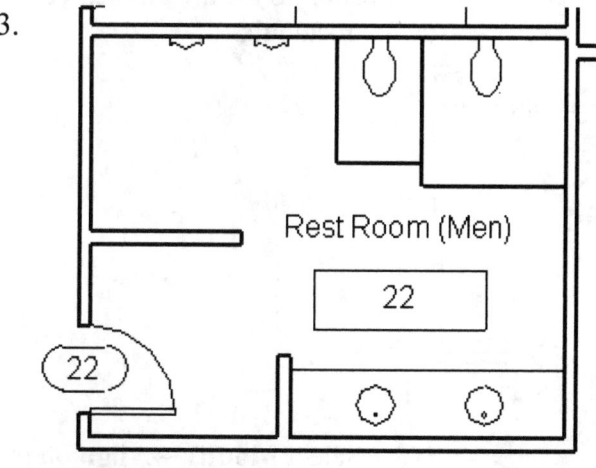 We see the urinals are included automatically in the copied group.

24. 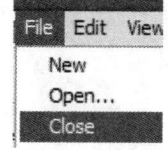 Save the file as *ex1-3a.rvt*.
Go to **File→Close** to close the file.

TIP: When using the ALIGN tool, the first element selected is the source, the element to be aligned to and the second element selected will shift or move to align to the first element.

Exercise 1-4
Using Align & Move

Drawing Name: i_Office_2.rvt
                    (This file can be found on the Supplemental Files CD.)
Estimated Time: 5 minutes

This exercise reinforces the following skills:

    ❑   Align
    ❑   Move

1.   Select the **Open** tool.

2.   File name: i_Office_2.rvt   Locate the *i_Office_2.rvt* file.

                                  Select **Open**.

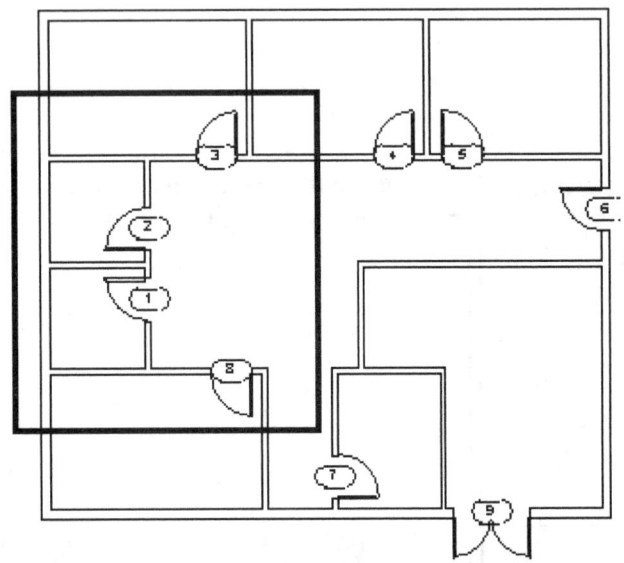

Right click in the graphics window and select **Zoom In Region**.

Zoom into the area indicated by the rectangle.

3.   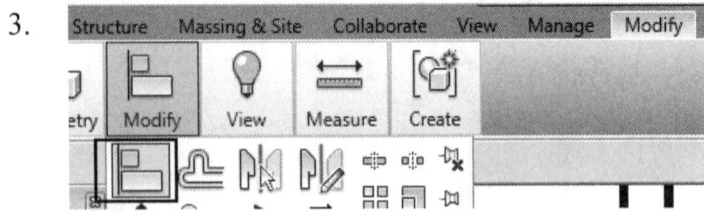   Select **Modify→Align** on the Modify Ribbon.

4.   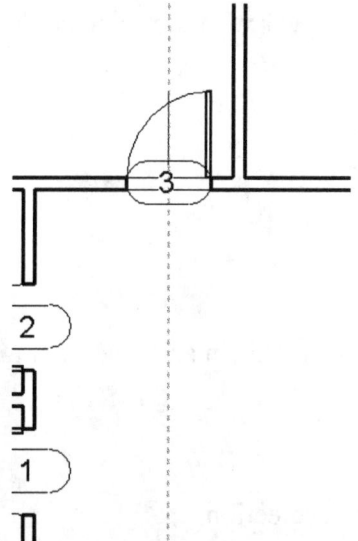 Select **Door 3**.

A dashed vertical line should appear.

Select **Door 8**.

5.   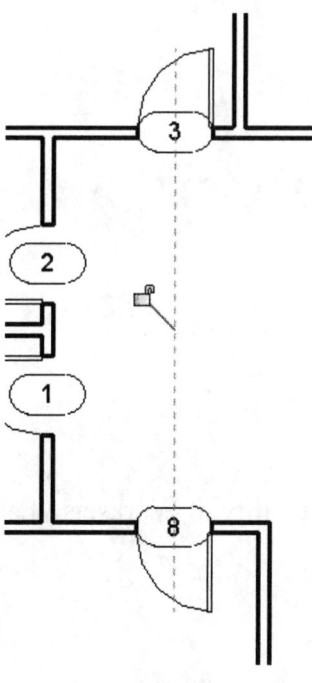 Door 8 jumps into position to be aligned with Door 3.

A lock icon appears next to Door 3.

The lock is used to fix Door 8 so it always will be aligned with Door 3.

6.    Left click on the lock to fix Door 3 into place, then select Door 8. The lock disappears.

Right click and select **Cancel** to exit the command.

7.   Pick Door 3 so it highlights.

8. 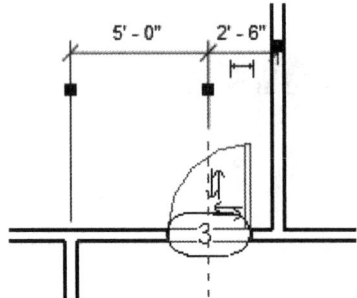 Temporary dimensions appear with the selected door.

9. 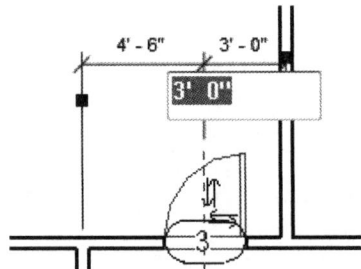 Left click on the 2'-6" dimension and change it to **3'-0"**.

Press **ENTER**.

Left click to release the selection.

10. Notice the Door 8 stays aligned with Door 3.

11. Close the file without saving.

The Collaborate Ribbon

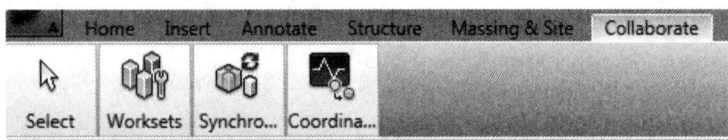

Collaborate is used if more than one user is working on the same project.

Use the Workset button to add, delete, rename and adjust editability of Worksets. Each user is assigned responsibility over a Workset.

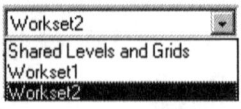 Then use the drop-down to switch between Worksets.

Revit's Menu

When you want to start a new project/building, you go to File→ New→Project or use the hot key by pressing Control and 'N' at the same time.

title block or annotation symbol.

New ▶

Project
Creates a Revit project file.

When you start a new project, you use a default template (default.rte). This template creates two Levels (default floor heights) and sets the View Window to the Floor Plan view of Level 1.

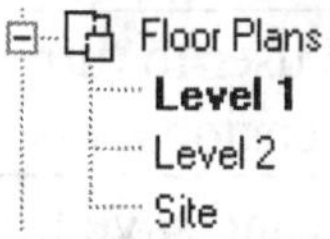

Floor Plans
Level 1
Level 2
Site

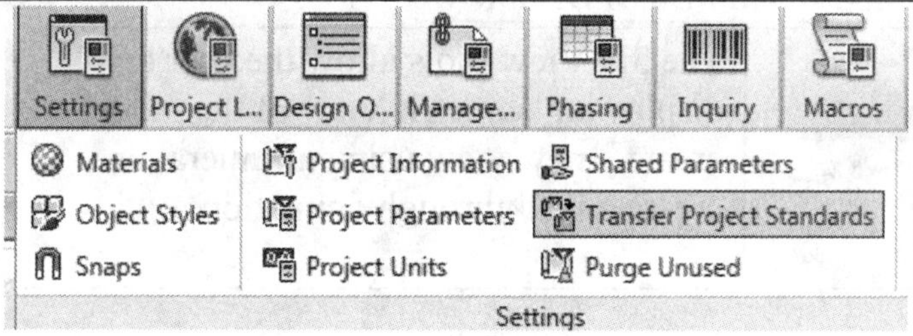

You can transfer the Project settings of an old project to a new one by opening both projects in one session of Revit, then with your new project active, select **Manage→ Settings→Transfer Project Standards**.
Check the items you wish to transfer, then click 'OK'.

TIPS:
- If you plan to export to .dwg or import existing .dwg details, it is important to set your import/export setting. This allows you to control the layers that Revit will export to and the appearance of imported .dwg files.
- Pressing the ESC Key twice will always take you to the Modify command.
- As you get more proficient with Revit, you may want to create your own templates based on your favorite settings. A custom template based on your office standards (including line styles, rendering materials, common details, door, window and room schedules, commonly used wall types, door types and window types and typical sheets) will increase project production.

The View Ribbon

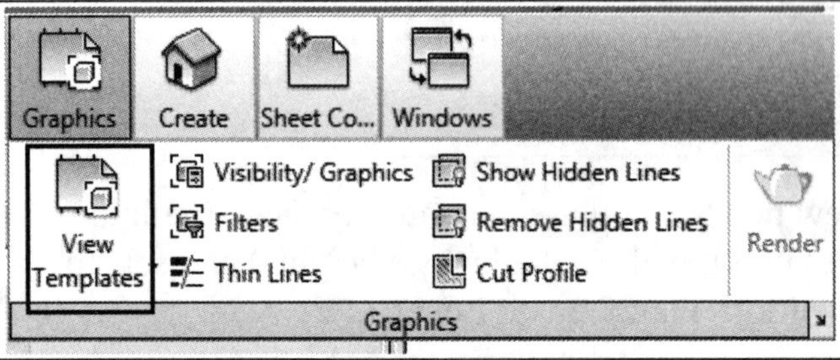 	View templates allow the user to save view settings and apply them to different views.
 Visibility/Graphics	Allow the user to turn off visibility of elements, such as elevation links, dimensions, floors, walls, etc.
 Filters	Users can create and save filters used to create selection sets.
 Thin Lines	Displays all lines in the view in a single line width. 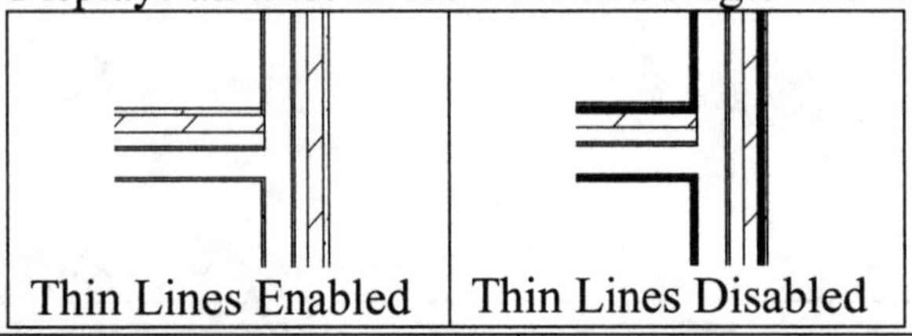 Thin Lines Enabled Thin Lines Disabled
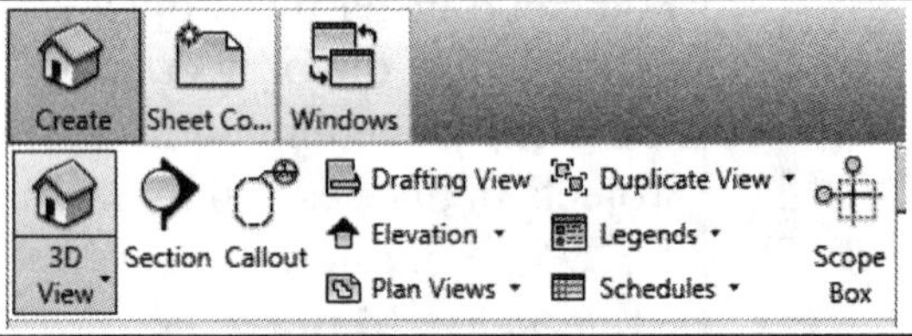	The 3D View tools allow the user to display an isometric view of the model, create a new view using a camera, or create a walkthrough animation.
 Section	Creates a section view.
 Callout	Creates a detail view callout, useful for framing and foundation views.
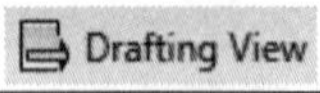 Drafting View	Creates a drafting view, useful in creating elevation details.
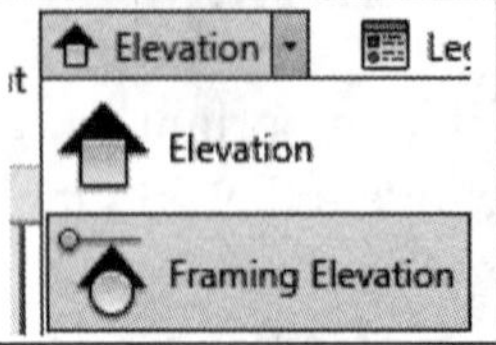 Elevation / Framing Elevation	Creates an elevation or framing elevation view.

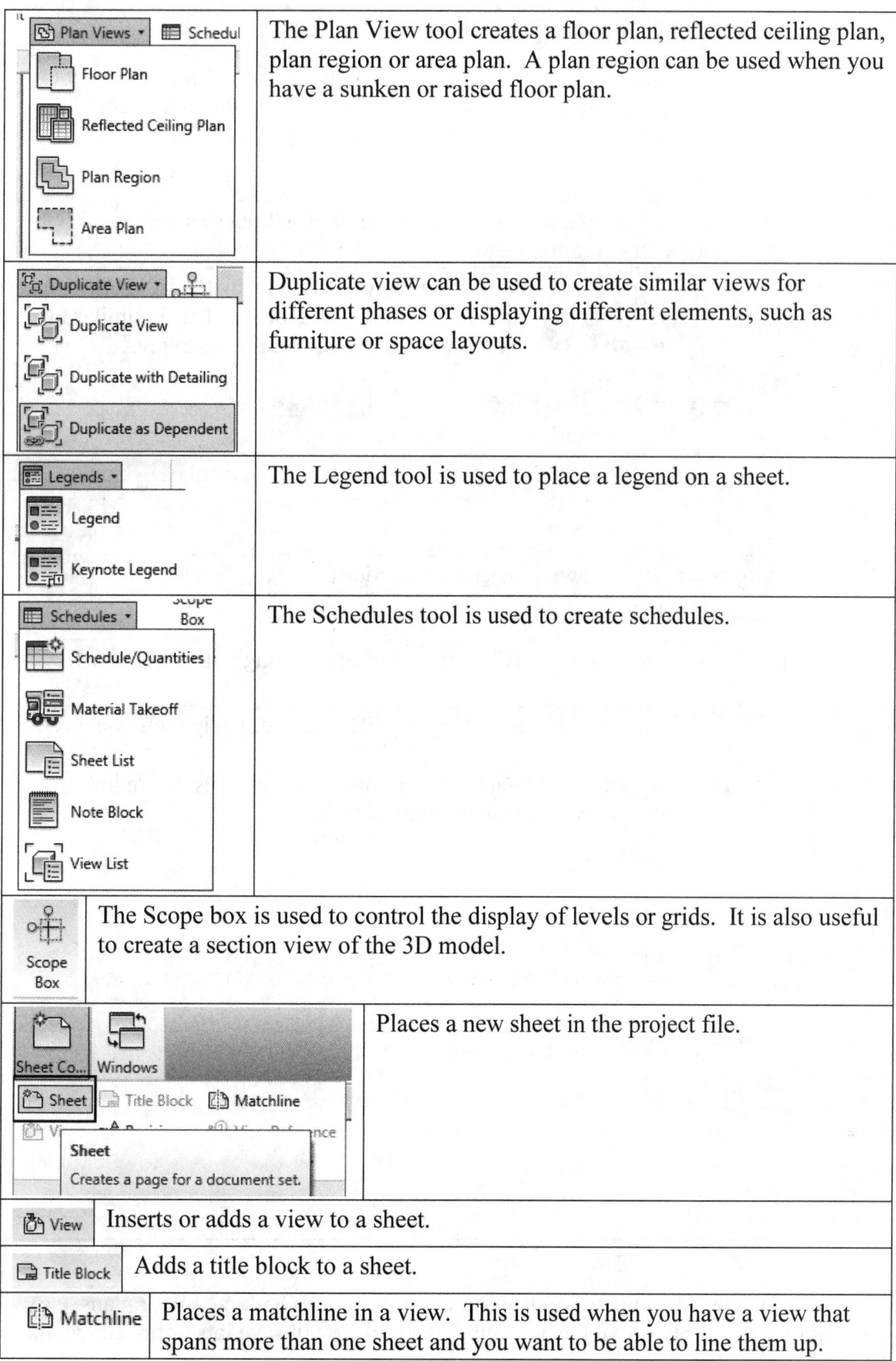

Plan Views / Schedul Floor Plan Reflected Ceiling Plan Plan Region Area Plan	The Plan View tool creates a floor plan, reflected ceiling plan, plan region or area plan. A plan region can be used when you have a sunken or raised floor plan.
Duplicate View Duplicate View Duplicate with Detailing Duplicate as Dependent	Duplicate view can be used to create similar views for different phases or displaying different elements, such as furniture or space layouts.
Legends Legend Keynote Legend	The Legend tool is used to place a legend on a sheet.
Schedules Schedule/Quantities Material Takeoff Sheet List Note Block View List	The Schedules tool is used to create schedules.
Scope Box	The Scope box is used to control the display of levels or grids. It is also useful to create a section view of the 3D model.
Sheet Co... Windows Sheet Title Block Matchline Sheet Creates a page for a document set.	Places a new sheet in the project file.
View	Inserts or adds a view to a sheet.
Title Block	Adds a title block to a sheet.
Matchline	Places a matchline in a view. This is used when you have a view that spans more than one sheet and you want to be able to line them up.

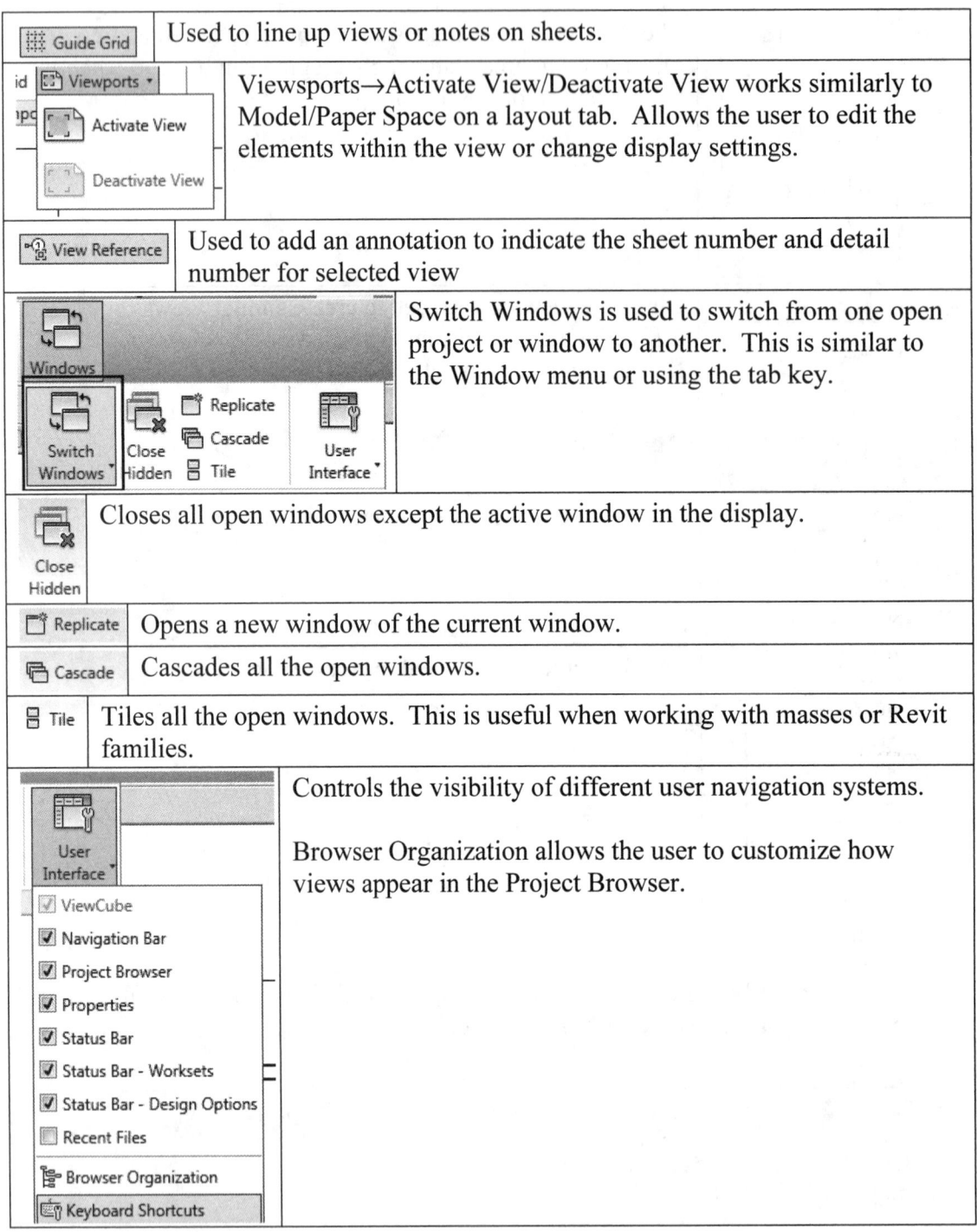

Guide Grid	Used to line up views or notes on sheets.
id Viewports · / Activate View / Deactivate View	Viewsports→Activate View/Deactivate View works similarly to Model/Paper Space on a layout tab. Allows the user to edit the elements within the view or change display settings.
View Reference	Used to add an annotation to indicate the sheet number and detail number for selected view
Windows / Switch Windows / Close Hidden / Replicate / Cascade / Tile / User Interface	Switch Windows is used to switch from one open project or window to another. This is similar to the Window menu or using the tab key.
Close Hidden	Closes all open windows except the active window in the display.
Replicate	Opens a new window of the current window.
Cascade	Cascades all the open windows.
Tile	Tiles all the open windows. This is useful when working with masses or Revit families.
User Interface / ViewCube / Navigation Bar / Project Browser / Properties / Status Bar / Status Bar - Worksets / Status Bar - Design Options / Recent Files / Browser Organization / Keyboard Shortcuts	Controls the visibility of different user navigation systems. Browser Organization allows the user to customize how views appear in the Project Browser.

TIP: Creating standard view templates (exterior elevations, enlarged floor plans, etc) in your project template or at the beginning of a project will save lots of time down the road.

The Manage Ribbon

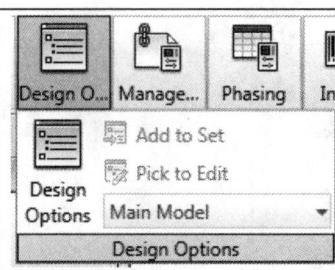	Design Options are used to design different options for a building model. This allows the user to create different versions of the same building to present to a client.
	Elements may be added to different option sets and then displayed.
	This is similar to a Configuration Manager.
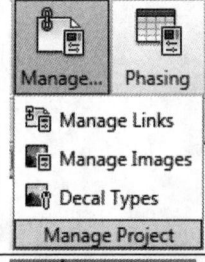	This is similar to the External Reference Manager in AutoCAD. This is used when you have inserted external cad files, such as topo files to be used in the model
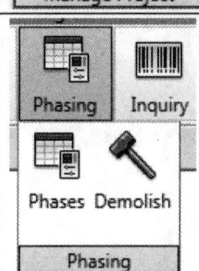	Phases are used to manage the different phases of a building project.

The Settings menu allows the user to customize the interface.

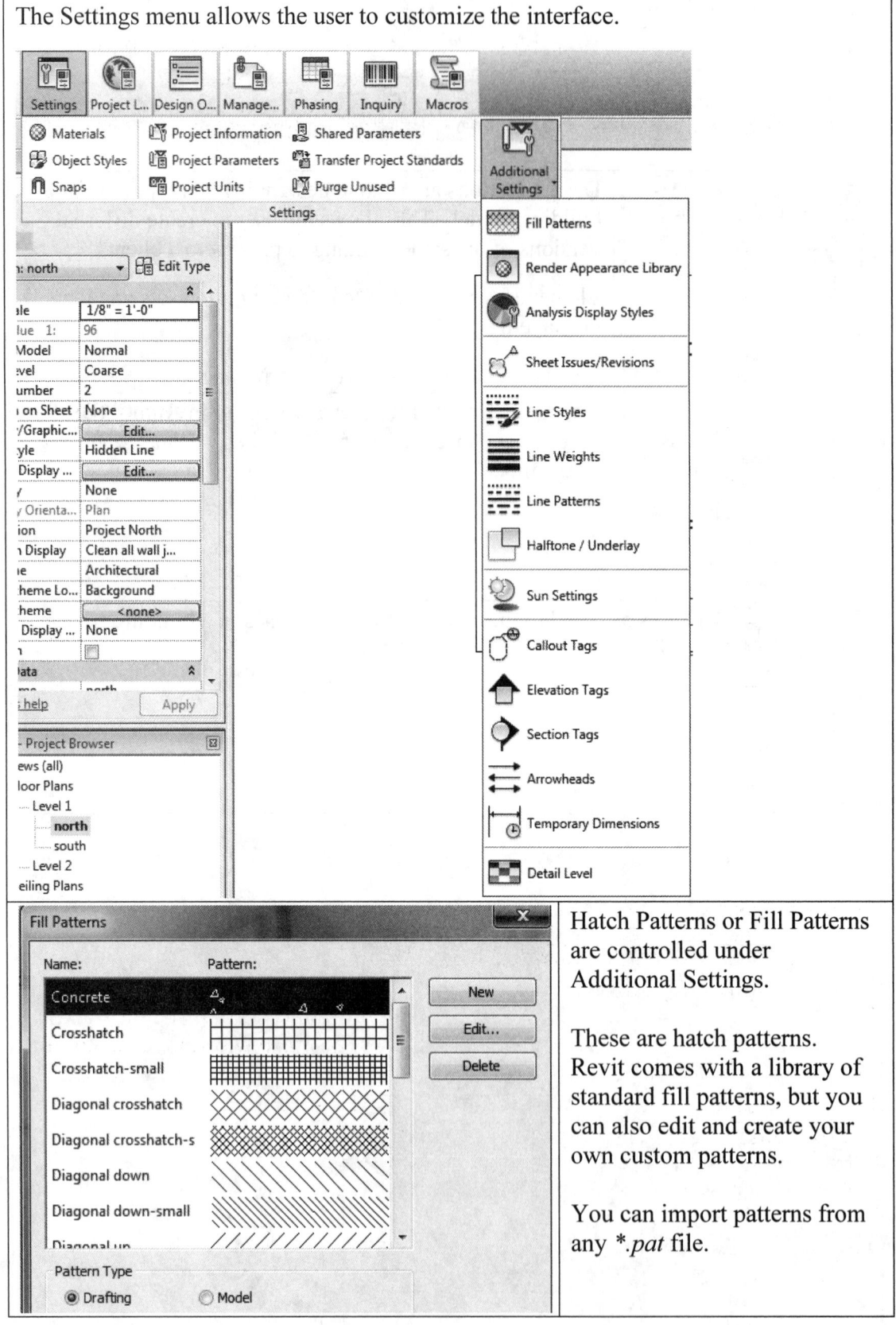

Hatch Patterns or Fill Patterns are controlled under Additional Settings.

These are hatch patterns. Revit comes with a library of standard fill patterns, but you can also edit and create your own custom patterns.

You can import patterns from any *.pat file.

 Materials

Revit comes with a library of materials, which can be applied to walls, windows, doors, etc. You can also edit and create your own custom materials.

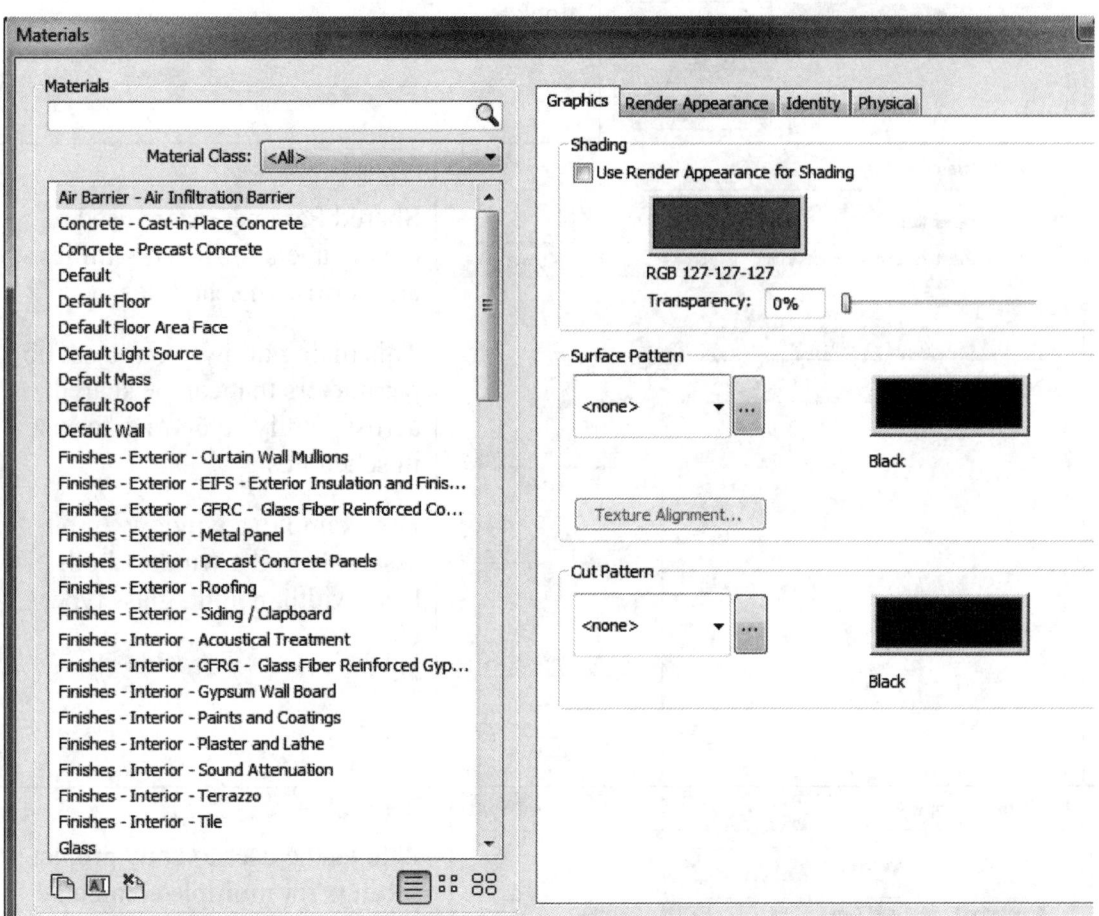

Any image file can be used to create a material.

My favorite sources for materials are fabric and paint websites.

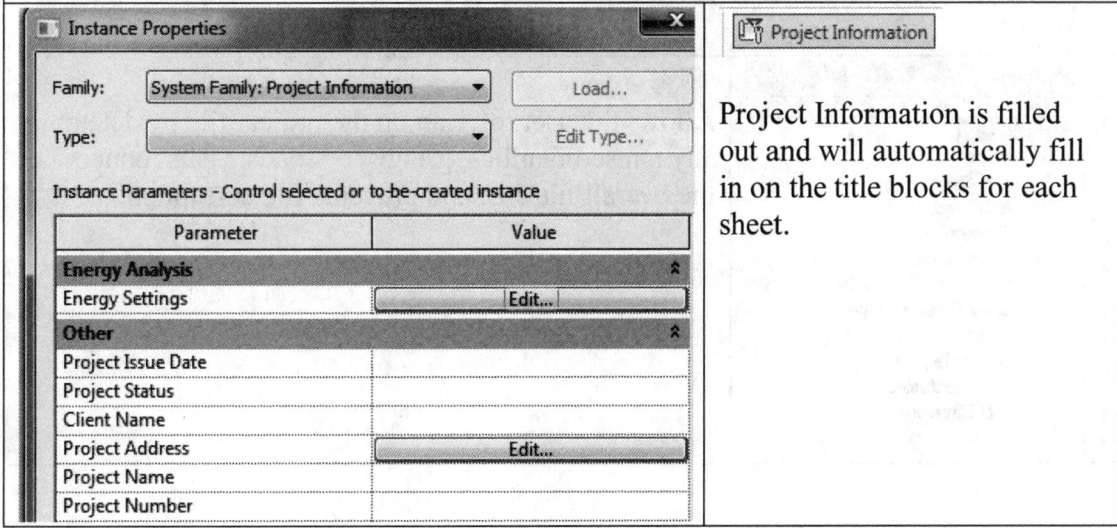

Project Information is filled out and will automatically fill in on the title blocks for each sheet.

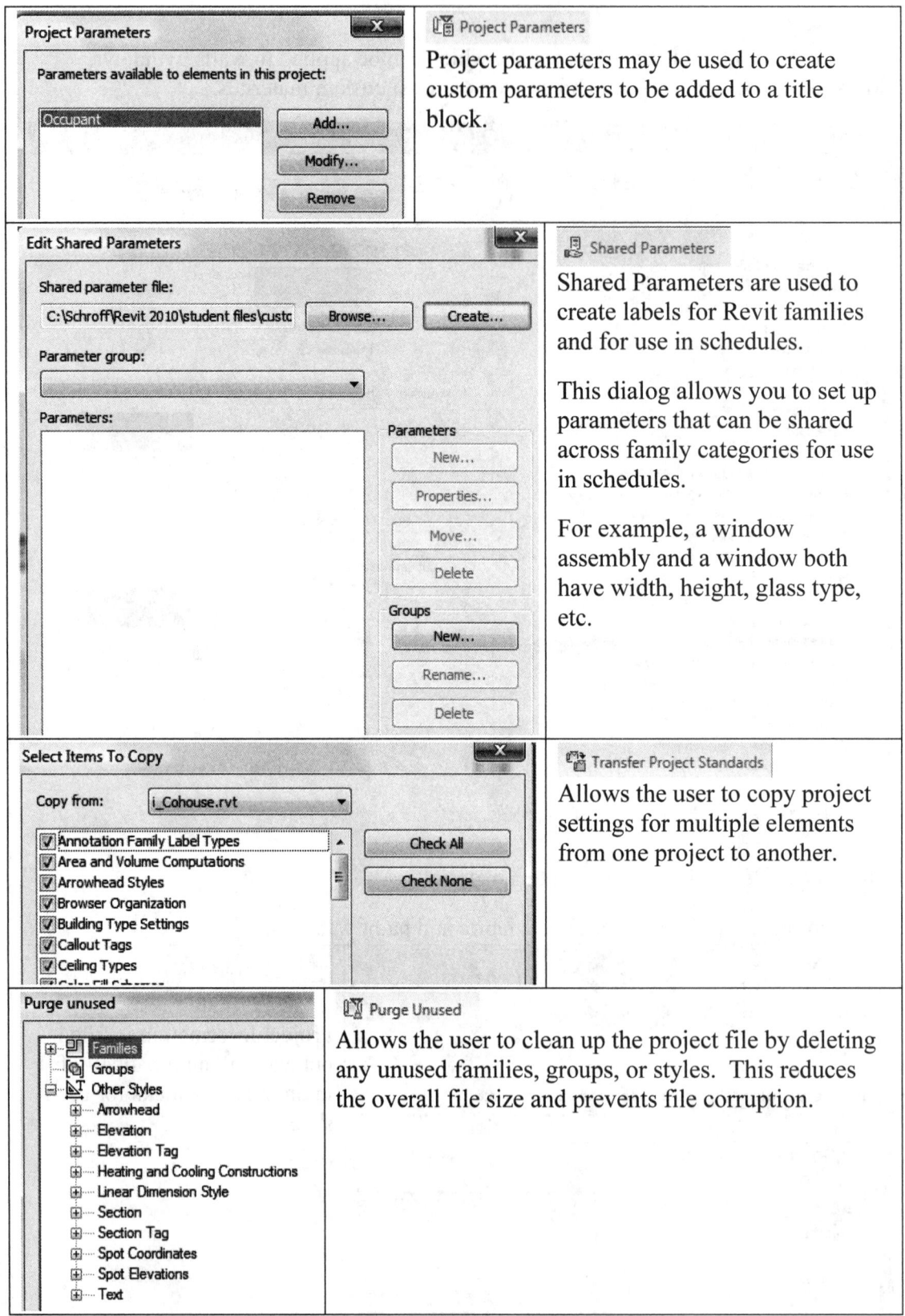

Project Parameters

Project parameters may be used to create custom parameters to be added to a title block.

Shared Parameters

Shared Parameters are used to create labels for Revit families and for use in schedules.

This dialog allows you to set up parameters that can be shared across family categories for use in schedules.

For example, a window assembly and a window both have width, height, glass type, etc.

Transfer Project Standards

Allows the user to copy project settings for multiple elements from one project to another.

Purge Unused

Allows the user to clean up the project file by deleting any unused families, groups, or styles. This reduces the overall file size and prevents file corruption.

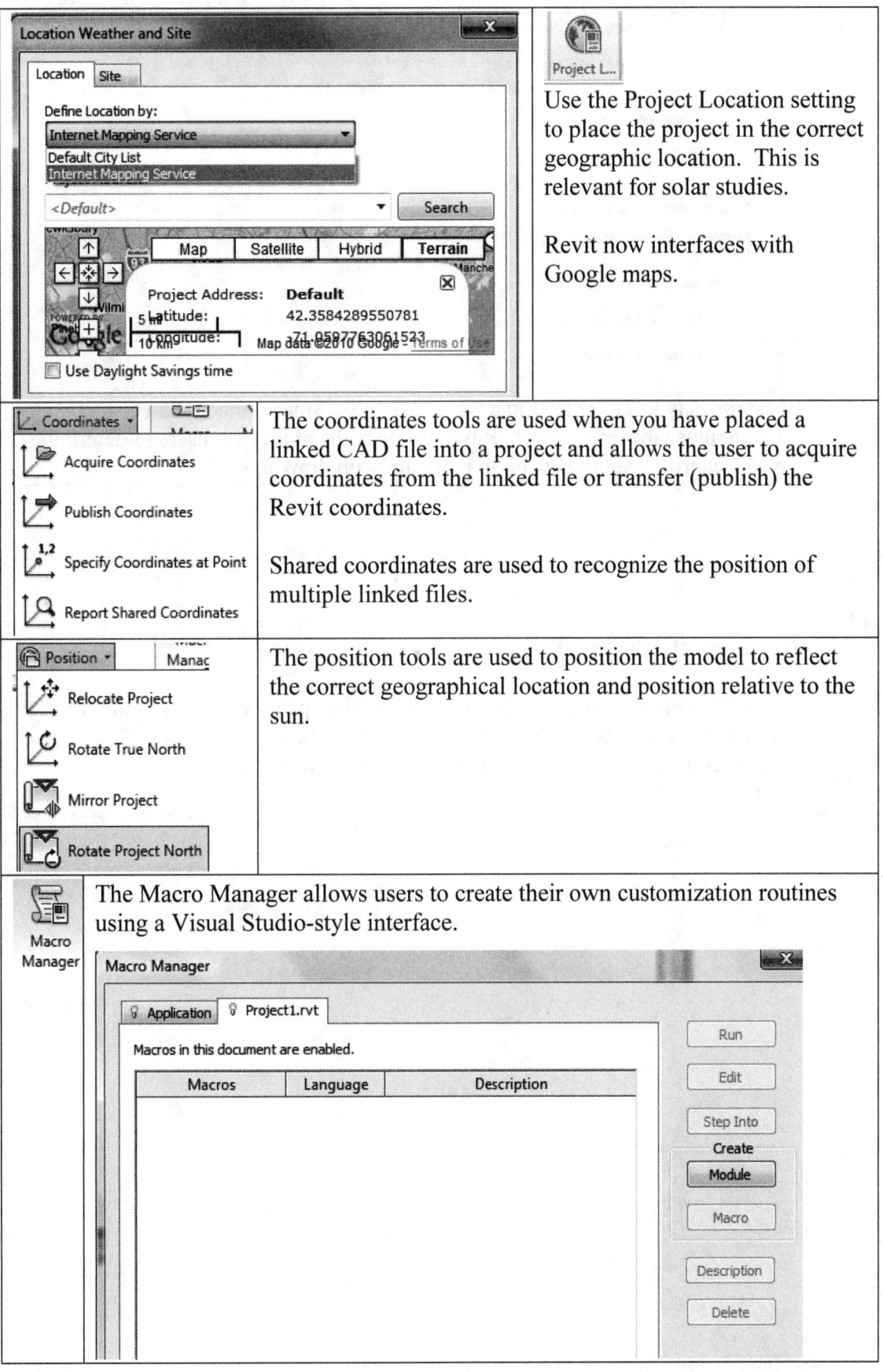

Use the Project Location setting to place the project in the correct geographic location. This is relevant for solar studies.

Revit now interfaces with Google maps.

The coordinates tools are used when you have placed a linked CAD file into a project and allows the user to acquire coordinates from the linked file or transfer (publish) the Revit coordinates.

Shared coordinates are used to recognize the position of multiple linked files.

The position tools are used to position the model to reflect the correct geographical location and position relative to the sun.

The Macro Manager allows users to create their own customization routines using a Visual Studio-style interface.

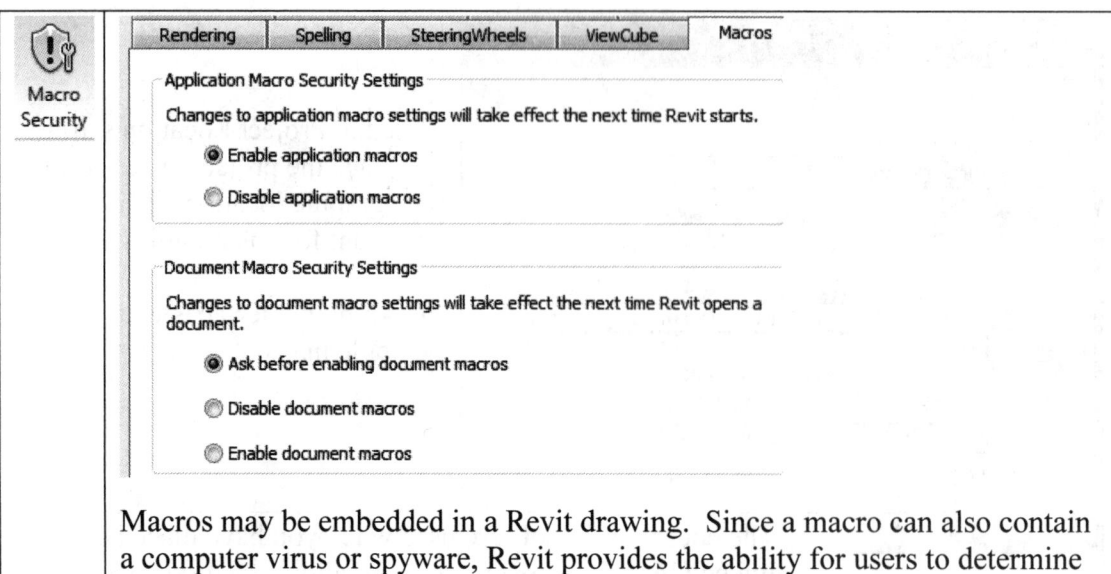

Macros may be embedded in a Revit drawing. Since a macro can also contain a computer virus or spyware, Revit provides the ability for users to determine what security level they want to maintain with drawings.

TIP:

> By default, the Browser lists all sheets and all views.

> If you have multiple users of Revit in your office, place your family libraries and rendering libraries on a server and designate the path under the File Locations tab under Options, this allows multiple users to access the same libraries and materials.

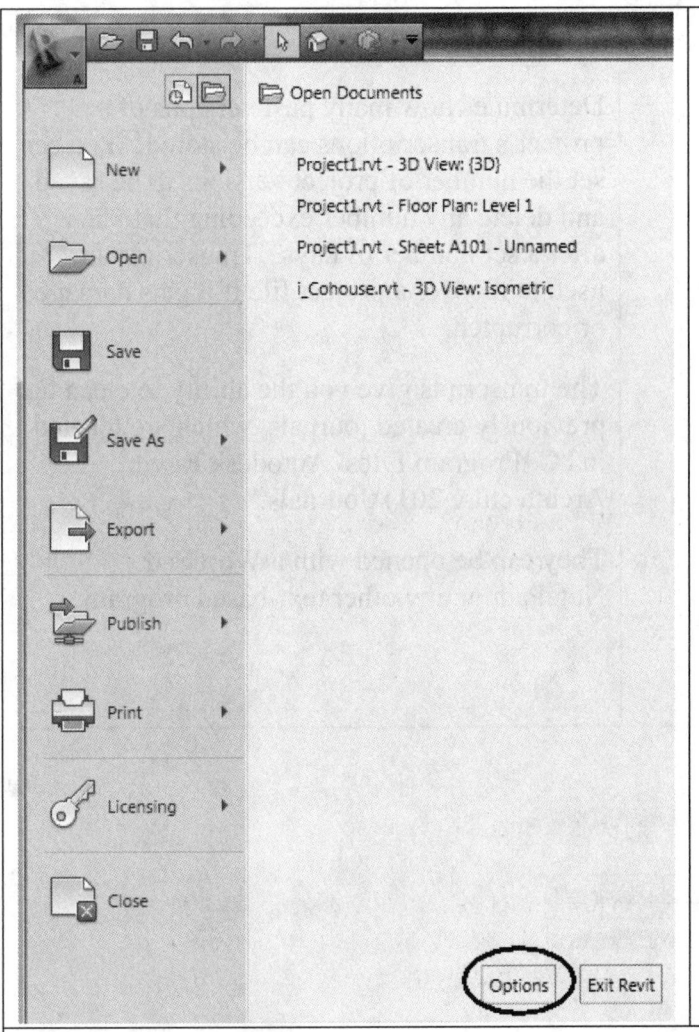

To access the System Options:

Go to the Revit menu and select the Options button located at the bottom of the dialog.

Save Reminder interval:

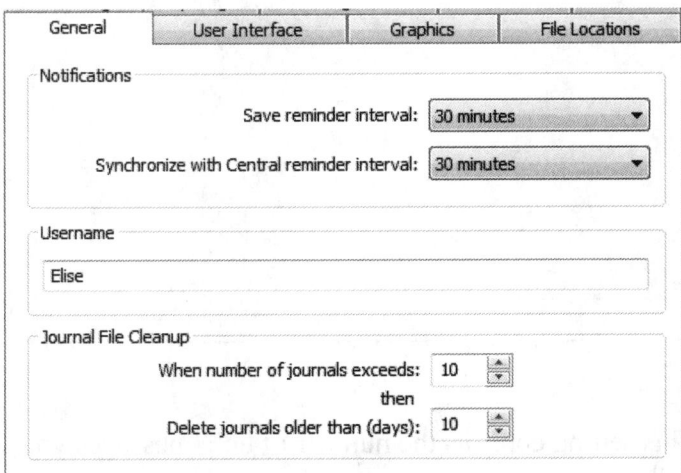

Notifications

You can select any option from the drop-down. This is not an auto-save feature. Your file will not be saved unless you select the 'Save' button. All this does is bring up a reminder dialog at the selected interval.

User Name	This indicates the user name that checks in and checks out documents. This is only applicable if you are working in a collaborative environment. You cannot change the user name unless you have saved all work.

Journal File Cleanup

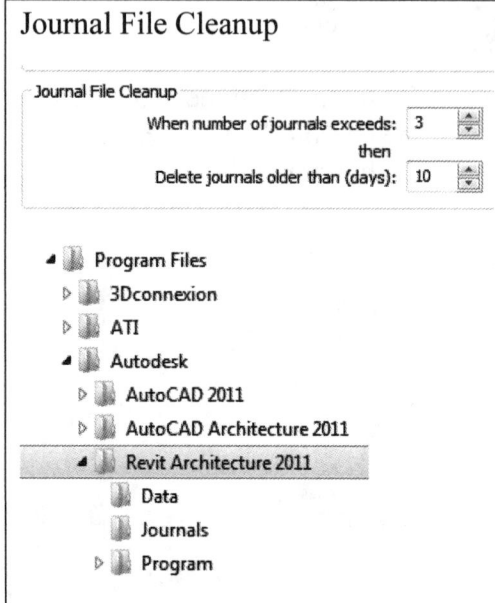

There is currently no option to place the journal file anywhere but the default location.

Determines how many past versions of a project's transcriptions can be stored. You can set the number of project versions to be saved and delete any number exceeding that value after a set number of days. Transcripts are used to recover a project file if it gets damaged or corrupted.

The transcripts give you the ability to clean up previously created journals, which are located in "C:\Program Files\ Autodesk Revit Architecture 2011\Journals."

They can be opened with a WordPad, NotePad, or any other text-based program.

The User Interface Options

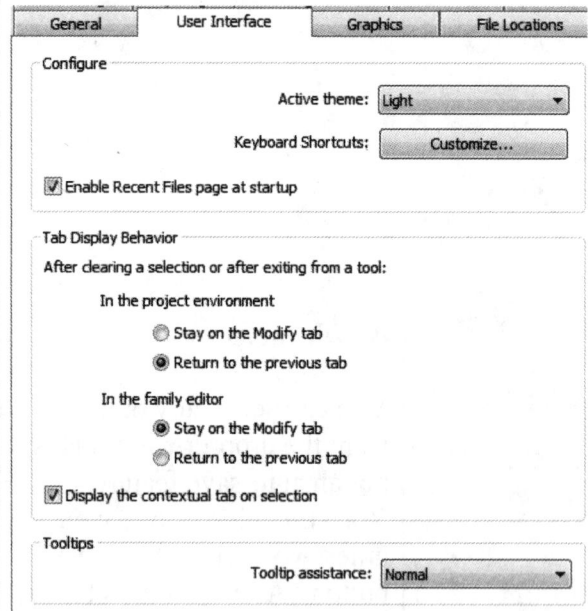

Tooltip Assistance

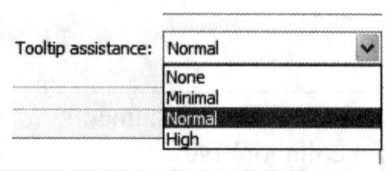

This setting controls the number of help messages you will see as you work.

The Graphics tab

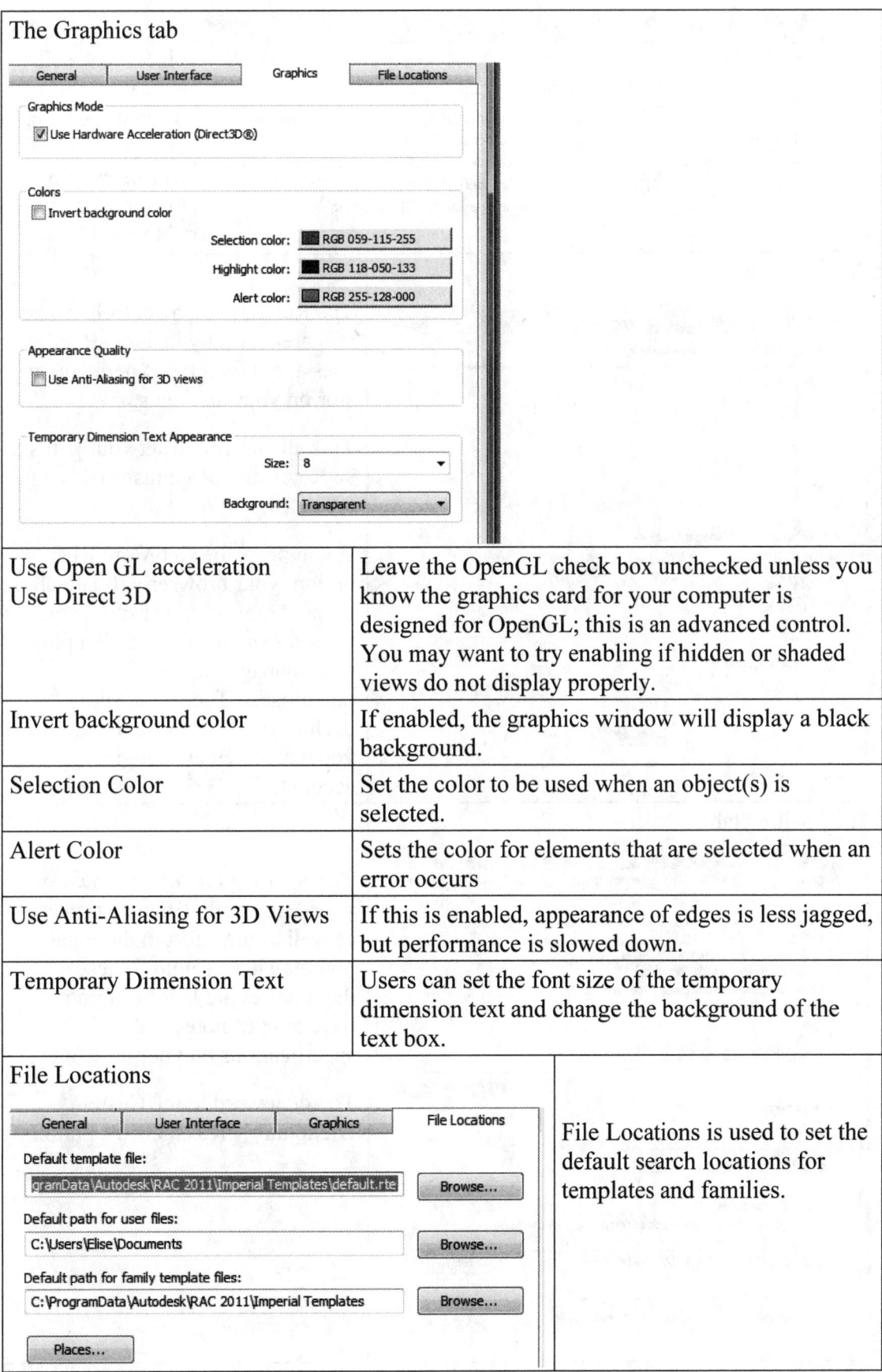

Use Open GL acceleration Use Direct 3D	Leave the OpenGL check box unchecked unless you know the graphics card for your computer is designed for OpenGL; this is an advanced control. You may want to try enabling if hidden or shaded views do not display properly.
Invert background color	If enabled, the graphics window will display a black background.
Selection Color	Set the color to be used when an object(s) is selected.
Alert Color	Sets the color for elements that are selected when an error occurs
Use Anti-Aliasing for 3D Views	If this is enabled, appearance of edges is less jagged, but performance is slowed down.
Temporary Dimension Text	Users can set the font size of the temporary dimension text and change the background of the text box.

File Locations

File Locations is used to set the default search locations for templates and families.

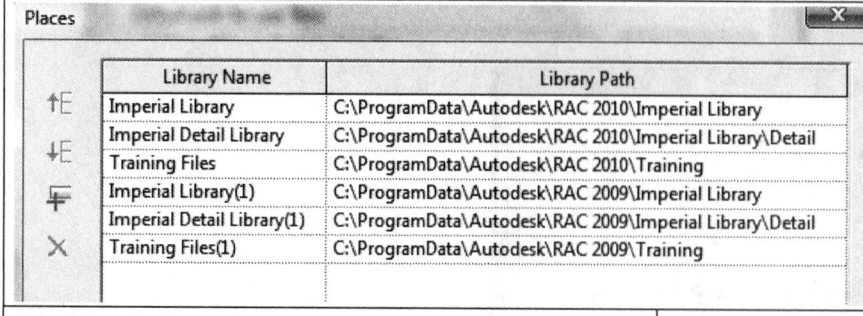

Places lists all the places that will appear on the left pane of the Open dialog. Use for templates, project locations, and libraries.

The Rendering tab

The Rendering tab controls where you are storing your AccuRender files and directories where you are storing your materials.

This allows you to set your paths so Revit can locate materials and files easily.

If you press the Get More RPC button, your browser will launch to the Archvision website. You must download and install a plug-in to manage your RPC downloads. There is a free exchange service for content, but you have to create a login account.

The Spelling tab

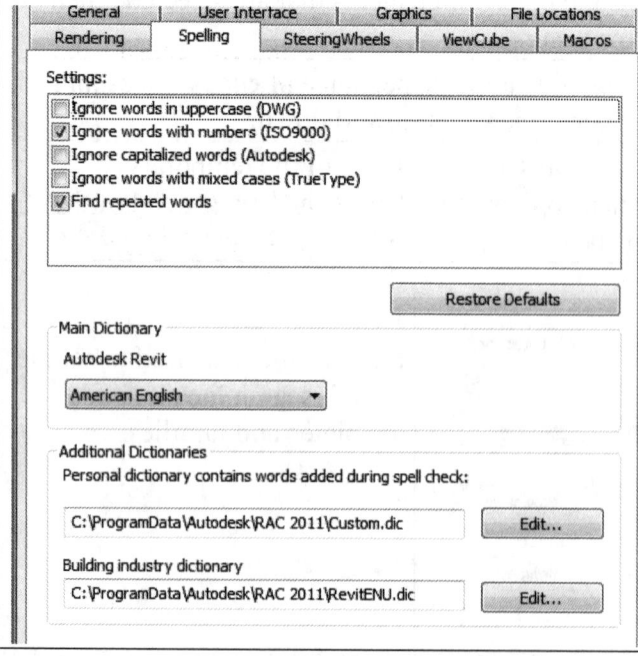

The Spelling tab allows you to use your Microsoft Office dictionary as well as any custom dictionaries you may have set up. These dictionaries are helpful if you have a lot of notes and specifications on your drawings.

To add a word to the Custom Dictionary, press the **Edit** button.

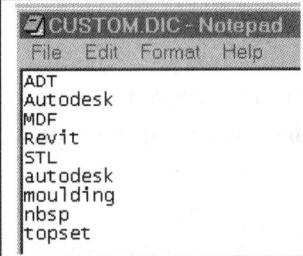	Notepad will open and you can just type in any words you want to add to the dictionary. Save the file.

The SteeringWheels tab

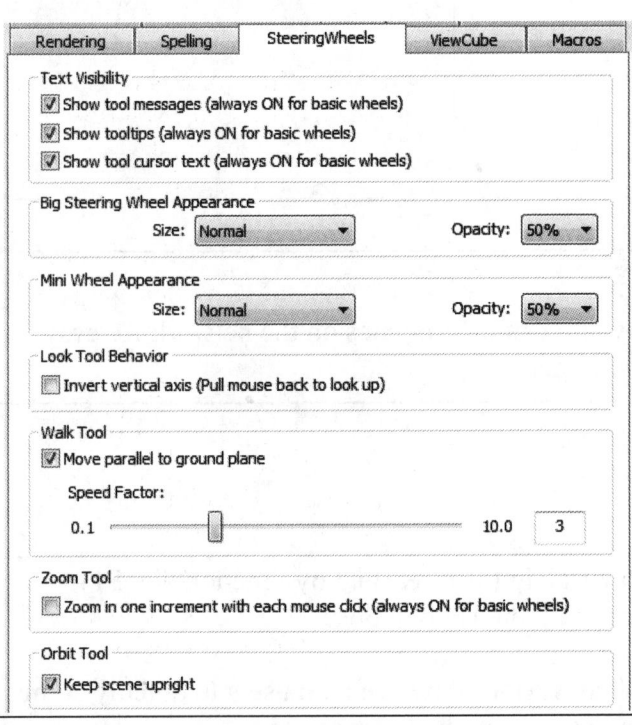

The SteeringWheels tab controls the appearance and functionality of the steering wheels.

Steering Wheels are used to change the display.

The ViewCube tab

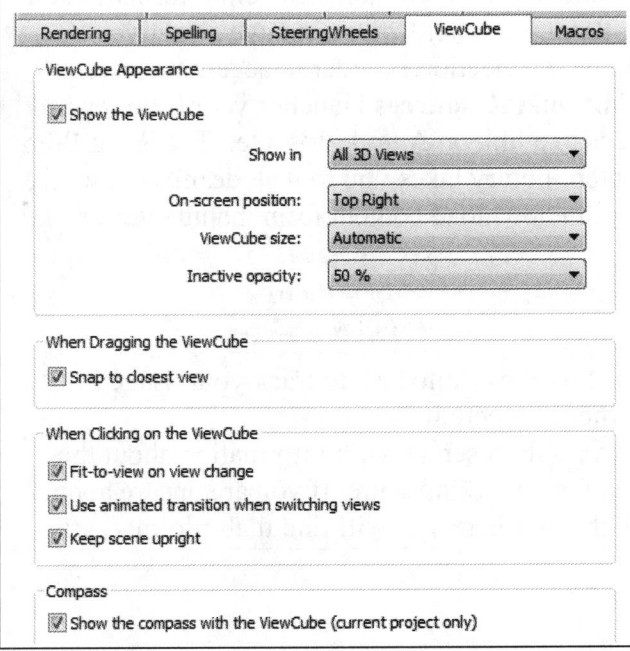

The ViewCube tab controls the appearance and location of the ViewCube.

The user can also determine how the display changes when the ViewCube is selected.

The Macros tab 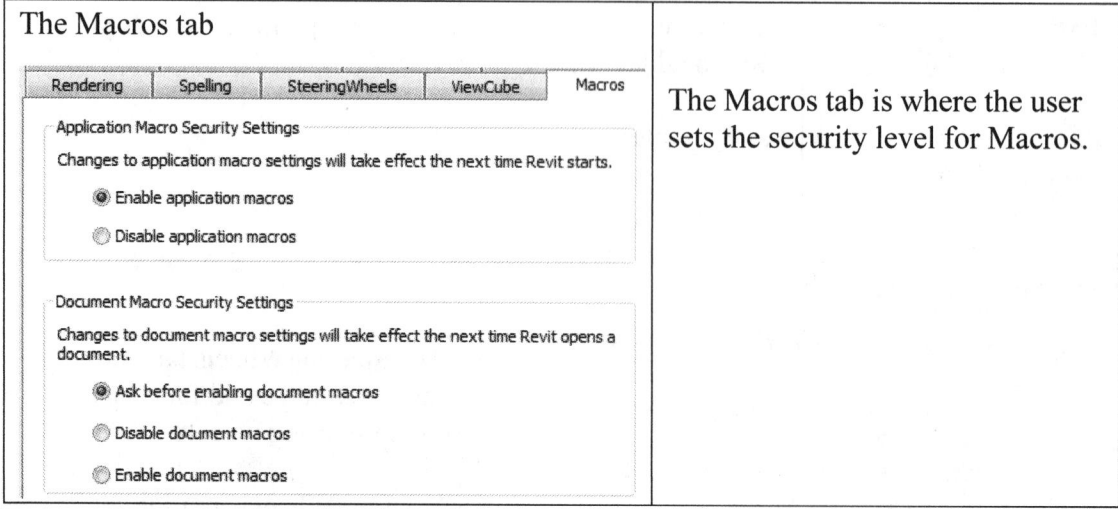	The Macros tab is where the user sets the security level for Macros.

TIP: To boost productivity, store all your custom templates on the network for easy access and set the pointer to the correct folder.

The Help Menu

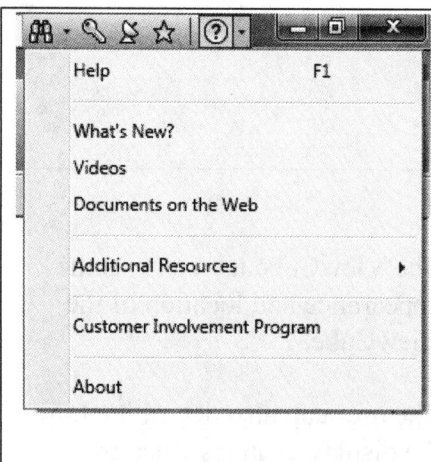

Revit Help (also reached by function key F1) brings up the Help dialog.

What's New allows veteran users to quickly come up to speed on the latest release.

Documents on Web launches help information on the Revit web site. You must have an active Internet connection in order to access the site.

Additional Resources launches your browser and opens to a link on Autodesk's site. The Revit Web Content library takes you to Autodesk Seek, where you can download content from manufacturers.

The **Customer Involvement Program** is used by Autodesk to track your usage of their software remotely using your internet connection.

About Revit Architecture 2011 reaches a splash screen with information about the version and build of the copy of Revit you are working with. If you are unsure about which Service Pack you have installed, this is where you will find that information.

Exercise 1-5
Setting File Locations

Drawing Name: Close all open files
Estimated Time: 5 minutes

This exercise reinforces the following skills:

- ❑ Options
- ❑ File Locations

1. Close all open files or projects.

2. 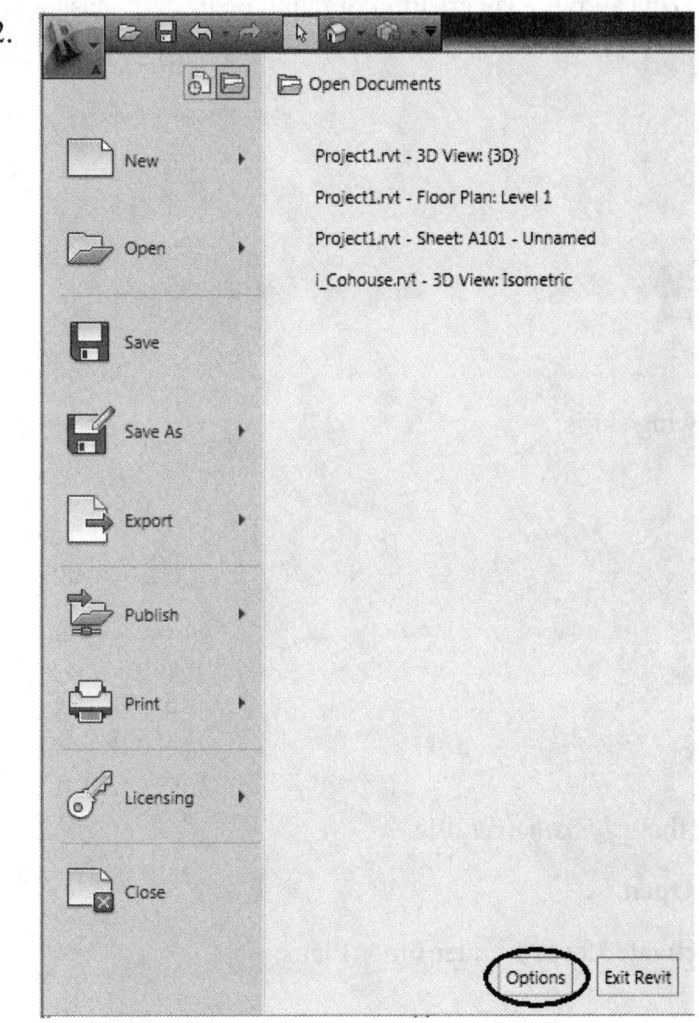 Go to **Applications Menu**.

   Select the **Options** button at the bottom of the window.

3. ⌐ File Locations ⌐   Select the **File Locations** tab.

4.  In the **Default path for users** section, pick the **Browse** button.

5. Default path for user files:

E:\Schroff\Revit 2011 Basics\exercise files\

Navigate to the local or network folder where you will save your files. When the correct folder is highlighted, pick **Open**. Your instructor or CAD manager can provide you with this file information.

I recommend to my students to bring a flash drive to class and back up each day's work onto the flash drive. That way you never will lose your valuable work.

Revit has 4D capabilities allowing users to set up phases, i.e. existing construction, demolition, new work, future phases, etc. Phase filters control how objects on different phases are displayed. For example, existing walls can be displayed as grey with a hatch pattern and new walls can be displayed black, demolition walls red. A user can choose to not display a phase on any view. This allows easy creation of demo plans and phased construction documents.

Exercise 1-6
Setting up Phases

Drawing Name: c_phasing.rvt
Estimated Time: 75 minutes

This exercise reinforces the following skills:

- ❑ Properties
- ❑ Filter
- ❑ Phases
- ❑ Rename View
- ❑ Copy View
- ❑ Graphic Settings for Phases

1. Select the **Open** tool.

2. File name: c_Phasing.rvt   Locate the *c_phasing.rvt* file.

   Select **Open**.

3. 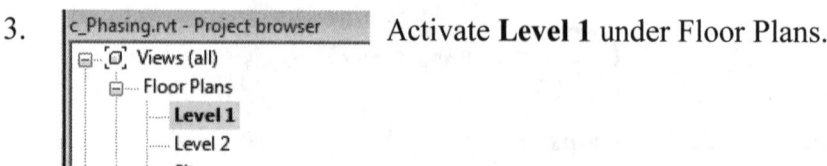 Activate **Level 1** under Floor Plans.

4. 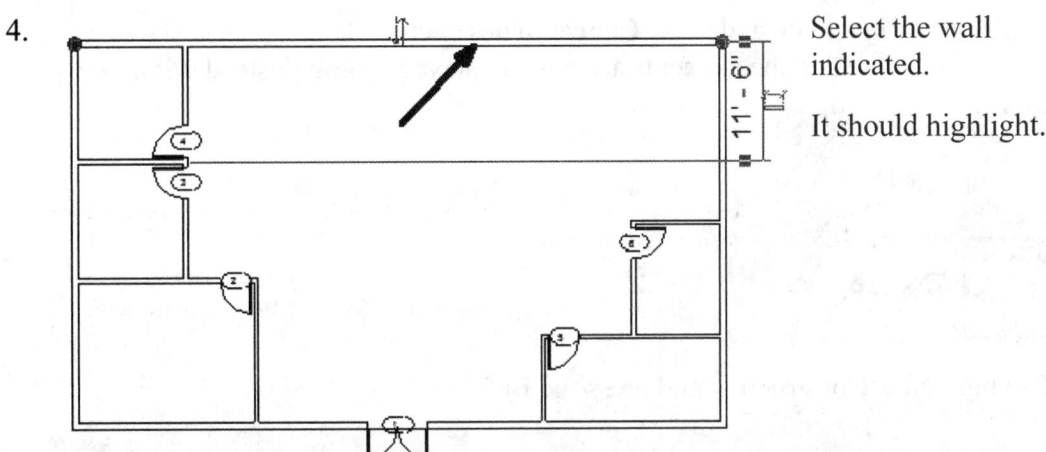 Select the wall indicated.

It should highlight.

5. 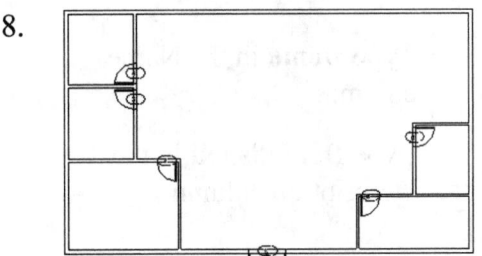 Scroll down to the Phasing category in the Properties panel on the upper left.

6. This wall was created in the New Construction Phase. Note that it is not set to be demolished.

7. Right click and press **Cancel** to deselect the wall. [Cancel]

8. Window around the entire building to select everything.

9. Select the **Filter** tool.

10. 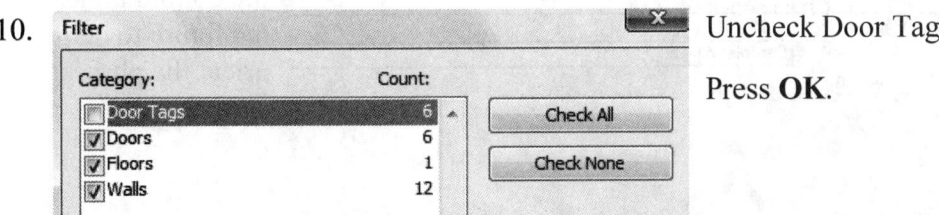 Uncheck Door Tags.

Press **OK**.

Note: If Door Tags are selected, you will not be able to access Phases in the Properties dialog.

11. In the Properties pane:

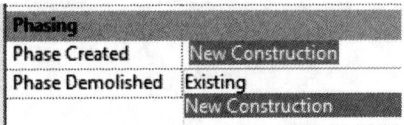 In the Phase Created drop-down list, select **Existing**. This moves all the selected items into the Existing Phase.

12. [Cancel]   Right click and press **Cancel** to deselect.
Note that the elements are now displayed as gray instead of black.

13. 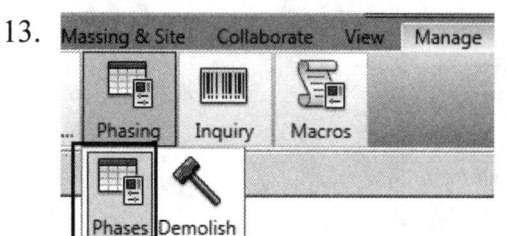   Go to the **Manage** ribbon.

Select **Phasing→Phases**.

14. Highlight New Construction and press the **Before** button.

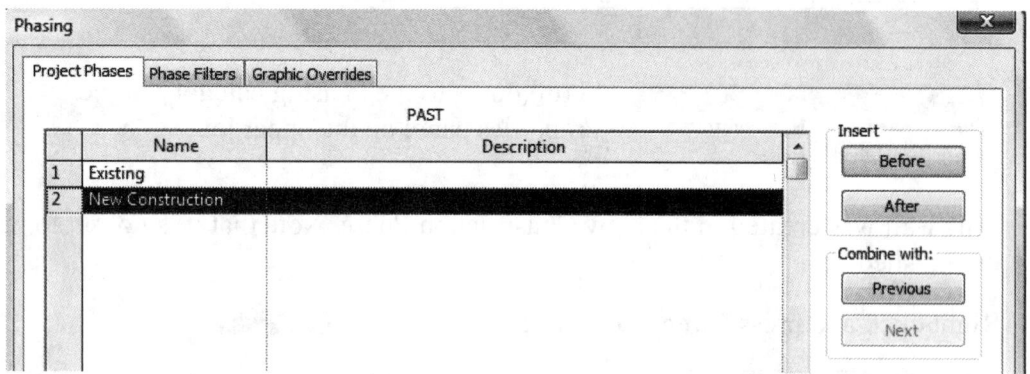

15. Type **Demo** in the Name column.

Type **Demolished** in the Description column.

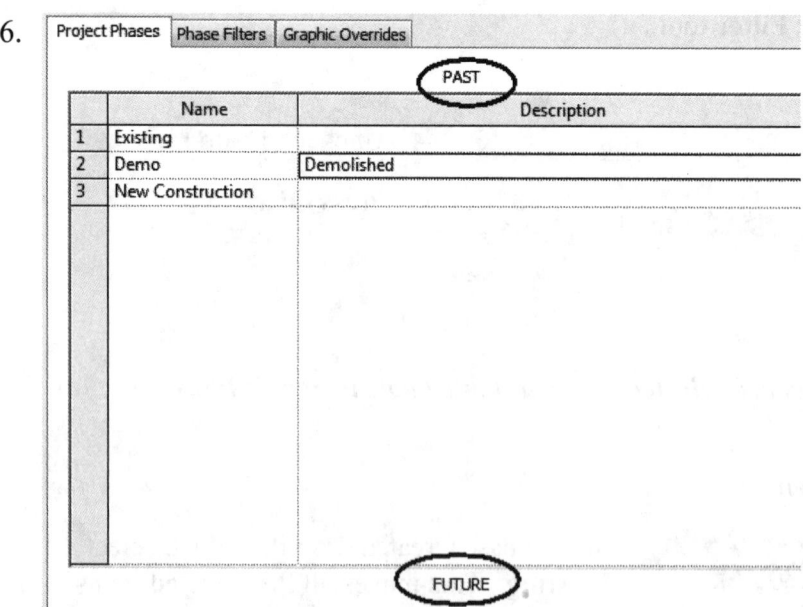

16. Note that the top indicates the past and the bottom indicates the future to help orient the phases.

17. Select the Graphic Overrides tab.

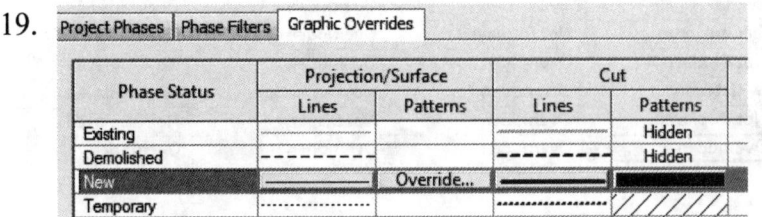

18. Note that in the Lines column for the Existing Phase, the line color is set to gray.

19. 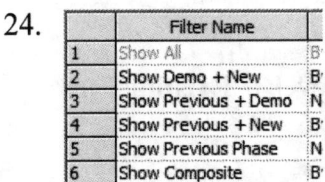 Click in the **Lines** column and the Line Graphics dialog will display.

20. Set the Color to **Green** for the Existing phase by selecting the color button.

    Set the Color to **Blue** for the Demolished phase.

    Set the Color to **Magenta** for the New phase.

    Change the colors for both Projection/Surface and Cut.

21. Select the **Phase Filters** tab.

22. *Note that there are already phase filters pre-defined that will control what is displayed in a view.*

23. Pres the **New** button on the bottom of the dialog.

24. Change the name for the new phase filter to **Show Composite**.

25. 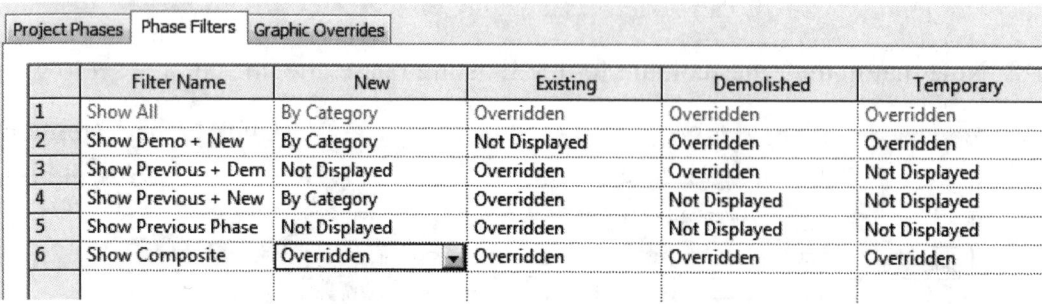 In the New column, select **Overridden**.

This means that the default display settings will use the new color assigned.

	Filter Name	New	Existing	Demolished	Temporary
1	Show All	By Category	Overridden	Overridden	Overridden
2	Show Demo + New	By Category	Not Displayed	Overridden	Overridden
3	Show Previous + Dem	Not Displayed	Overridden	Overridden	Not Displayed
4	Show Previous + New	By Category	Overridden	Not Displayed	Not Displayed
5	Show Previous Phase	Not Displayed	Overridden	Not Displayed	Not Displayed
6	Show Composite	Overridden	Overridden	Overridden	Overridden

26. Press **Apply** and **OK** to close the Phases dialog.
Note all the elements on the existing layer are now displayed in green.

If only the doors or only the walls are displayed in green, go back and verify that the colors in both columns are set properly.

27. Highlight **Level 1** under Floor Plan.

Right click and select **Rename**.

28. 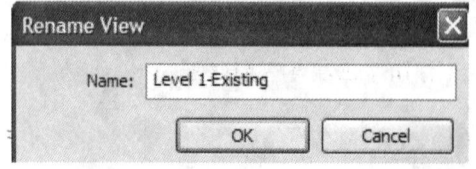 Rename the view **Level 1- Existing**.

Press **OK**.

29. 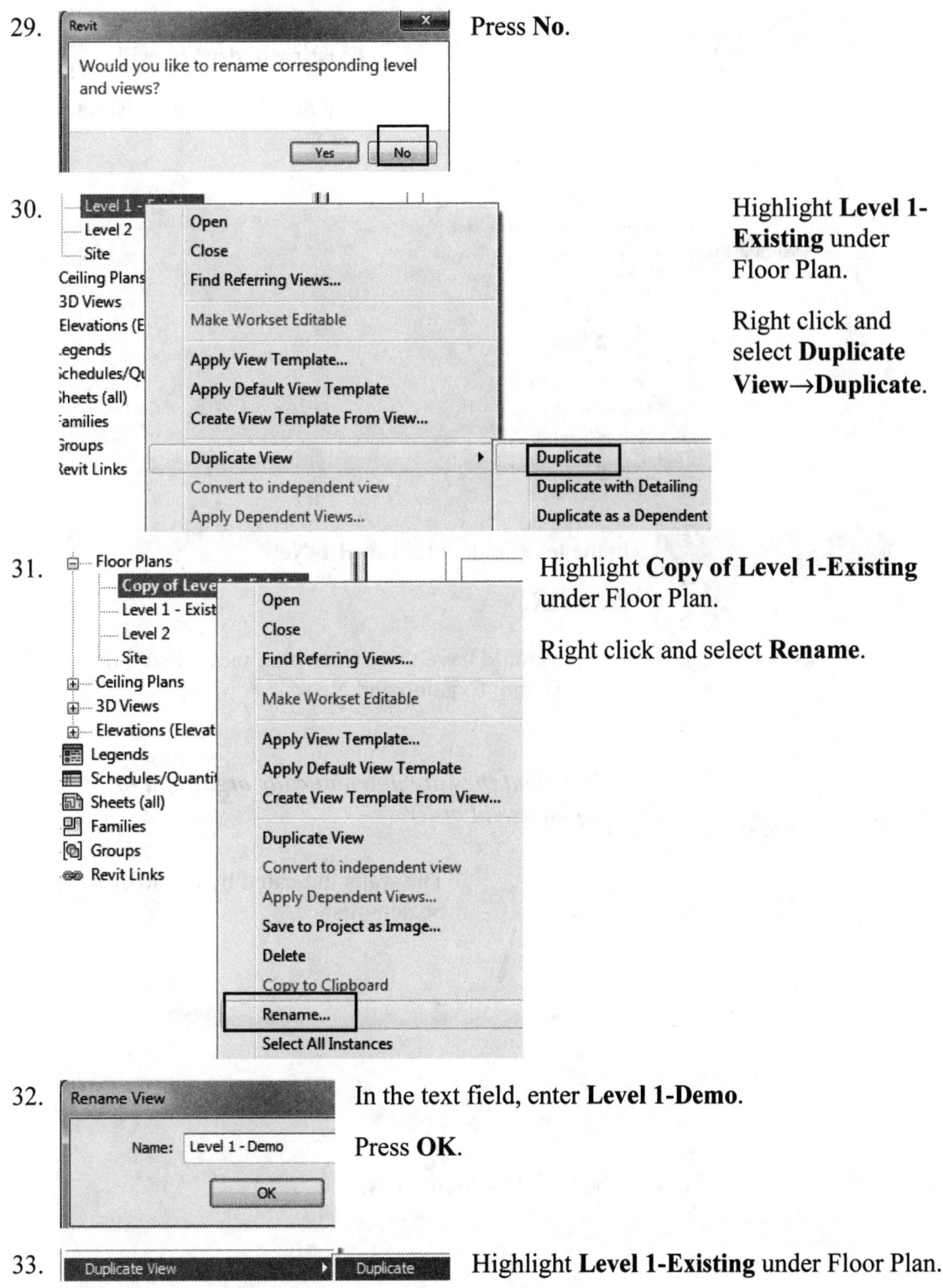 Press **No**.

30. Highlight **Level 1-Existing** under Floor Plan.

Right click and select **Duplicate View→Duplicate**.

31. Highlight **Copy of Level 1-Existing** under Floor Plan.

Right click and select **Rename**.

32. In the text field, enter **Level 1-Demo**.

Press **OK**.

33. Highlight **Level 1-Existing** under Floor Plan.

34. Right click and select **Duplicate View→Duplicate**.

35. 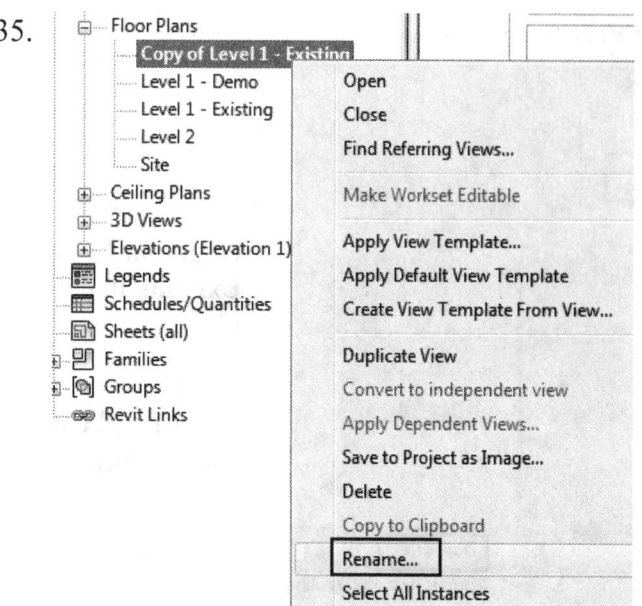 Highlight **Copy of Level 1-Existing** under Floor Plan.

Right click and select **Rename**.

36. In the text field, enter **Level 1-New**.

Press **OK**.

37. You should have three floor plan views listed for Level 1 – Demo, Existing and New.

Note that they are automatically organized in alphabetical order.

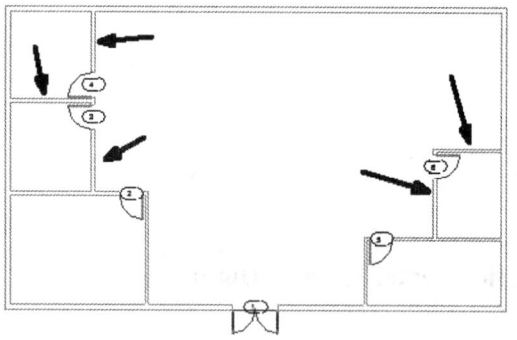 The walls indicated by the arrows are to be demolished.

38. Activate the **Level 1-Demo** view.

39. In the Properties dialog:

Set the Phase Filter to **Show Previous + Demo**. The previous phase to demo is Existing. This means the view will display elements created in the existing and demolished phase.

Set the Phase to **Demo**.

40. 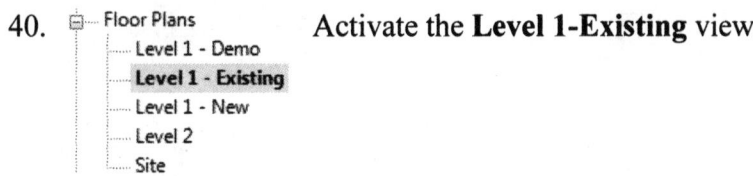 Activate the **Level 1-Existing** view.

41. In the Properties dialog:

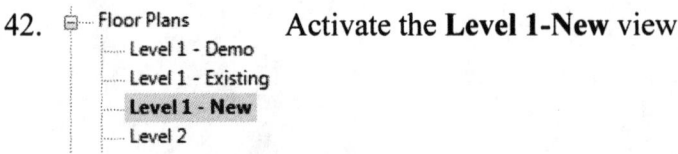 Set the Phase Filter to **Show Composite**.
The composite filter shows the overridden displays.
Set the Phase to **Existing**.

42. Activate the **Level 1-New** view.

43. In the Properties dialog:

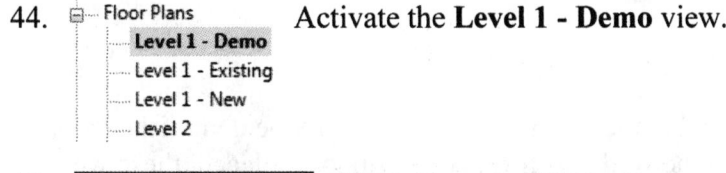 Set the Phase Filter to **Show Previous + New**.
This will display elements created in the Existing
Phase and the New Phase, but not the Demo phase.
Set the Phase to **New**.

44. Activate the **Level 1 - Demo** view.

45. Hold down the Ctrl button.

Select the two walls indicated.

46. In the Properties pane:

Scroll down to the bottom.
In the Phase Demolished drop-down list, select **Demo**.

47. Press **OK**.

48. The demolished walls change appearance based on the graphic overrides.
Release the selected walls using right click→Cancel or by pressing ESCAPE.

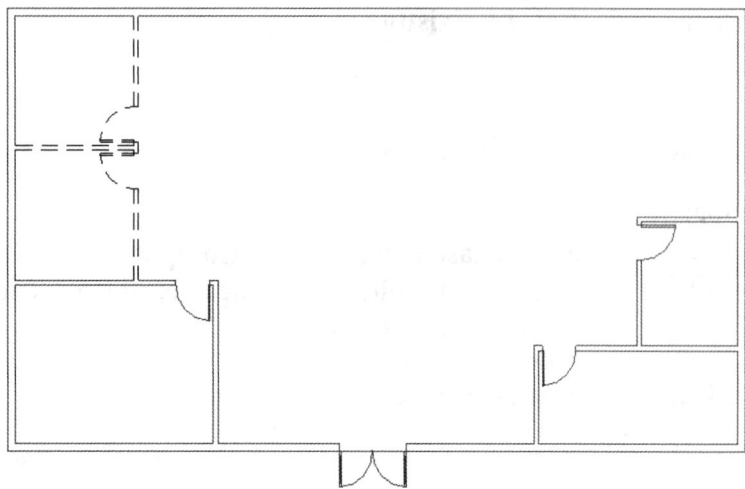

49. 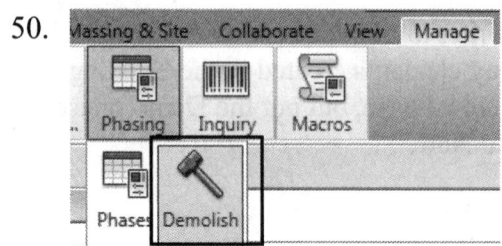 Select the Manage Ribbon.

50. Use the **Demolish** tool under Phasing to demolish the walls indicated.

51. 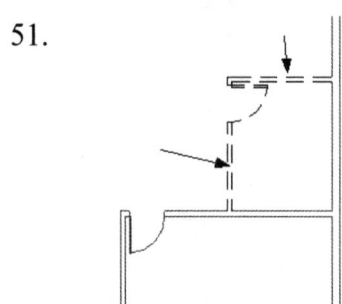 Note that the doors will automatically be demolished along with the walls. If there were windows placed, these would also be demolished. That is because those elements are considered *wall-hosted*.

Right click and select Cancel to exit the Demolish mode.

52. 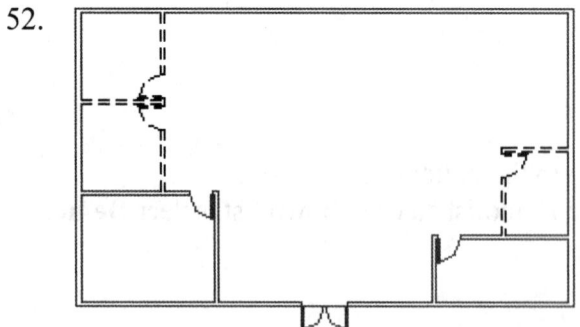 This is how the Level 1- Demo view should appear.

If it doesn't, check the walls to verify that they are set to Phase Created: Existing, Phase Demolished: Demo.

53. 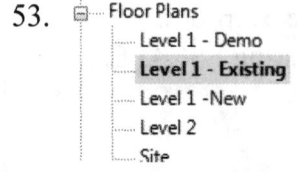 Double left click on the Level 1- Existing floor plan view to activate it.

54.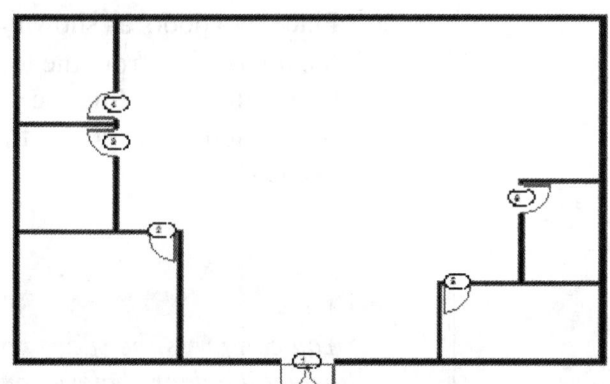

The view should update as displayed.

55.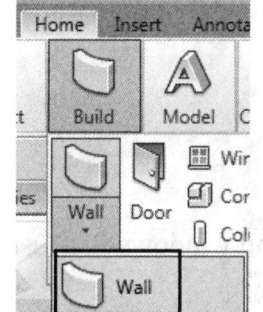

Activate the **Level 1-New** view.

Floor Plans
Level 1 - Demo
Level 1 - Existing
Level 1 - New
Level 2

56. Select the **Home** ribbon.

Select the **Wall** tool under Build→Wall.

57.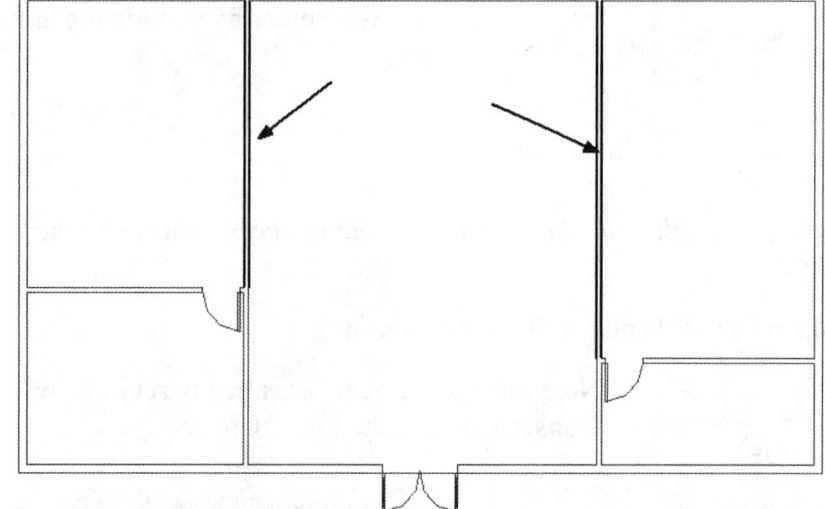

Place two walls as shown. Select the end points of the existing walls and simply draw up.

Right click and select **Cancel** to exit the Draw Wall mode.

58.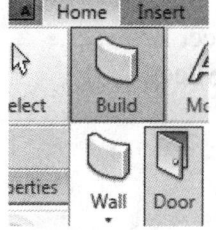

Select the **Door** tool under the Build panel.

59. 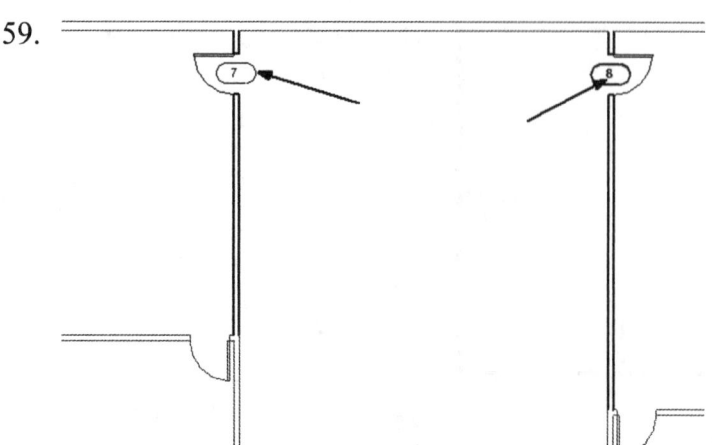 Place two doors as shown. Set the doors 3′ 6″ from the top horizontal wall. Flip the orientation of the doors if needed.

You can press the space bar to orient the doors before you left click to place.

60. 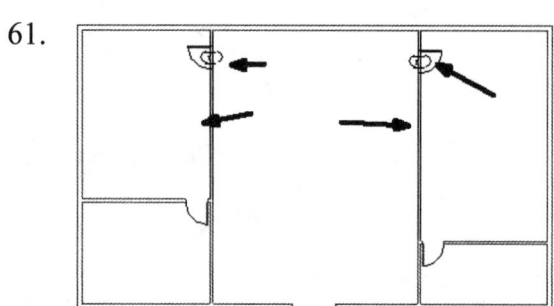 Note that the new doors and windows are a different color than the existing walls.

61. Select the doors and windows you just placed.

You can select by holding down the CONTROL key or by windowing around the area.

Note: If Door Tags are selected, you will not be able to access Phases in the Properties dialog.

62. Look in the Properties panel and scroll down to Phasing.

 Note that the elements are already set to **New Construction** in the Phase Created field.

63. Switch between the three views to see how they display differently.

64. 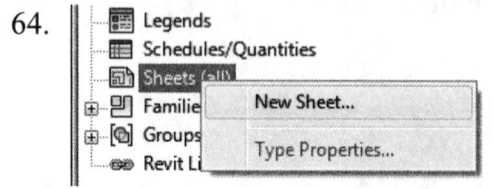 Highlight **Sheets** in the Project Browser. Right click and select **New Sheet**.

65. 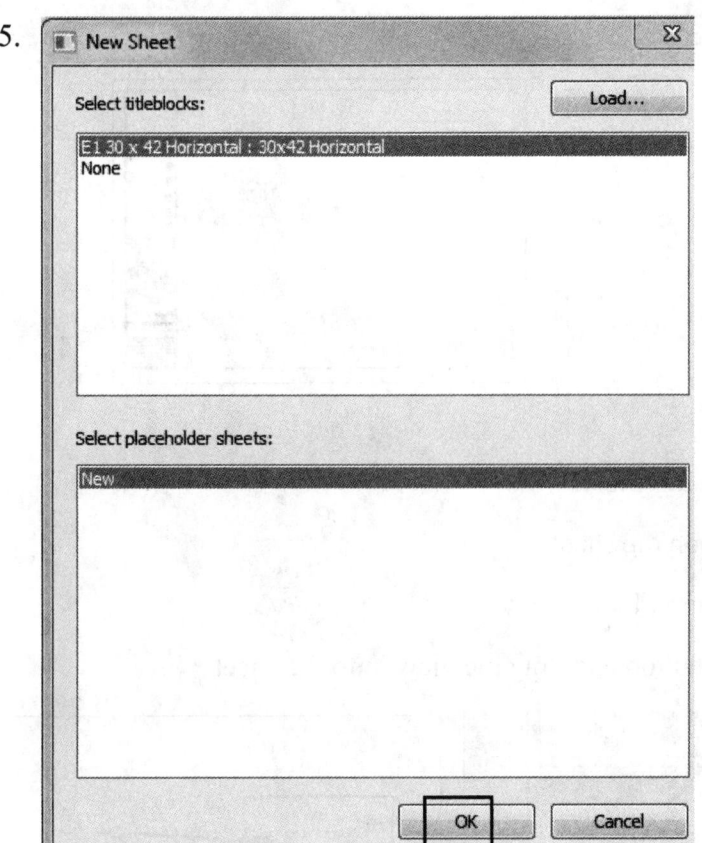 Press **OK** to accept the default title block.

66. A view opens with the new sheet.

67. 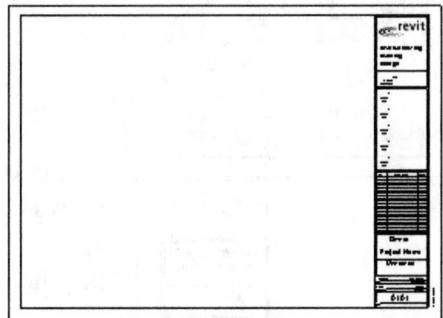 Highlight the Level 1 - Existing Floor plan.

Hold down the left mouse button and drag the view onto the sheet.

68.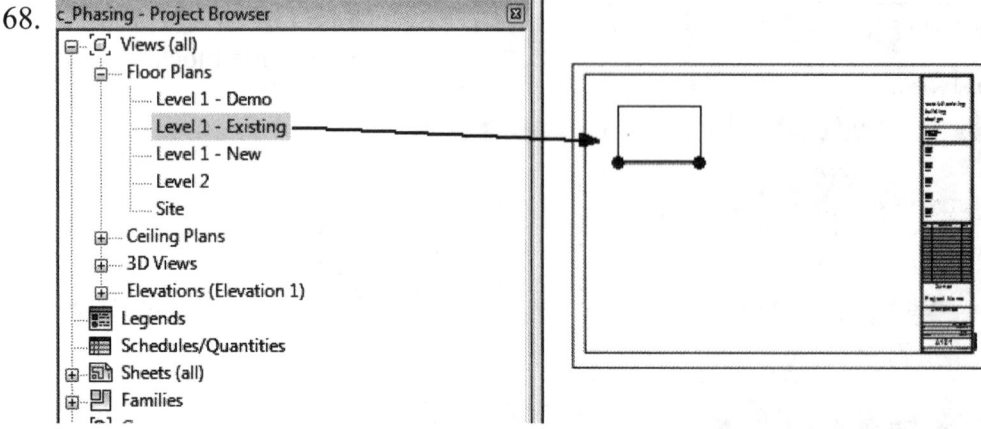

A preview will appear on your cursor.

Left click to place the view on the sheet.

69. Highlight the Level 1 - Demo Floor plan.

   Hold down the left mouse button and drag the view onto the sheet.

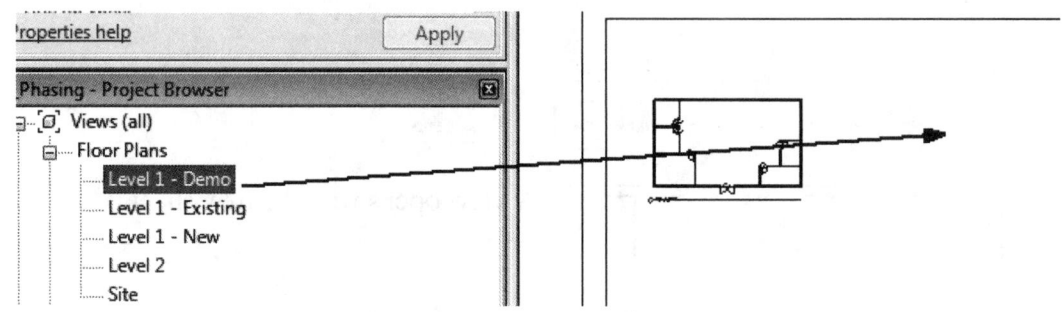

70. The two views appear on the sheet.

71. Highlight the Level 1 - New Floor plan.

Hold down the left mouse button and drag the view onto the sheet.

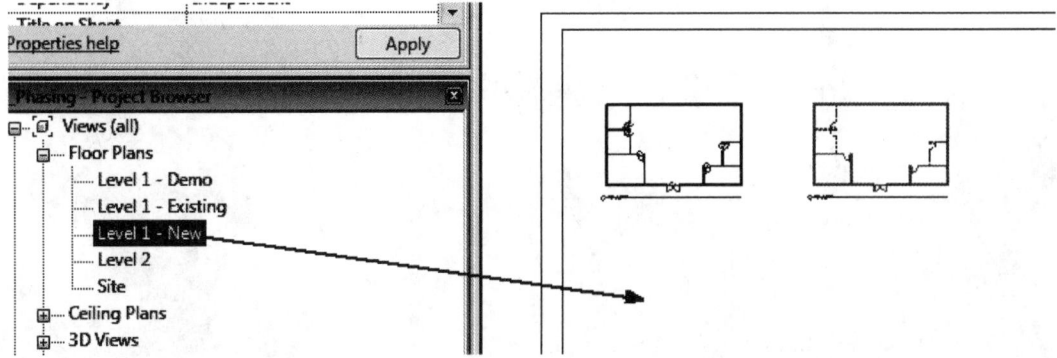

72. Zoom in to inspect the views.

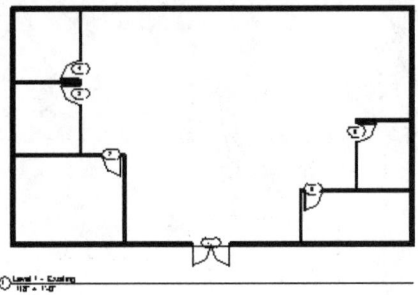

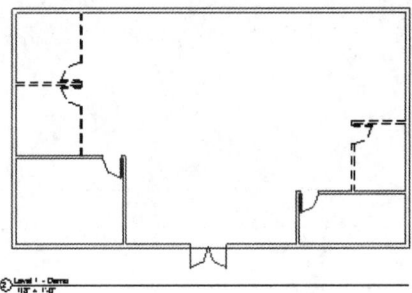

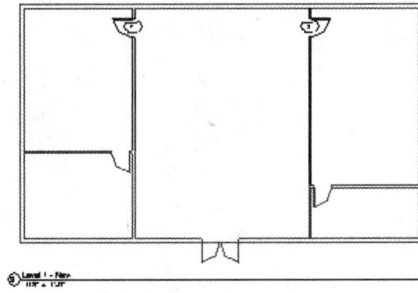

73. Close without saving.

Notes:

Lesson 1 Quiz

True or False

1. If you Ungroup a previously created group, the entities in the group are deleted.
2. The Align tool lets you lock an alignment relationship so two entity edges or faces are always aligned no matter how the design otherwise changes.
3. Revit Warnings do not interrupt commands, so they can be ignored and later reviewed.
4. Deactivate View on the View menu is used to remove Views from Sheets
5. Demolish is the same as Delete.

Multiple Choice [Select the Best Answer]

6. Phases are used to:

    A. Assign building elements to different stages of construction.
    B. Control the visibility of elements.
    C. Control the transparency of elements.
    D. Manage a building design.

7. When you select an object, you can access the element properties by:

    A. Right click and select Element Properties.
    B. Select Element Properties→Instance Properties on the Ribbon Bar.
    C. Go to File→Properties.
    D. Using the Properties pane located on the left of the screen.

8. The interface item that changes appearance constantly depending on entity selections and command status is _____.

    A. Ribbon
    B. Project Browser
    C. Menu Bar
    D. Status Bar

9. View Styles available in Revit are _____.

    A. Wireframe
    B. Hidden Line
    C. Shaded
    D. Consistent Colors
    E. All of the Above

10. The shortcut key to bring up the steering wheel is _____.

        A. F2
        B. F3
        C. VV
        D. F8

ANSWERS:
    1) A; 2) T; 3) T; 4) F; 5) F; 6) B; 7) D; 8) A; 9) E; 10) D

Lesson 2
Mass Elements

Mass Elements are used to give you a conceptual idea of the space and shape of a building without having to take the time to put in a lot of detail. It allows you to create alternative designs quickly and easily and get approval before you put in a lot of effort.

Massing Tools

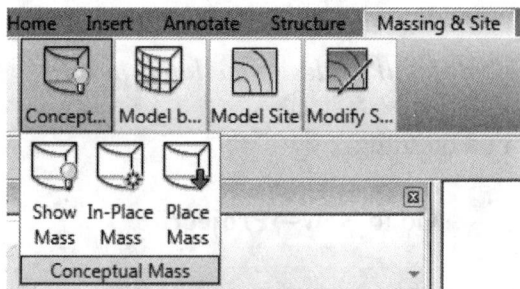

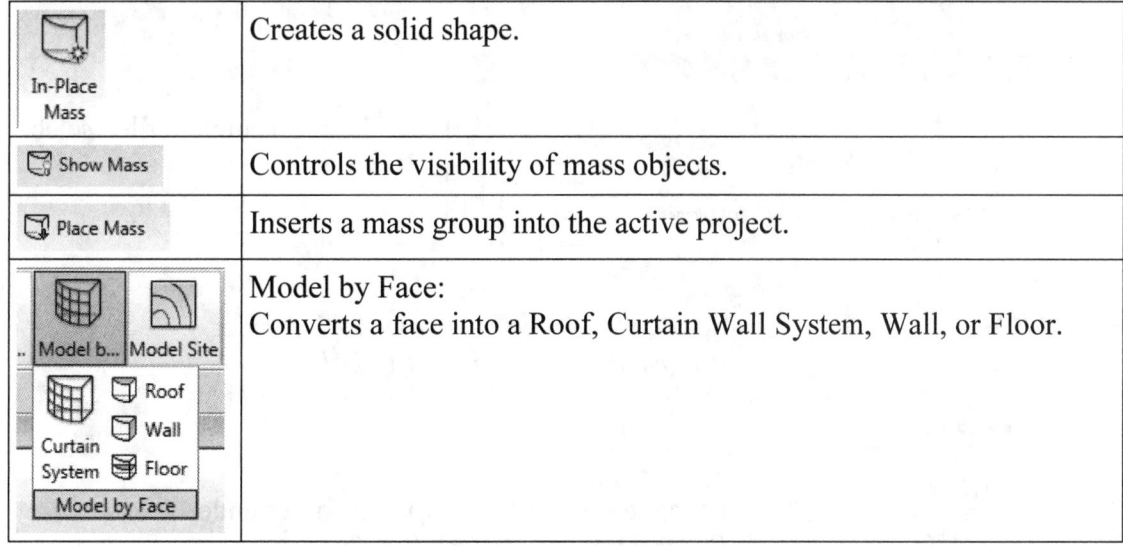	
In-Place Mass	Creates a solid shape.
Show Mass	Controls the visibility of mass objects.
Place Mass	Inserts a mass group into the active project.
Model b... Model Site — Curtain System, Roof, Wall, Floor — Model by Face	Model by Face: Converts a face into a Roof, Curtain Wall System, Wall, or Floor.

Exercise 2-1
Adding a Level

Drawing Name: default.rte [metric default.rte]
Estimated Time: 5 minutes

This exercise reinforces the following skills:

- Switching Elevation Views
- Basics
- Add a Level

This tutorial uses metric or Imperial units. Metric units will be designated in brackets.

Revit uses a level to define another floor or story in a building.

1. 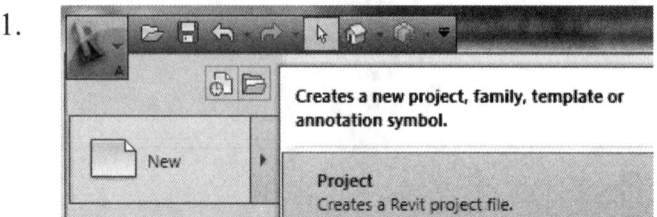   Go to **New→Project**.

2. 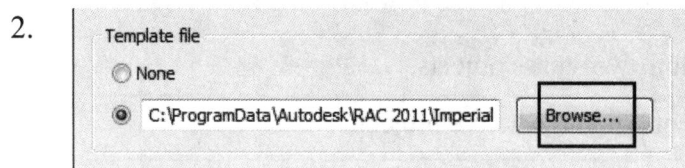   Under the Template file: select **Browse**.

3. 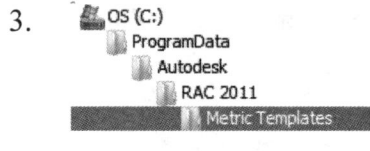   Locate the *Metric Templates* folder under *ProgramData/Autodesk/RAC2011*.

   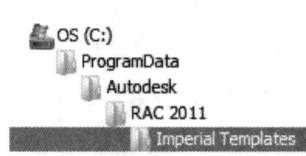   Locate the *Imperial Templates* folder under *ProgramData/Autodesk/RAC2011*.

4. 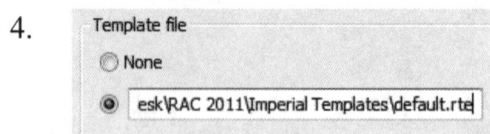   Select the *default.rte [DefaultMetric.rte]* template.

   Brackets indicate metric is selected as an alternative.

   Press **OK**.

If you accidentally picked Metric when you wanted Imperial or vice versa, you can change the units at any time. Revit will automatically switch any dimensions over to the active units.

To change Project Units, go to the Manage Ribbon.

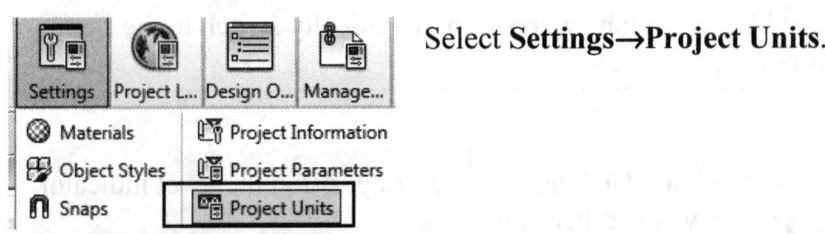

Select **Settings→Project Units**.

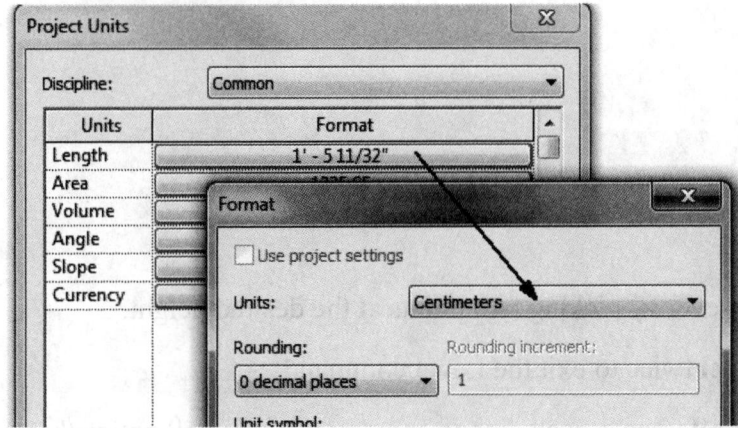

Left click the Length button, then select the desired units from the drop-down list.

5. Elevations (Building Elevation)
   - East
   - North
   - South
   - West

Double click **East** under Elevations.

This activates the East view orientation.

6. Home   Select the **Home** ribbon.

7. Select the **Level** tool under Datum. (This adds a floor elevation.)

8. Level 3   22' - 0"

Move your mouse to set an elevation of **12′ [3650 mm]**. Pick to start the elevation line.

Level 2   10" - 0"

9.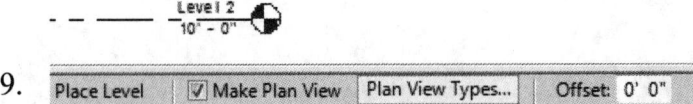

In the Options bar located on the lower left of the screen, enable **Make Plan View**.

This should be enabled if you want Revit to automatically create a floor plan view of this level. If you forget to check this box, you can create the floor plan view later using the **View** Ribbon.

TIP: Double click on the blue elevation symbol to automatically switch to the floor plan view for that elevation.

10.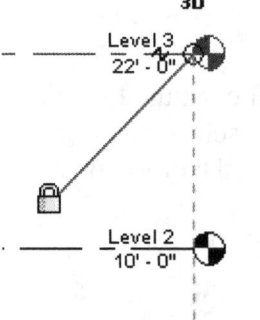

Pick to place the end point to position the level indicator above the other indicators.

11. Basically, you place a new level by picking two points at the desired height.

Right click and select **Cancel** twice to exit the Level command.

Revit is always looking for references even among annotations, you will notice that your level tags snap and lock together so when you move one to the right or left, all those in line with it will follow.

The jogged line allows the user to create a jog if desired.

If you need to adjust the position of the tag, just click on the line, 3 blue grips will appear. These can be clicked and dragged as needed. You can also right click on a level tag and select 'Hide annotation in view' and the tag and level line will disappear in that view only.

Hide Annotation in View is only enabled if an object is selected first.

12. Save the file as a project as *ex2-1.rvt*.

Exercise 2-2
Adding Mass Elements

Drawing Name: ex2-1.rvt
Estimated Time: 10 minutes

This exercise reinforces the following skills:

    ❑   Switching Elevation Views
    ❑   Add Mass

1.   Open or continue working in the file *ex2-1.rvt*.

2.   Activate the **Level 1** view.

    Views (all)
      Floor Plans
        Level 1
        Level 2
        Level 3
        Site

3.   Massing & Site   Select the **Site & Massing** ribbon.

4.   Select the **In-Place Mass** tool.

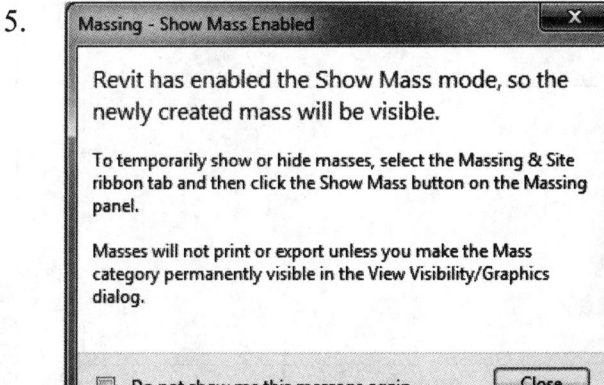

5.

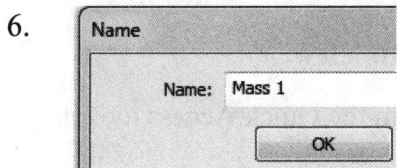

Masses, by default, are invisible. However, in order to create and edit masses you need to see what you are doing. Revit brings up a dialog to let you know that the software is switching the visibility of masses to ON, so you can work.

Press **Close**.

*If you don't want to bugged by this dialog, enable the **Don't show me this message again** option.*

6.   Enter **Mass 1** in the Name field.

    Name   Press **OK**.

    Name: Mass 1

7. 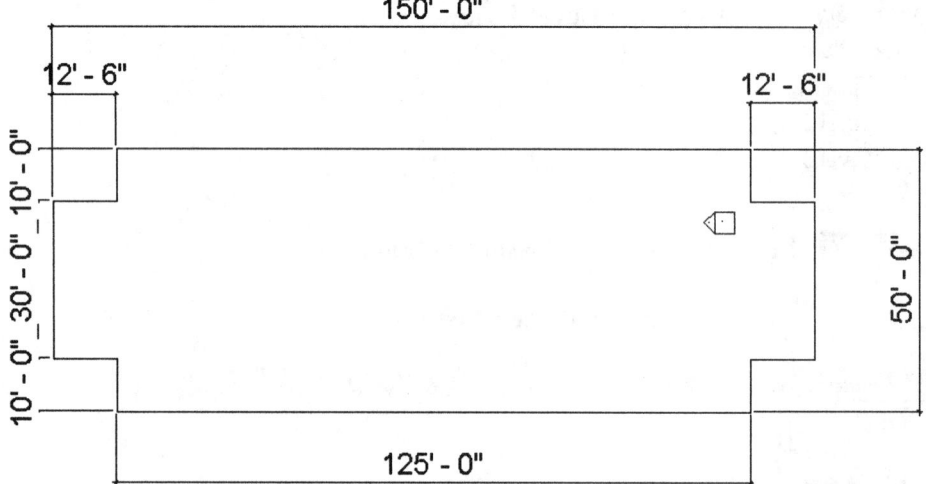 Select the **Line** tool located under the Draw panel.

8. ☑ Chain   Offset: 0' 0"   ☐ Radius: 1' 0"

Enable **Chain** in the Options bar located on the bottom of the screen.
This allows you to draw lines without always having to pick the start point.

9. Create the shape shown.
The top figure shows the units in Imperial units.
The bottom figure shows the units in millimeters.

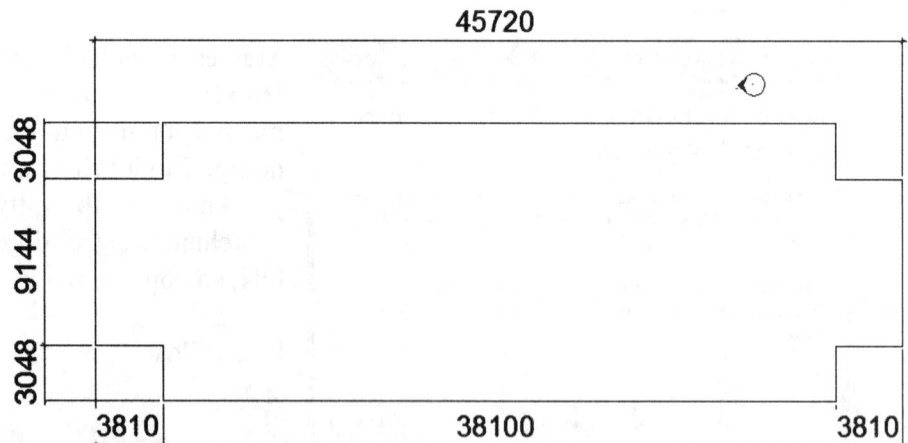

10.  Switch to a 3D view.
Activate the **View** ribbon and select **3D View**.

You can also switch to a 3D view from the Quick Access toolbar.

11. Window around the entire figure so it is highlighted.

12. 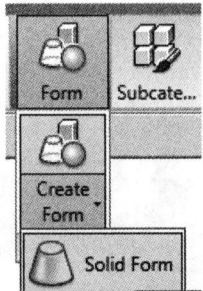 Select **Form→Create Form→Solid Form**.

13. 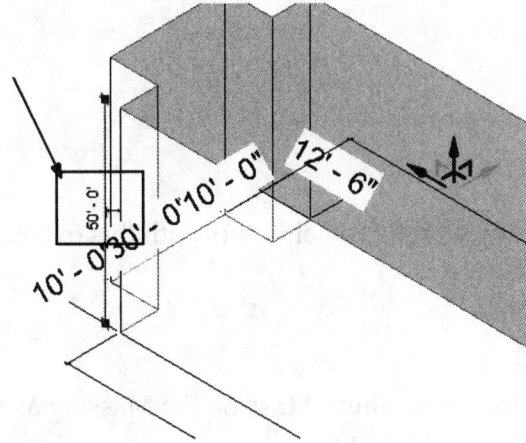 An extrusion distance is displayed. This can be edited, if desired.

14.  Select the green check box to **Finish Mass**.

The Mass is created.

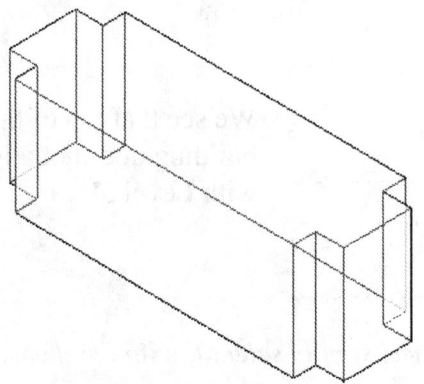

15. Save the file as *ex2-2.rvt*.

TIP: Object tracking will only work if the sketch objects are active and available in the current sketch. You can use **Pick** to copy entities into the current sketch.

Exercise 2-3
Modifying Mass Elements

Drawing Name: ex2-2.rvt
Estimated Time: 30 minutes

This exercise reinforces the following skills:

- ❑ Show Mass
- ❑ Align
- ❑ Modify Mass
- ❑ Mirror
- ❑ Create Form
- ❑ Save View

A short video of this exercise is available on my website to help users with this exercise. Access at *www.mossdesigns.com/ex3-3-revit.avi.*

1. Open *ex2-2.rvt.*

2. 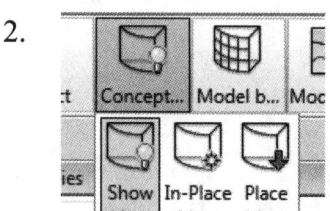 If you don't see the mass, **Show Mass** on the Massing & Site ribbon to turn mass visibility ON.

3. 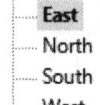 Elevations (Building Elevation)   Activate the **East** Elevation.
   East
   North
   South
   West

4. 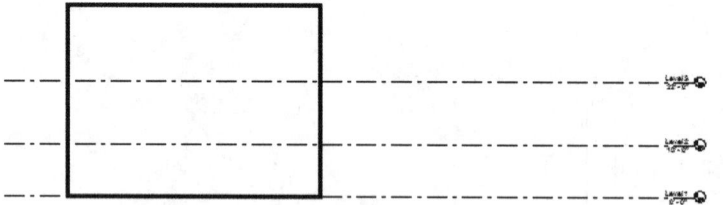 We see that top of the building does not align with Level 3.

   To adjust the horizontal position of the level lines, simply select the line and use the grip to extend or shorten it.

5. Modify   Select the **Modify** Ribbon.

6. 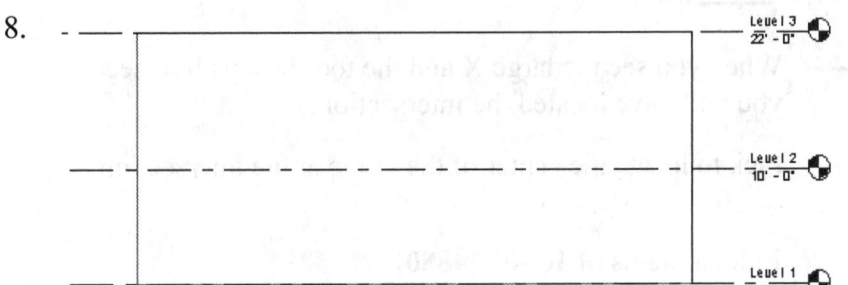 Select the **Align** tool.

When using Align, the first element selected acts as the source, the second element selected shifts position to align with the first element.

7. Select the top level line (Level 3) then select the top of the extrusion.

Right click and select **Cancel** to exit the Align command.

8. 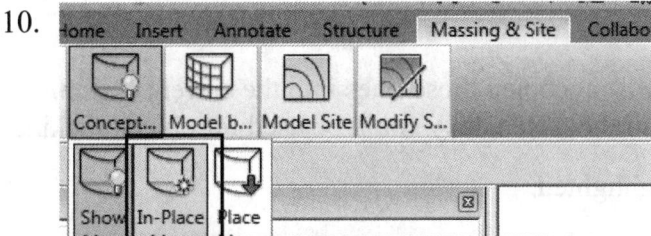 The top of the extrusion now aligns to level 3.

9. Activate **Level 2** under Floor Plans.

10. Select **In-Place Mass**.

11. Name the new mass **Tower**.

Name: Tower

Press **OK**.

12. 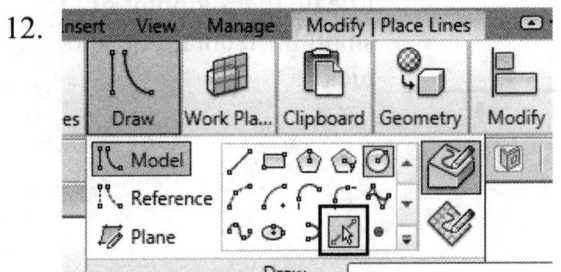 You can use object tracking to locate the intersection between the two corners.

To activate object tracking, enable the **Pick Lines** tool located under Draw. Then select the two lines you want to align with.

13. 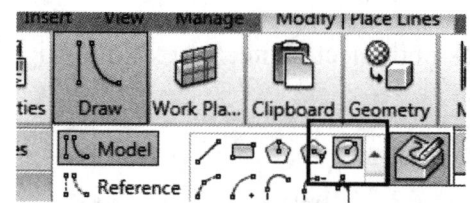 Select the two lines indicated to be used for object tracking to locate the center of the circle.

14. Select the **Circle** tool under Draw.

15. When you see the large X and the tooltip says Intersection, you will have located the intersection.

Pick to locate the center of the circle at the intersection.

16. Enter a radius of **16'-0"** [**4880**].

16'

When you used the Pick Line tool, you copied those lines into the current sketch. Once the lines were part of the current sketch, they could be used for object tracking.

17. Select the circle sketch so it is highlighted.

18. 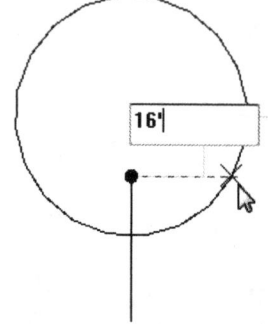 Select the **Draw Mirror Axis** tool under the **Mirror** tool.

19. 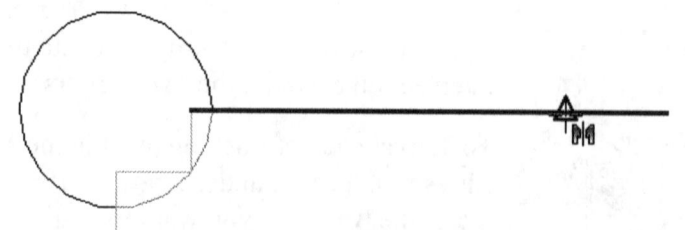 Locate the midpoint of the small horizontal line and pick.

20. 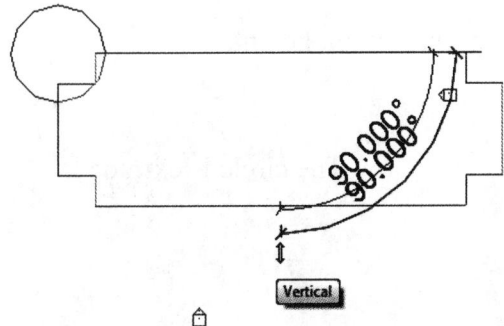 Bring your mouse down in the Vertical direction and pick for the second point of the mirror axis.

21. 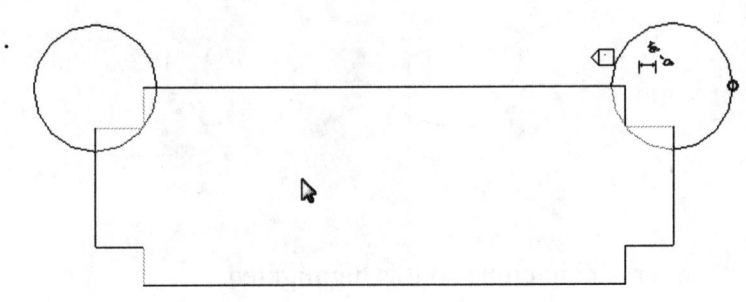 The circle sketch is mirrored.

Left click to release the selection.

22. 3D Views {3D} Switch to a 3D view using the Project Browser.

23. 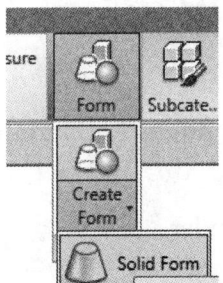 Select one of the circles so it is highlighted.

Select **Form→Create Form→Solid Form**.

24. 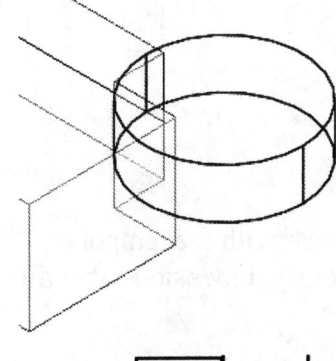 A small toolbar will appear with two options for extruding the circle.

Select the option that looks like a cylinder.

25. 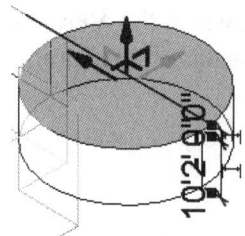 A preview of the extrusion will appear with the temporary dimension. You can edit the temporary dimension to modify the height of the extrusion.

Press ENTER to accept the default height.

26. 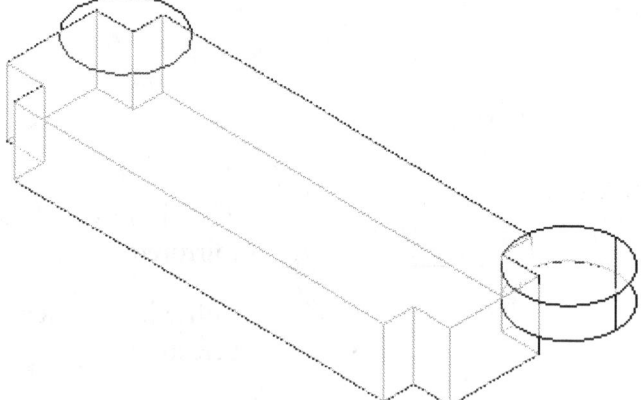 The circle is extruded.

27. 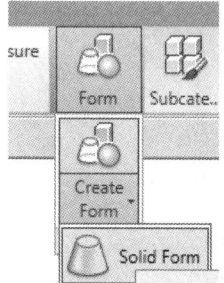 Select the remaining circle so it is highlighted.

Select **Form→Create Form→Solid Form**.

28. 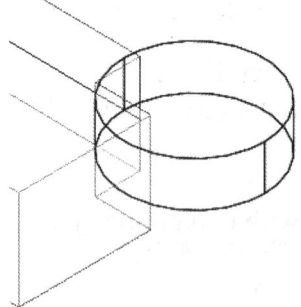 A small toolbar will appear with two options for extruding the circle.

Select the option that looks like a cylinder.

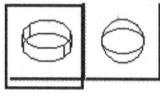

29. 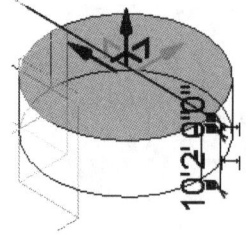 A preview of the extrusion will appear with the temporary dimension. You can edit the temporary dimension to modify the height of the extrusion.

Press ENTER to accept the default height.

30.

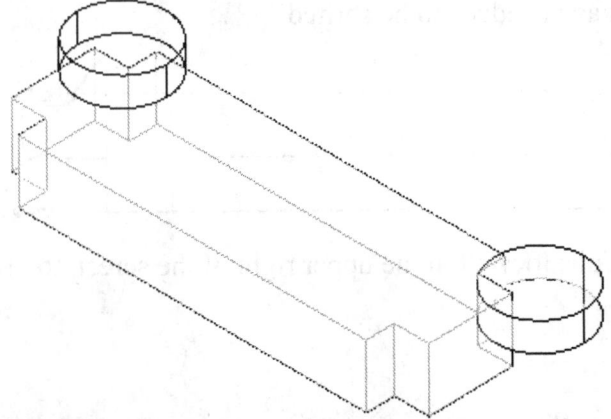

Both circles are now extruded.

31. 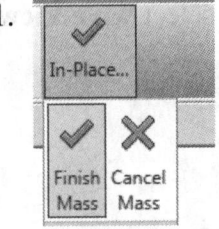 Select **Finish Mass**.

32. Activate the **South** Elevation.

- Elevations (Building Elevation)
  - East
  - North
  - **South**
  - West

33. Select each level line.

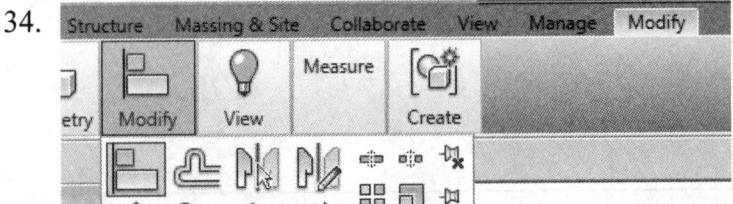

Right click and select **Maximize 3D Extents**.
This will extend each level line so it covers the entire model.

34. Activate the Modify ribbon.

Select the **Align** tool from the Modify Panel.

35.  On the Options bar, enable **Multiple Alignment**.

36.

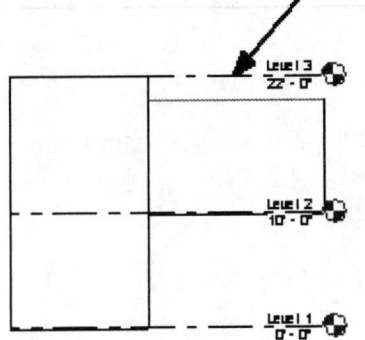

Select the Level 3 line as the source object.

37. Select the top of the two towers as the edges to be shifted.

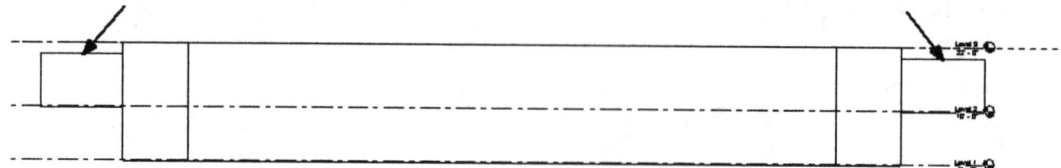

38.  Use the ViewCube located in the upper right of the screen to orbit the model.

39. To save the new orientation, right click on the ViewCube and select **Save View**.

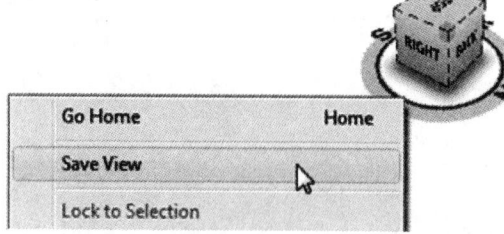

Go Home	Home
Save View	
Lock to Selection	

40. Enter name for new 3D View

    Name: 3D Ortho 2

    OK

    Enter **3D Ortho 2** for the name of the view.

    Press **OK**.

41. 3D Views
    — 3D Ortho 2
    — {3D}

    The **Saved** view is now listed in the Project browser under 3D Views.

42. Save the file as *ex2-3.rvt*.

> ➤ Pick on a mass element to activate the element's grips. You can use the grips to change the element's shape, size, and location.
> ➤ You can only use the **View→Orient** menu to activate 3D views when you are already in 3D view mode.

Exercise 2-4
Creating Wall by Face

Drawing Name: ex2-3.rvt
Estimated Time: 15 minutes

This exercise reinforces the following skills:

- Wall by Face
- Trim
- Show Mass

You can add doors and windows to your conceptual model to make it easier to visualize.

1.   Open *ex2-3.rvt*.

2.   3D Views
         3D Ortho 2
         {3D}   Activate the **SAVED** view under 3D Views.

3.   Massing & Site   Activate the **Massing & Site** ribbon.

4.   nsert Annotate Structure Massing & Site   Select **Model by Face→Wall**.

      Model b... Model Site Modify S...

         Roof
      Curtai   Wall

5.   Properties   Note the wall type currently enabled
                                              in the Properties pane. A different
      Basic Wall   wall type can be selected from the
      Generic - 8"   drop-down list available using the
                                              small down arrow.

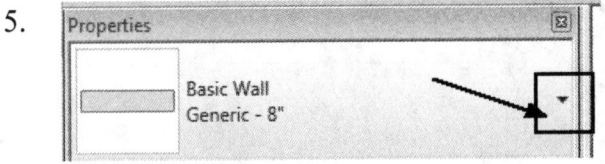

      Imperial: *Metric:*
      Set the Default Wall Type to: Set the Default Wall Type to:
      Basic Wall: Generic- 8 in.   **Basic Wall: Generic- 200 mm**.

6.   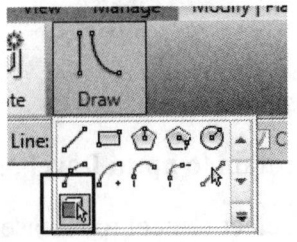   Enable **Pick Faces** from the Draw Panel on the ribbon.

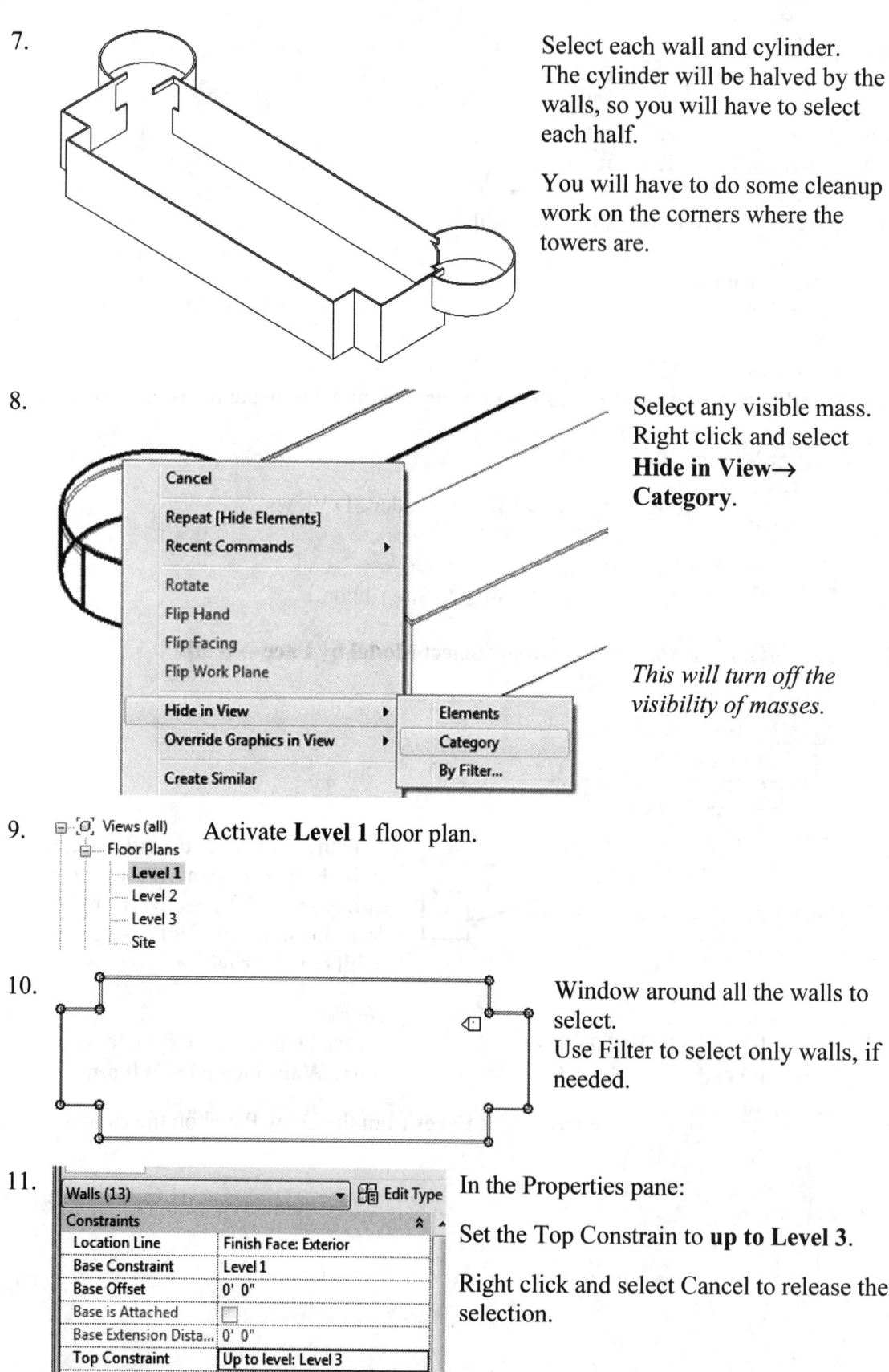

7. Select each wall and cylinder. The cylinder will be halved by the walls, so you will have to select each half.

You will have to do some cleanup work on the corners where the towers are.

8. Select any visible mass. Right click and select **Hide in View→ Category**.

Cancel

Repeat [Hide Elements]
Recent Commands

Rotate
Flip Hand
Flip Facing
Flip Work Plane

This will turn off the visibility of masses.

Hide in View   Elements
Override Graphics in View   Category
Create Similar   By Filter...

9. Views (all)
   Floor Plans
      Level 1
      Level 2
      Level 3
      Site

Activate **Level 1** floor plan.

10. Window around all the walls to select.
Use Filter to select only walls, if needed.

11. Walls (13)   Edit Type

In the Properties pane:

Set the Top Constrain to **up to Level 3**.

Right click and select Cancel to release the selection.

Constraints	
Location Line	Finish Face: Exterior
Base Constraint	Level 1
Base Offset	0' 0"
Base is Attached	☐
Base Extension Dista...	0' 0"
Top Constraint	Up to level: Level 3
Unconnected Height	22' 0"
Top Offset	0' 0"

12.   Hold down the Ctrl Key.
Select the four walls indictaed.

13. In the Properties pane:

Set the Top Constrain to **up to Level 2**.

Right click and select Cancel to release the selection.

Walls (4)	▼ 🔲 Edit Type
Constraints	⌃ ▲
Location Line	Finish Face: Exterior
Base Constraint	Level 1
Base Offset	0' 0"
Base is Attached	☐
Base Extension Dista...	0' 0"
Top Constraint	Up to level: Level 2
Unconnected Height	10' 0"

14. Activate **Level 2** under Floor Plans.

```
Floor Plans
    Level 1
    Level 2
    Level 3
```

15. In the Properties Pane:

Set the Underlay to **None**.

Visibility/Graphics ...	Edit...
Visual Style	Hidden Line
Graphic Display Opt...	Edit...
Underlay	None
Underlay Orientation	Plan

This will turn off the visibility of all entities located below Level 2.

16. Select the **Trim** tool from the Modify ribbon to clean up where the tower joins with the walls.

17. When you select to trim, be sure to select the section you want to keep.

18. 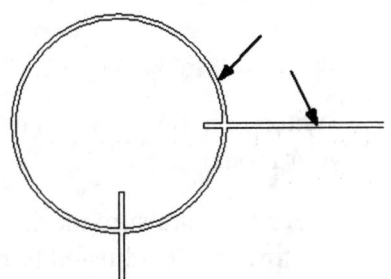 Select the arc and wall indicated.

19. 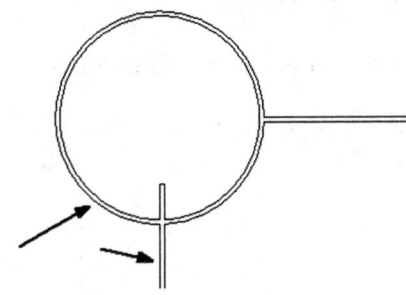 Select the arc and wall indicated.

> Select the first line or wall to trim/extend. (Click on the part you want to keep)

Note that you have some instructions in the lower left of the screen to assist you.

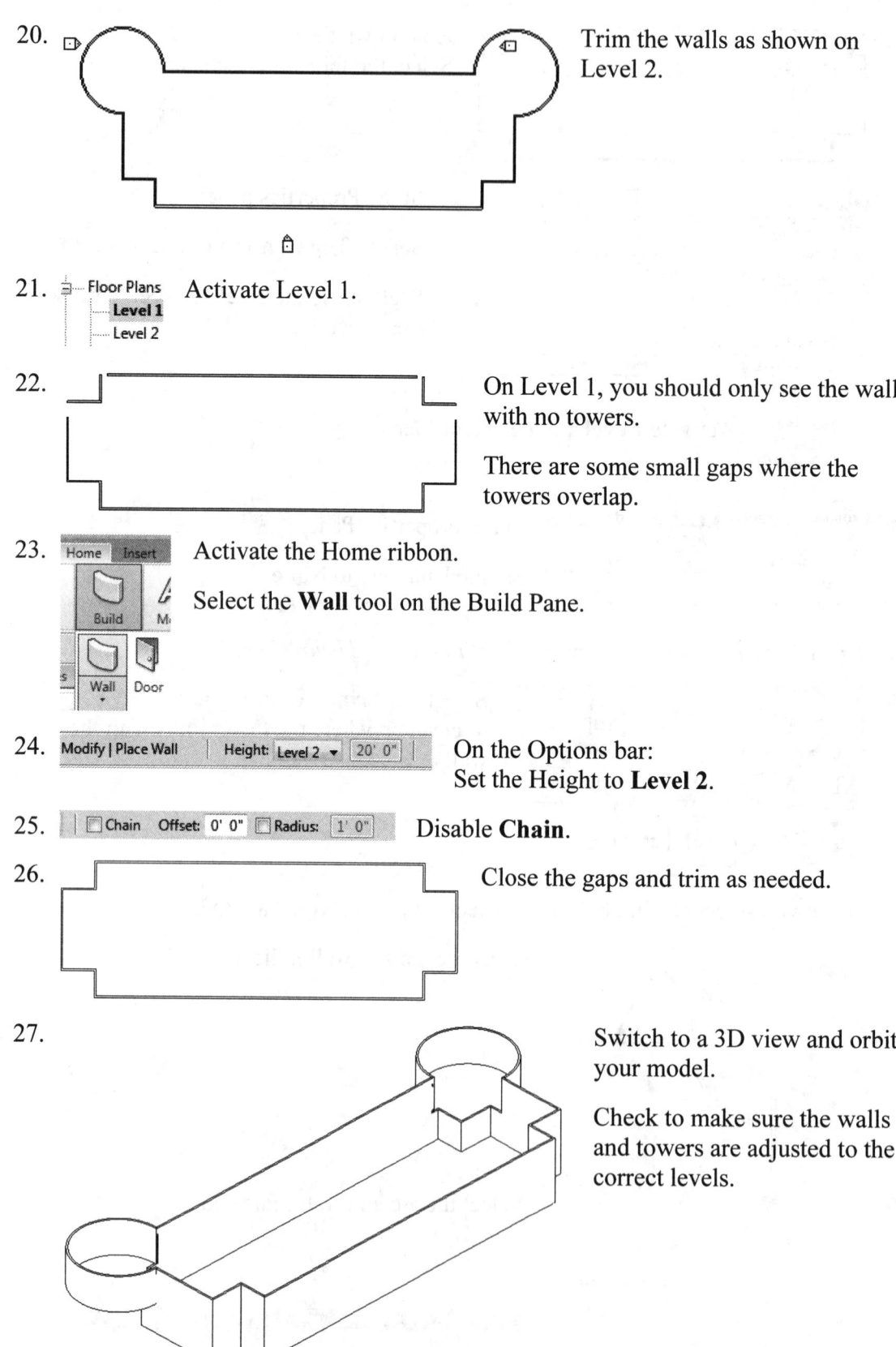

20. Trim the walls as shown on Level 2.

21. Floor Plans
    Level 1
    Level 2

    Activate Level 1.

22. On Level 1, you should only see the walls with no towers.

    There are some small gaps where the towers overlap.

23. Home Insert

    Build

    Wall Door

    Activate the Home ribbon.

    Select the **Wall** tool on the Build Pane.

24. Modify | Place Wall   Height: Level 2 ▾   20' 0"

    On the Options bar:
    Set the Height to **Level 2**.

25. ☐ Chain Offset: 0' 0" ☐ Radius: 1' 0"

    Disable **Chain**.

26. Close the gaps and trim as needed.

27. Switch to a 3D view and orbit your model.

    Check to make sure the walls and towers are adjusted to the correct levels.

28. Save as *ex2-4.rvt*.

Exercise 2-5
Adding Doors and Windows

Drawing Name: ex2-4.rvt
Estimated Time: 30 minutes

This exercise reinforces the following skills:

    ❑ Basics
    ❑ Door
    ❑ Load from Library
    ❑ Window
    ❑ Array
    ❑ Mirror
    ❑ Shading

You can add doors and windows to your conceptual model to make it easier to visualize.

1.   Open *ex2-4.rvt*.

2.   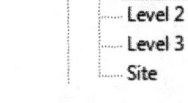   Activate **Level 1** under Floor Plans.

3.   Level 1 should appear like this.

4.   Home   Activate **Home ribbon**.

5.   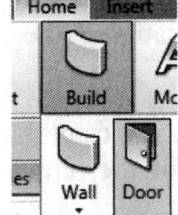   Select the **Door** tool under the Build panel.

6.   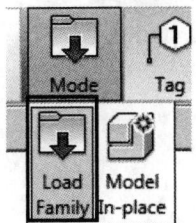   Select **Load Family** under the Mode panel.

7.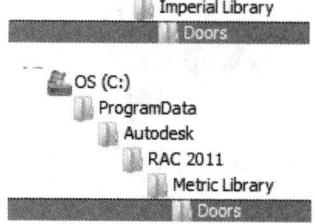

Browse to the **Doors** folder under the Imperial or Metric library – use Imperial if you are using Imperial units or use Metric if you are using Metric units.

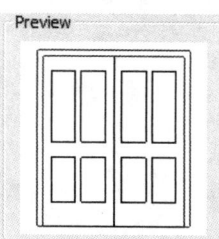

As you highlight each file in the folder, you can see a preview of the family.

8.

For Imperial Units:
Locate the *Double-:Panel2.rfa* file.

For Metric Units:
Locate the *M_Double-Panel 2.rfa* file.

Press **Open**.

9.

62' - 2"   62' - 2"

Place the door so it is centered on the wall as shown.
Doors are wall-hosted. So, you will only see a door preview when you place your cursor over a wall.

10.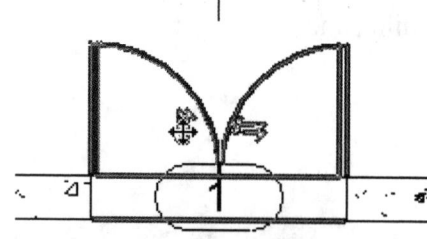

If you press the space bar before you pick to place, you can control the orientation of the door.

After you have placed the door, you can flip the door by picking on it then pick on the vertical or horizontal arrows.

11.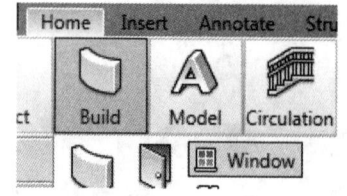

Pick the **Window** tool from the Build panel.

12. 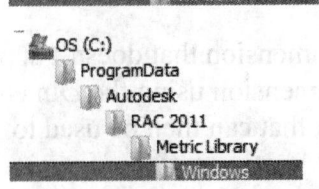 Select **Load Family** from the Mode panel.

13. Browse to the **Windows** folder under the Imperial or Metric library – use Imperial if you are using Imperial units or use Metric if you are using Metric units.

14. For Imperial Units:
Located the *Casement with Trim.rfa* file.

For Metric Units:
Locate the *M_Casement with Trim.rfa* file.

Press **Open**.

15. For Imperial Units:

From the drop-down list, select the 24″ x 48″ size for the Casement with Trim window.

Access the list of available sizes using the small down arrow indicated.

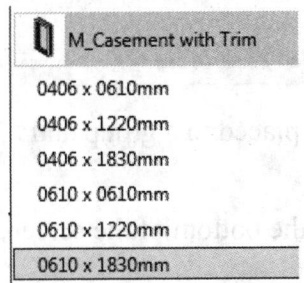

For Metric Units:

From the drop-down list, select the 0610 x 1830 mm size for the M_Casement with Trim window.

16.   **6' - 6"**   Place the window **6'-6"** [**3000 mm**] from the inner left wall.

Right click and select **Cancel** to exit the command.

Dimensions in Revit work differently. Revit uses *temporary* dimensions and *permanent* dimensions. Permanent dimensions are the parametric dimensions attached to each object. You can modify these dimensions by clicking on the object. Temporary dimensions are the dimensions you place using the Dimension tool or typing 'DI'. The dimension values of temporary dimensions can only be modified by changing the permanent dimensions.

If you want to define the position of an object using a dimension that doesn't appear when you pick the object, you can apply a temporary dimension using the Dimension tool. This will add a permanent dimension to the object that can then be used to position the object.

17.   **6' - 6"**   Pick the window so it highlights.

18.   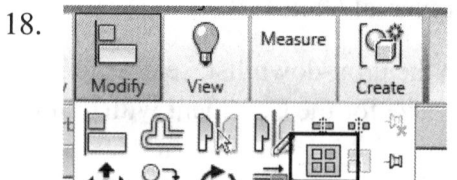   Select the **Array** tool under the Modify panel.

19.   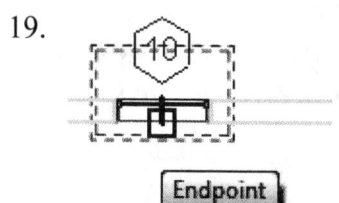   Select the midpoint of the window as the basepoint for the array.

20.   Modify | Windows   ☑ Group And Associate   Number: 5   Move To: ○ 2nd ● Last   ☐ Constrain

Enable Group and Associate. This assigns the windows placed to a group and allows you to edit the array.

Set the array quantity to **5** on the options bar located on the bottom of the screen. Enable **Last**.

Array has two options. One option allows you to place elements at a set distance apart. The second option allows you to fill a distance with equally spaced elements. We will fill a specified distance with five elements equally spaced.

21.

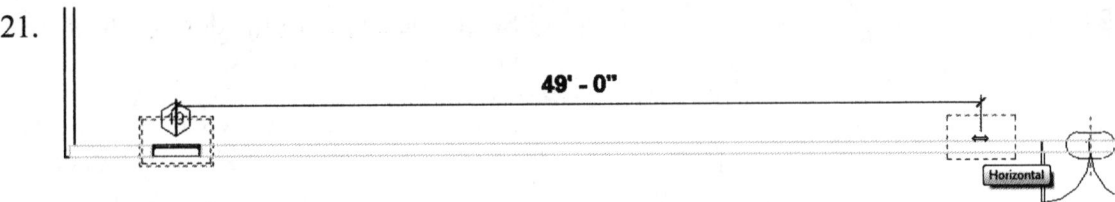

Pick a point 49'-0" [**14,935.20**] from the first selected point to the right.

22.

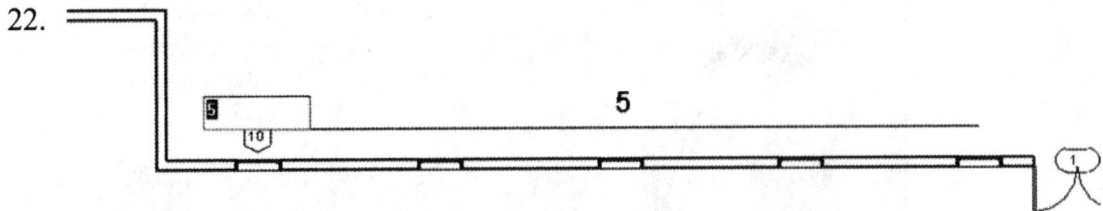

You will see a preview of how the windows will fill the space.

Press **ENTER** to accept.

23.

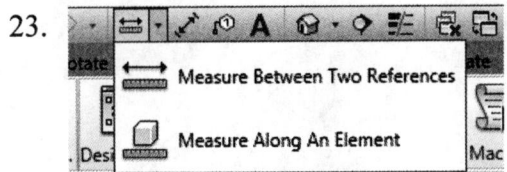

Select the **Measure** tool on the Quick Access toolbar.

24.

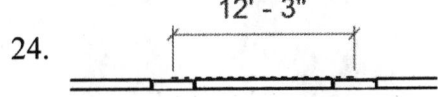

Check the distance between the windows and you will see that they are all spaced equally.

25.

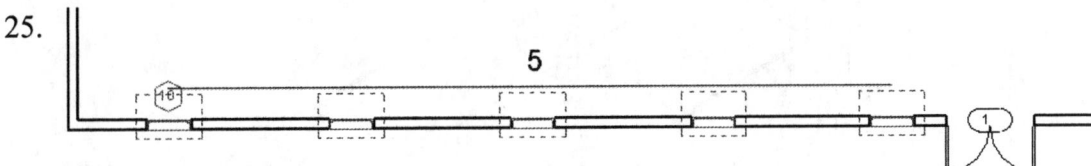

Window around the entire array to select all the windows.

The array count will display.

26.

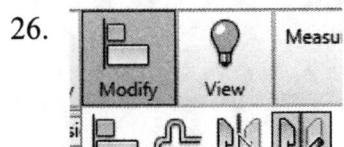

Use the **Mirror→Draw Mirror Axis** tool to mirror the windows to the other side of the wall opposite the door.

27.

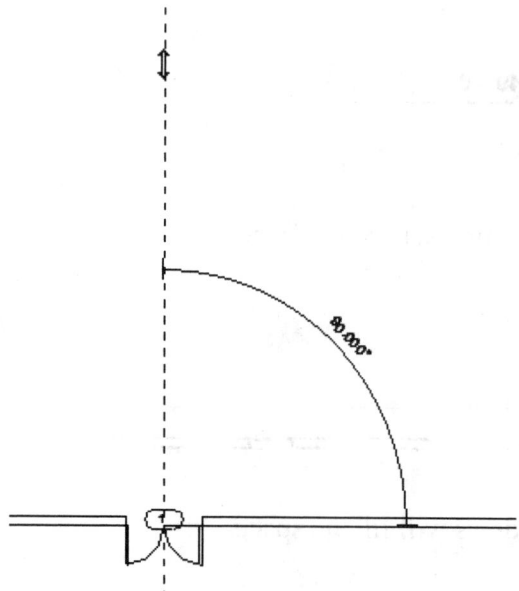

Select the center of the door as the start point of the mirror axis.

Move the cursor upwards at a 90 degree angle and pick a point above the door.

28. Left pick anywhere in the graphics window to complete the command.

29. 3D Views
　　　3D Ortho 2
　　　{3D}

Switch to a **3D** View.

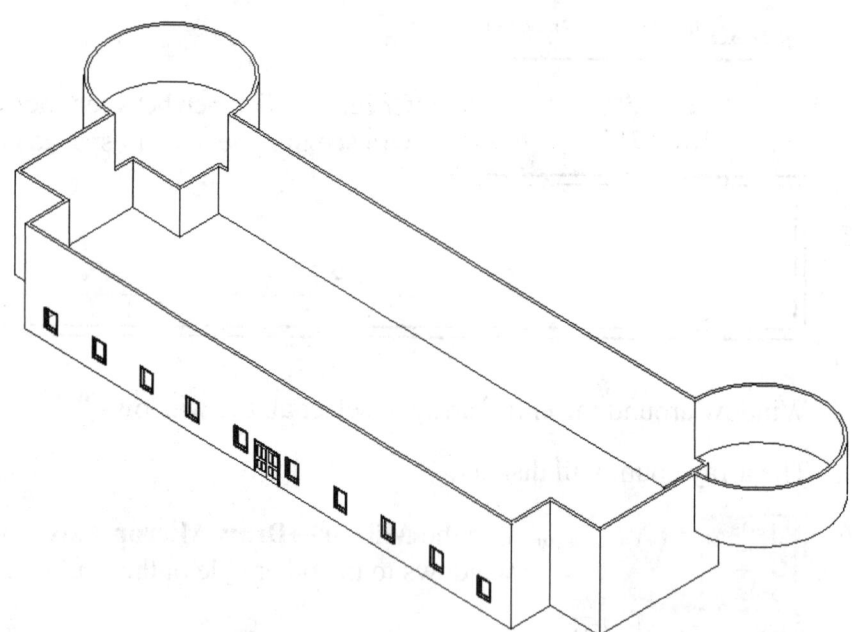

30.

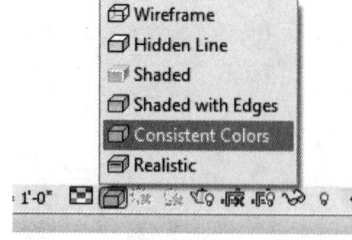

Set the Model Graphics Style to **Consistent Colors**.

We have created a conceptual model to show a client.

31. Save the file as *ex2-5.rvt*.

Additional Projects

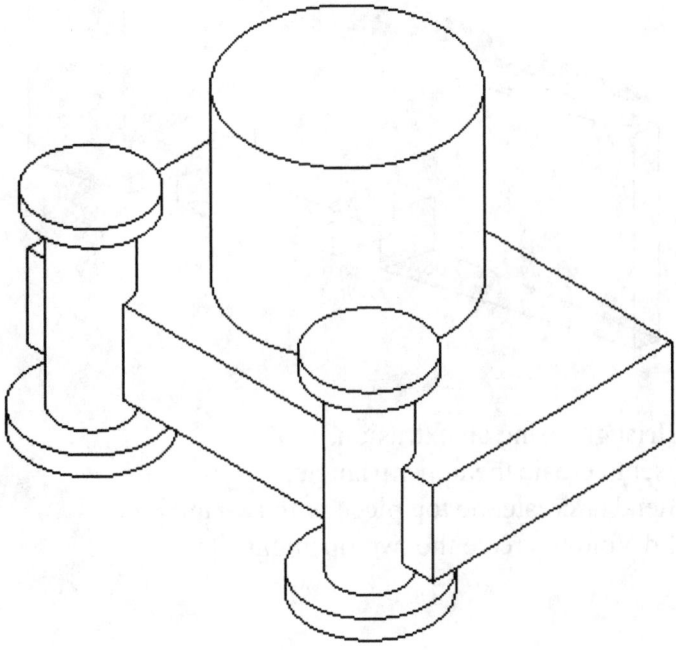

1)   Create a conceptual model like the one shown using an extruded rectangle, an extruded cylinder and a revolve.

2)   Make the shape shown using a Blend. The base is a rectangle and the top is a circle located at the center of the rectangle.

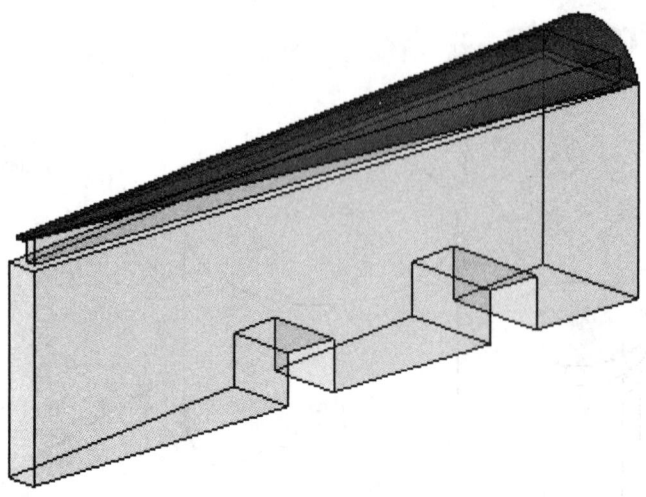

3)   Make a triangle using an extrusion.
      Use Offset to create the upper triangle.
      Use a Blend to create the top piece with two arcs.
      Use Solid Void to create the two openings.

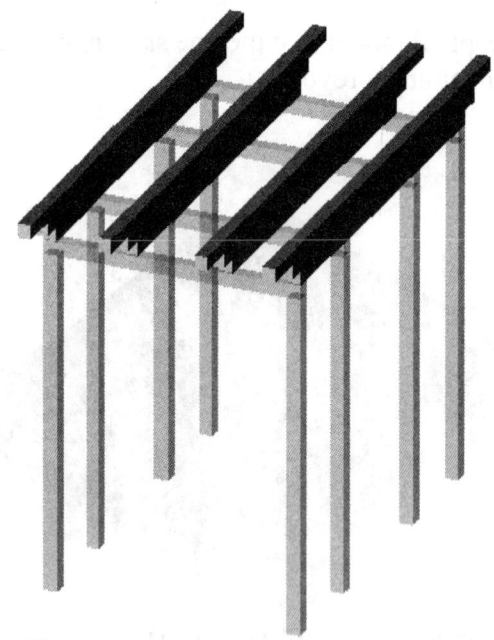

4) Design a pergola using 4″ x 4″ posts and beams.

Lesson 2 Quiz

True or False

1. Masses can be created inside Projects or as a Conceptual Mass file.
2. Forms are always created by drawing a sketch, selecting the sketch, and clicking ⬚ Create Form.
3. In order to see masses, Show Mass must be enabled.
4. Masses are level-based.

Multiple Choice [Select the Best Answer]

5. Faces on masses can be converted to the following:

   A. Walls
   B. Ceilings
   C. Floors
   D. Doors
   E. A, B, and C, but NOT D

6. You can adjust the distance a mass is extruded by:

   A. Editing the temporary dimension that appears before a solid form is created
   B. Use the ALIGN tool.
   C. Use the 3D drag tool
   D. Using the Properties pane located on the left of the screen.

ANSWERS:
   1) T; 2) T; 3) T; 4) T; 5) E; 6) A, B, and C

Notes:

Lesson 3
Floor Plans

> ➢ Put a semi-colon between snap increments, not a comma.
> ➢ If you edit the first grid number to 'A' before you array, Revit will automatically increment them alphabetically for you; A, B, C, etc.
> ➢ You will need to 'Ungroup' an element in an array before you can modify any of the properties.
> ➢ To keep elements from accidentally moving, you can select the element and use **Pin Objects** or highlight the dimension string and lock the dimensions.
> ➢ You can purge the unused families and components in your project file in order to reduce the file space. Go to **File→Purge Unused**.
> ➢ Revit creates stairs from the center of the run, so it may be helpful to place some reference planes or detail lines defining the location of the starting points for the runs of any stairs.
> ➢ Floor plans should be oriented so that North is pointing up or to the right.
> ➢ The direction you draw your walls (clockwise or counterclockwise) controls the initial location of the exterior face of the wall. Drawing a wall from left to right places the exterior on the top. Drawing a wall from right to left places the exterior on the bottom. When you highlight a wall, the blue flip orientation arrows are always adjacent to the exterior side of the wall.

Throughout the rest of the text, we will be creating new types of families. Here are the basic steps to creating a new family.

1. Select the element you want to define (wall, window, floor, stairs, etc.).
2. Select **Edit Type** from the Properties pane.
3. Select **Duplicate**.
4. Rename: Enter a new name for your family type.
5. Redefine: Edit the structure, assign new materials, change the dimensions.
6. Reload or Reassign: Assign the new type to the element.

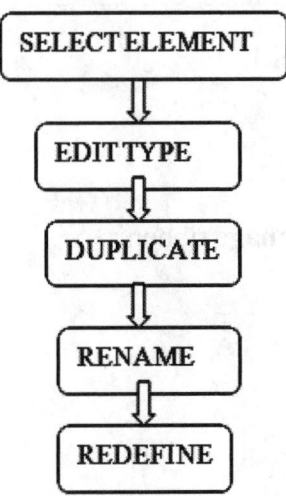

Exercise 3-1
Placing a Grid

Drawing Name: default.rte [DefaultMetric.rte]
Estimated Time: 30 minutes

This exercise reinforces the following skills:

- □ Units
- □ Snap Increments
- □ Grid
- □ Array
- □ Ungroup
- □ Dimension
- □ Dimension Settings

1. Start a new project.

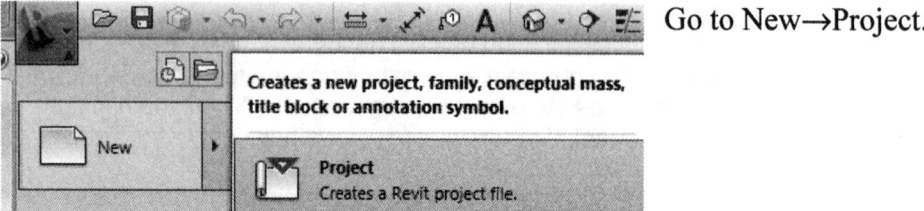 Go to New→Project.

2. Press **OK** to accept the default project settings.

3. Activate **Level 1**.

Views (all)
  Floor Plans
    Level 1
    Level 2
    Site

4. Manage   Activate the **Manage** ribbon.

 Under **Settings**, select **Snaps**.

5. ☑ Length dimension snap increments
   40';25';5'

   Set the snap increments for length to **40′; 25′; 5′ [1500;7620;1220]**.

   Use a semi-colon between the distance values.

   Press **OK**.

6. Home   Activate the **Home** ribbon.

7. Select **Grid** under the Datum panel.

   Datum Roor

   Level Grid

8. Click to enter grid start point   Pick on the left side of the graphics window to start the grid line.

9.   Pick a point above the first point.

   Right mouse click and select Cancel to exit the Grid mode

   Your first grid line is placed.

10. ☑   Select the Grid text to edit it.

   1
   3U

11. Change the text to **A**.

   A
   3U

   If you edit the first grid letter before you array, Revit will automatically increment the arrayed grid elements.

12. Select the grid line so it is highlighted.

Select the **Array** tool under the Modify panel.

13.

Set the Number to **8**.
Enable Move To: **2nd**.

14.

Pick the first point as just under the grid bubble.
Set the distance **25′** [**7620mm**] between grid lines.

15.

You will see a preview of the array.
Verify that the number of grids is set to **8**.

Left click to finish or press **ENTER**.

16. Select the **Grid** tool under the Datum panel.

17.

Draw a horizontal line near the bottom of the grid.

Right click and select Cancel to exit the command.

18. Edit the horizontal bubble text.
Change it to **1**.

19. The square boxes that appear at the end of the grid lines control the appearance of the grid bubbles. Place a check in both ends of the horizontal grid line.

20. 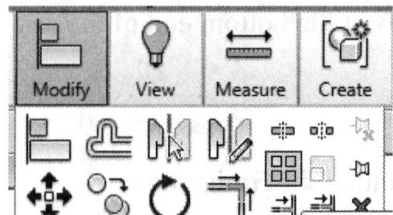 Select the horizontal grid line so it is highlighted.

Select the **Array** tool under the Modify panel.

21. ☑ Group And Associate   Number: 3   Move To: ◉ 2nd ○ Last

Set the Number to **3**.
Enable Move To: **2nd**.

22. 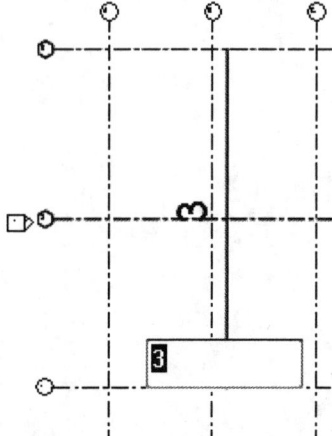 Pick the first point as just under the grid bubble.

Set a distance of **40′** [**12200**] between grid lines.

23. 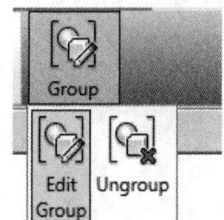 You will see a preview of the array.
Verify that the number of grids is set to **3**.

Left click to finish or press **ENTER**.

24. Select one of the vertical grid lines.
It should highlight in red.

25. Select **Edit Group** under the Group panel.

When we created an array, we grouped the grid lines.

26. Select the visible grid line.

27. Place a check in the square box at the bottom end of the grid line.

28. Select **Finish** from the Edit Group toolbar.

Left click to release the selection.

29. 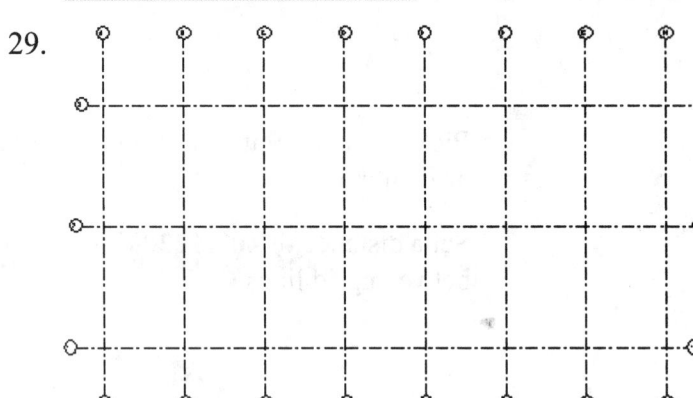 The grid lines will now have bubbles on each end.

The vertical bubbles should be labeled A through H.

The horizontal bubbles should be labeled 1 through 3.

30. Save the file as *ex3-1.rvt*.

Exercise 3-2
Placing Walls

Drawing Name: ex3-1.rvt
Estimated Time: 20 minutes

This exercise reinforces the following skills:

- Walls
- Mirror
- Filter
- Move

1.   Open or continue working in *ex3-1.rvt*.

2.   Home   Activate the Home ribbon.

3.   Type **VG** to launch the Visibility/Graphics dialog.
     Select the **Annotations Categories** tab.

4. Turn off the Visibility of Elevations in the Visibility/Graphics dialog by unchecking the box.

Press **OK**.

This turns off the visibility of the elevation tags in the display window. This does not DELETE the elevation tags or elevations.

Many users find the tags distracting.

5. Select the **Wall** tool from the Build panel on the Home ribbon.

6. Enable **Chain**.

This eliminates the need to pick a start and end point.

7. Place walls as shown.

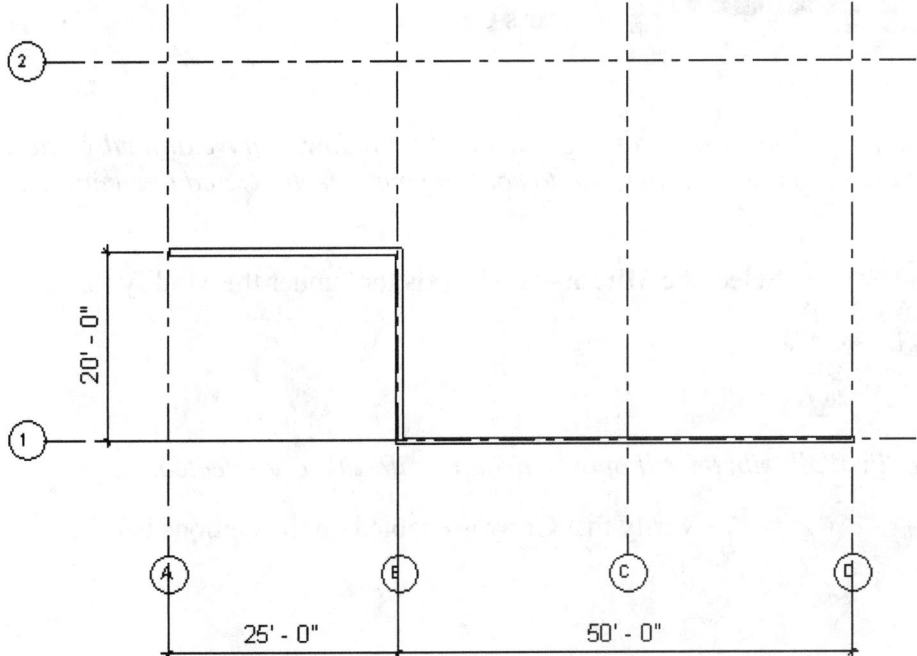

Dimensions are for reference only. Do not place dimensions.

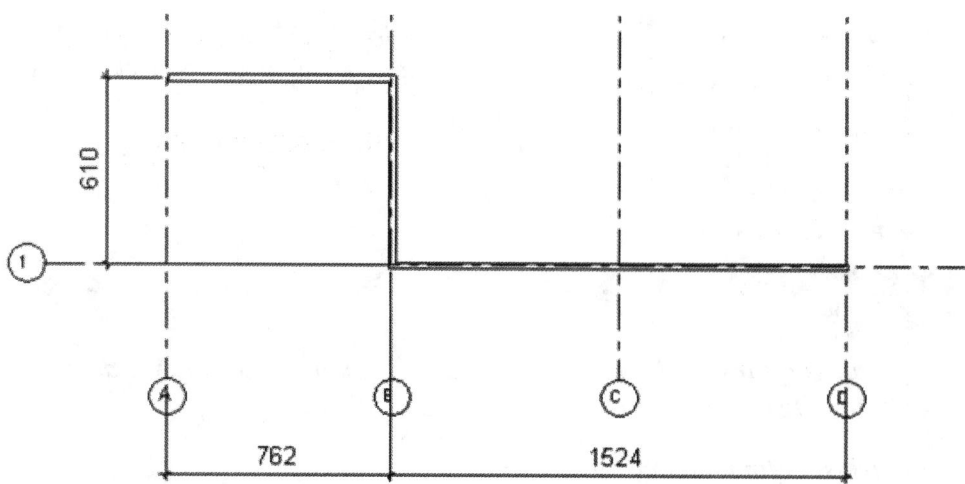

This layout shows units in centimeters.

8.   Window about the walls you just placed.

9.   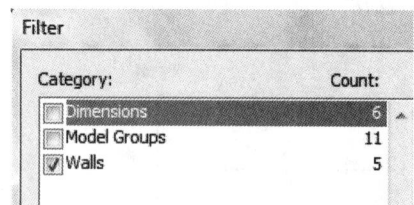   Select the **Filter** tool located in the lower right of the screen.

10.   You should just see Walls listed.

If you see other elements listed, uncheck them and this will select only the walls.

Press **OK**.

Many of my students use a crossing instead of a window or have difficulty selecting just the walls, so use the Filter tool to control your selections and that can save a lot of time.

11.   Select the **Mirror→Pick Axis** tool under the Modify Panel.

The Modify Walls ribbon will only be available if walls are selected.

12.   Verify that **Copy** is enabled on the Options bar.

13. 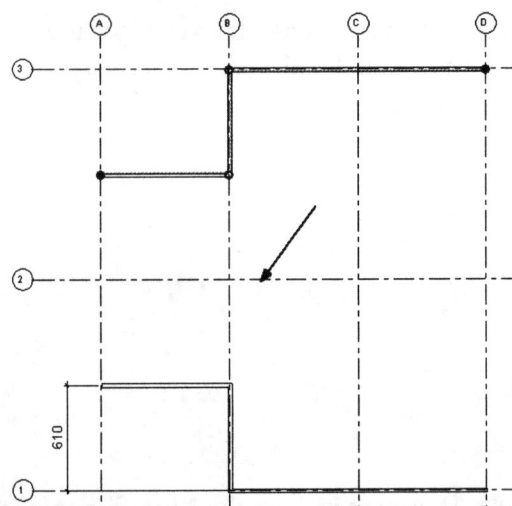 Select the grid line labeled 2 as the mirror axis.

The walls should mirror over.

14. 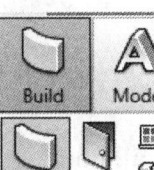 Select the **Wall** tool from the Build panel on the Home ribbon.

15. 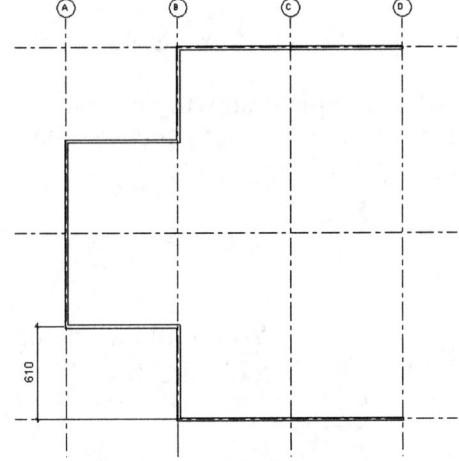 Draw a vertical wall to close the west side of the building.

16. 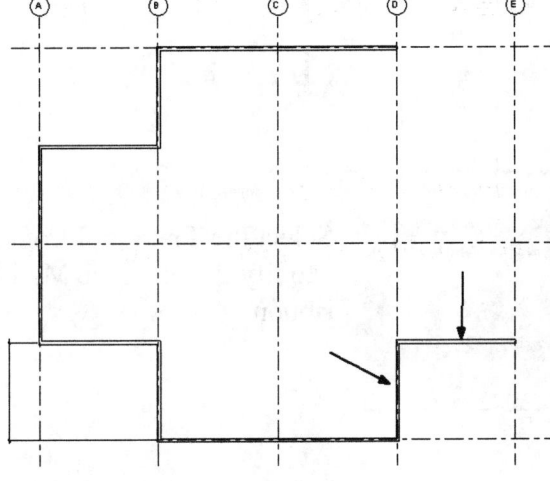 Draw two more walls.

Draw a small vertical wall.
Place a horizontal wall between D and E in the center of the bay.

17.

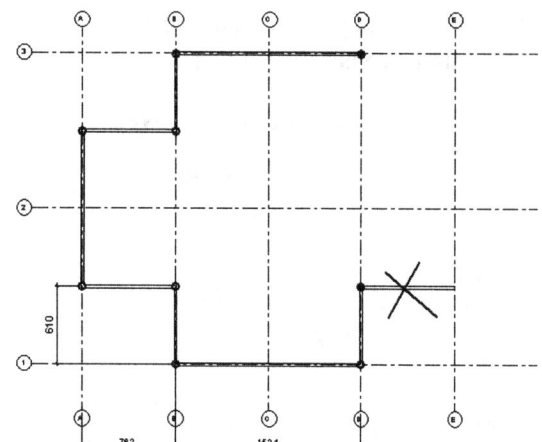

Select all the walls except for the horizontal wall located between D and E grids.

18.

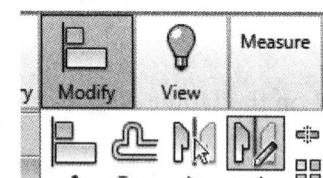

Select **Mirror→Draw Axis** from the Modify panel.

19.

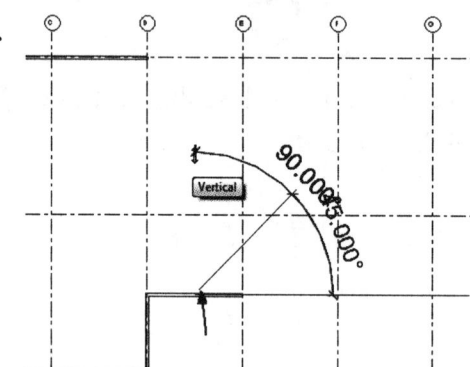

Select the midpoint of the small horizontal wall as the start point for the mirror axis.

Make sure you hold that axis at 90 degrees.

Left click to complete drawing the axis.

20.

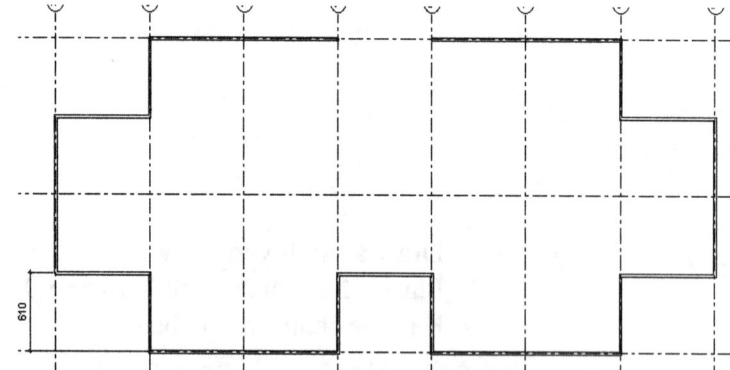

Your building should look like this.

21.

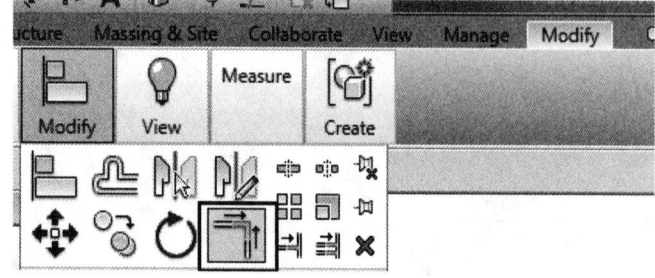

Select the **Trim** tool from the Modify Panel on the Modify ribbon.

22. 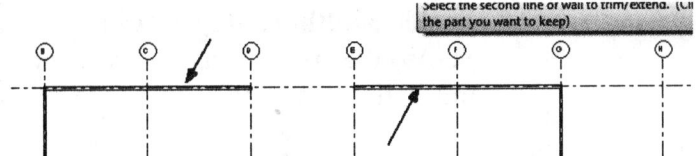 Select the two upper horizontal walls. The trim tool will join them together.

23. 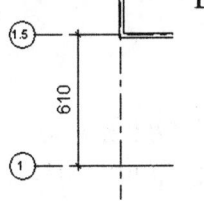 Select the **Grid** tool from the Datum panel on the Home ribbon.

24. 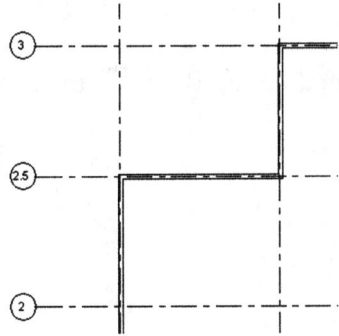 Add a grid line along the center line of the walls between Grids 1 and 2.

Label the grid **1.5**.

25. 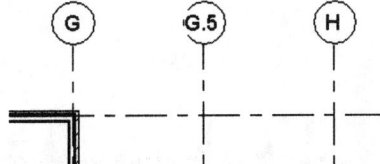 Add a grid line along the center line of the walls between Grids 2 and 3.

Label the grid **2.5**.

26. 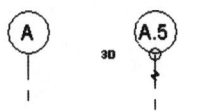 Add a vertical grid line centered between Grids A and B.

Label the grid **A.5**.

27. Add a vertical grid line centered between Grids G and H.

Label the grid **G.5**.

28. 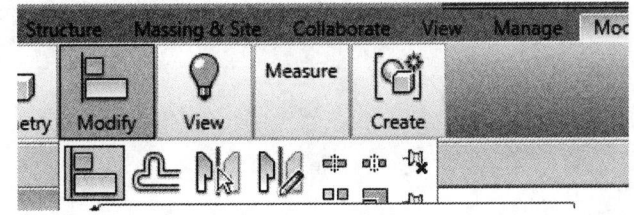 Activate the Modify Ribbon. Select the **Align** tool on the Modify Panel.

29. 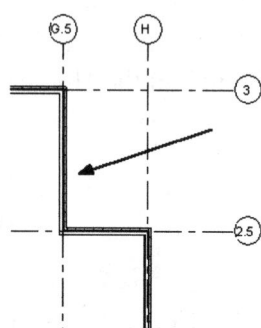 Enable **Multiple Alignment**.
Set **Wall centerline** as the preference in the Options bar.

30. Shift the walls located on the G grid to the G.5 grid using ALIGN.

31. 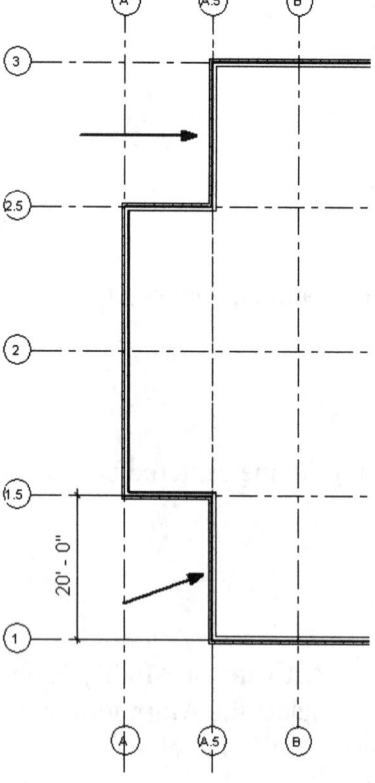 Shift the walls located on the B grid to the B.5 grid using ALIGN.

32. Save as *ex3-2.rvt*.

When drawing walls, it is important to understand the *location line*. This is the layer from which the wall is drawn and controlled from. The location line controls the position of the wall for flipping. It also sets the wall's position when wall thickness is modified. If you change the wall type, say from brick to wood stud, the stud location will be maintained. You can always select the walls and use 'Element Properties' to change the location line. The new user should experiment with this function to fully understand it.

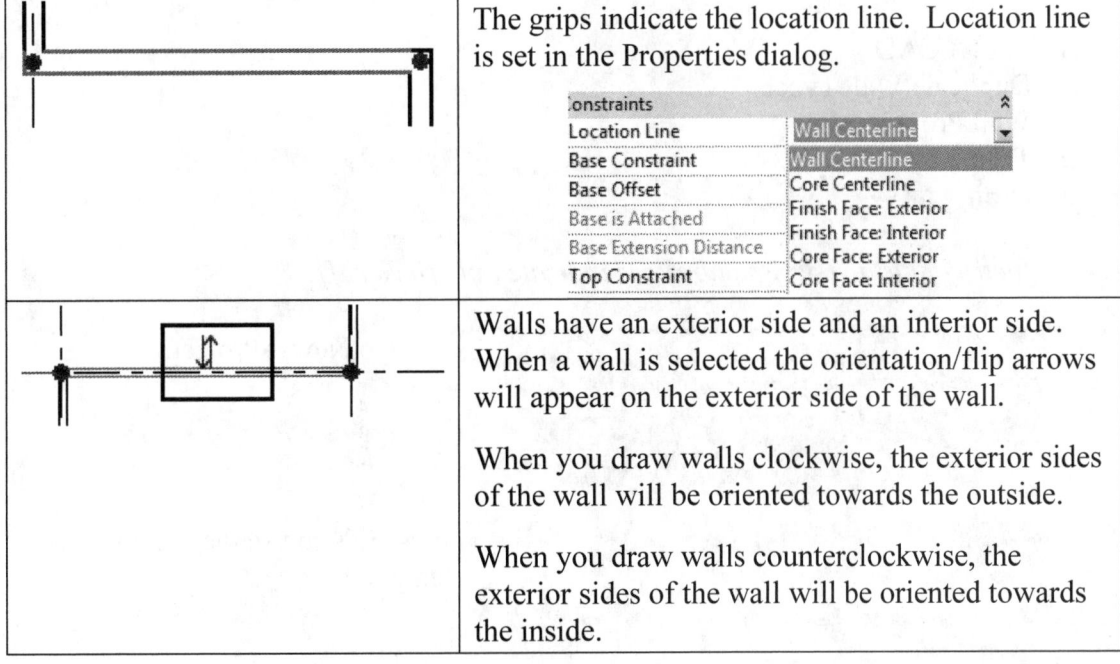	The grips indicate the location line. Location line is set in the Properties dialog.
	Walls have an exterior side and an interior side. When a wall is selected the orientation/flip arrows will appear on the exterior side of the wall.
	When you draw walls clockwise, the exterior sides of the wall will be oriented towards the outside.
	When you draw walls counterclockwise, the exterior sides of the wall will be oriented towards the inside.

Converting an AutoCAD Floor plan

Drawing Name: autocad_floorplan.dwg
Estimated Time: 30 minutes

This exercise reinforces the following skills:

- ❑ Import CAD
- ❑ Duplicate Wall Type
- ❑ Wall Properties
- ❑ Trim
- ❑ Orbit

Metric units and designations are indicated in brackets [].

1. 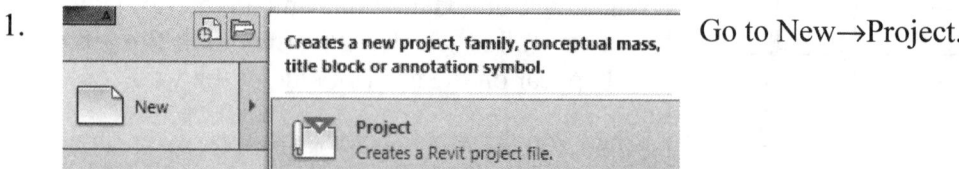 Go to New→Project.

2. Press **OK** to use the default template.

3. 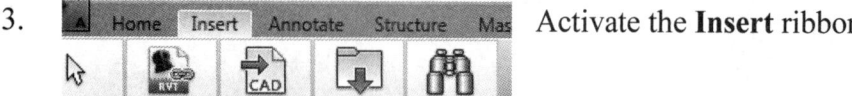 Activate the **Insert** ribbon.

4.  Select the **Import CAD** tool from the Import Panel.

5. File name: autocad_floor_plan.dwg   Locate the *autocad_floor_plan.dwg*.
   This file is located on the Supplemental Files CD.

6.

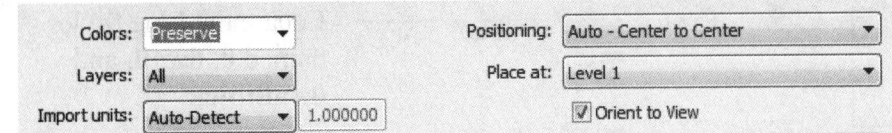

Set Colors to **Preserve**.
Set Layers to **All**.
Set Import Units to **Auto-Detect**.
Set Positioning to: **Auto- Center to Center**.
Press **Open**.

7.

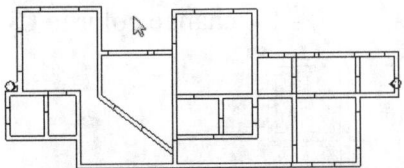

Pick the imported CAD data so it highlights.

8.

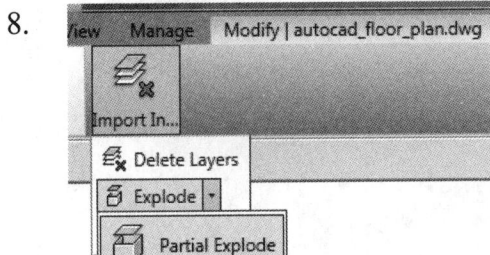

Select the **Partial Explode** tool under the
Import Instance panel.

9.

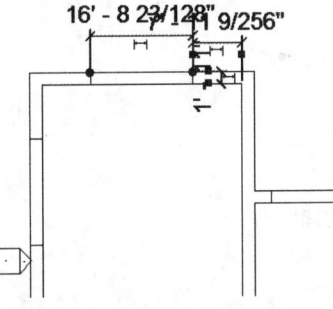

Select a line so it is highlighted.

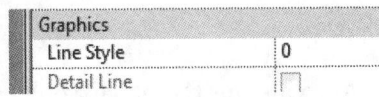

Note the Line Style listed in the Properties
pane.

10.

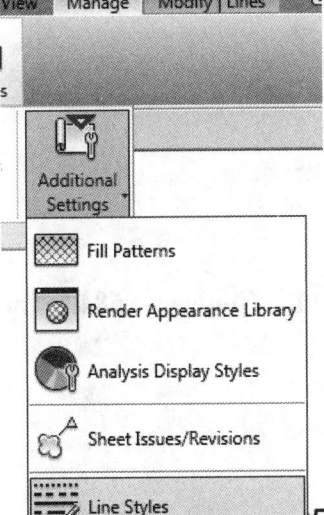

Activate the **Manage** ribbon.

Under Settings→Additional Settings:

Select **Line Styles**.

11. 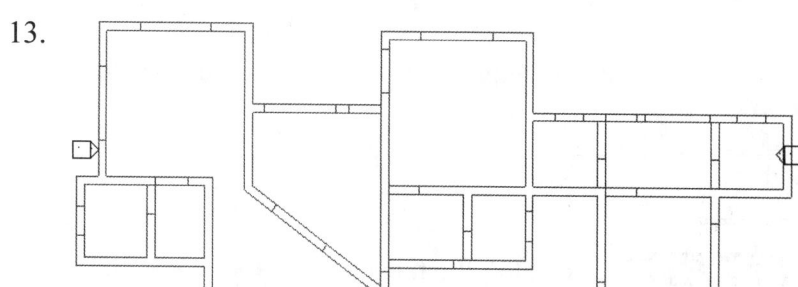 Locate the Line Styles named **0**, **0wall**, and **0wallthick**.

	Projection		
Lines	1	RGB 000-166-000	Solid
0	1	Black	Solid
0wall	1	Black	Solid
0wallthick	4	Black	Solid
<Area Boundary>	6	RGB 128-000-255	Solid

12. Change the color of **0**, **0wall**, and **0wallthick** line styles to **Cyan**.

Lines	1	RGB 000-166-00(
0	1	Cyan
0wall	1	Cyan
0wallthick	4	Cyan

Press **OK**.

13. The imported lines will change color to Cyan.

14. Select the **Measure** tool from the Quick Access toolbar.

Measure

15. Measure the wall thickness.

1' - 11"

16. Home Activate the **Home** ribbon.

17. Select the **Wall** tool under the Build panel.

18. ▾ Edit Type Select **Edit Type** from the Properties pane.

19. Duplicate... Select **Duplicate**.

20. Name: Generic - 1' 11" Change the Name to **Generic – 1' 11"** [**Generic – 584.2mm**].

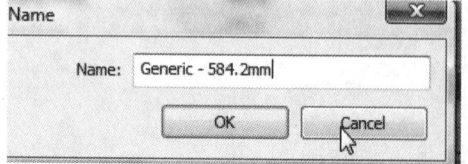 Press **OK**.

21. 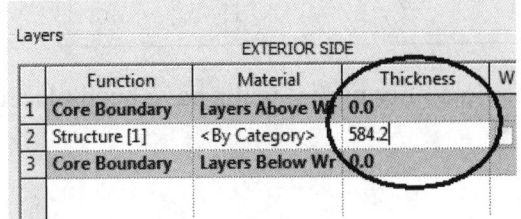 Select **Edit** next to Structure.

22. 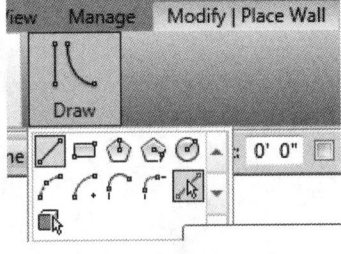 Change the thickness to **1′ 11″** [**584.2**].

Press **OK**.

23. Press **OK** to exit the Properties dialog.

24. Select the **Pick Lines** tool under the Draw panel.

25. On the Options bar, select **Finish Face: Exterior** for the Location Line.

This means you should select on the exterior side of the wall to place the wall correctly.

26. 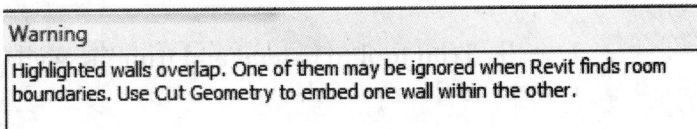 When you select the line, a preview will appear to indicate the wall orientation. To switch the wall orientation, press the SPACE bar or move the cursor to make a different selection. Select so the dashed line appears inside the wall.

27. Move around the model and select a section of each wall. Do not try to select the entire section of wall or you will get an error message about overlapping walls.

Warning

Highlighted walls overlap. One of them may be ignored when Revit finds room boundaries. Use Cut Geometry to embed one wall within the other.

Delete any overlapping walls.

28.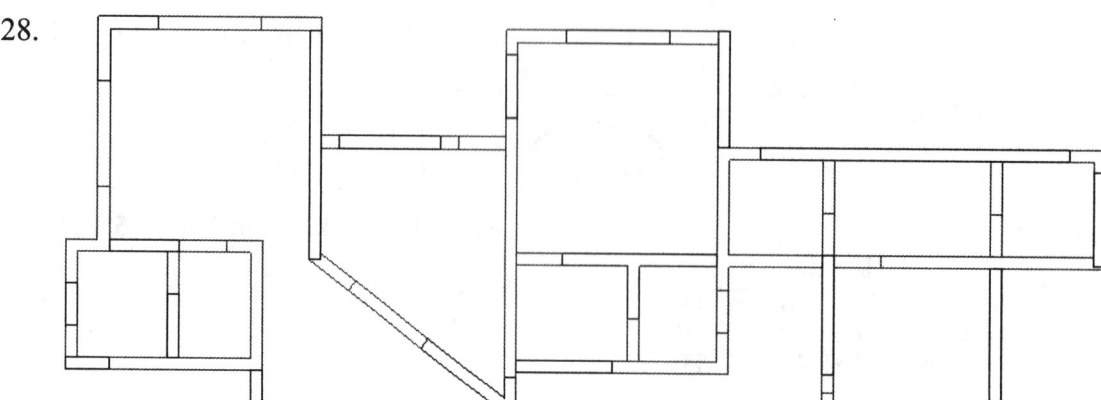

Your model should look similar to this. Note only partial walls have been placed on many of the sections.

29. Activate the View ribbon.

Select **3D View** from the Create panel.

30. The model shows the walls placed.

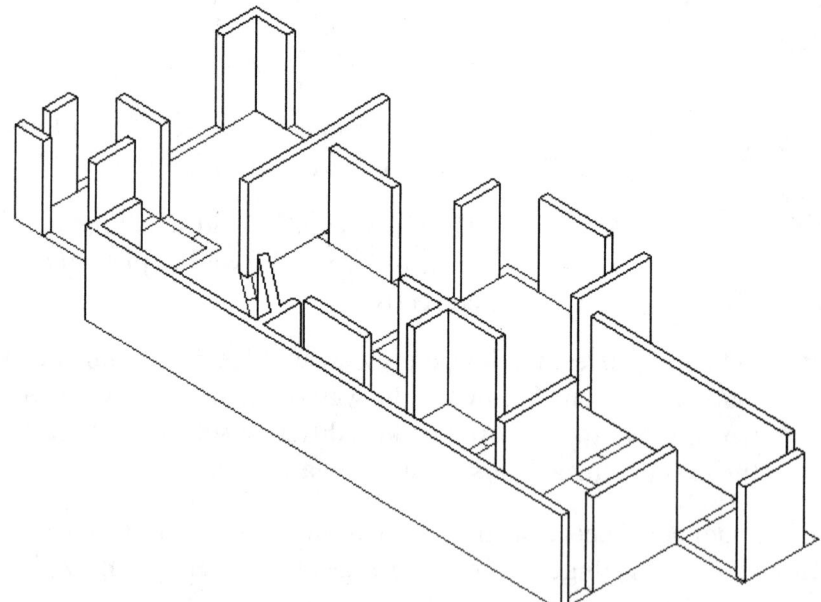

31. Use the Trim tool to extend and trim the walls to create the floor model.

32.

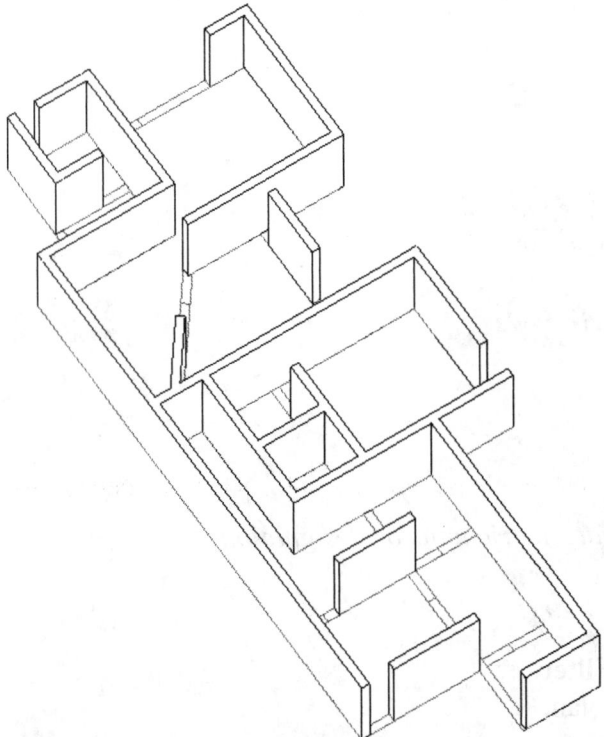

Not all walls can be connected using TRIM.

Some will require use of the EXTEND tool.

33.

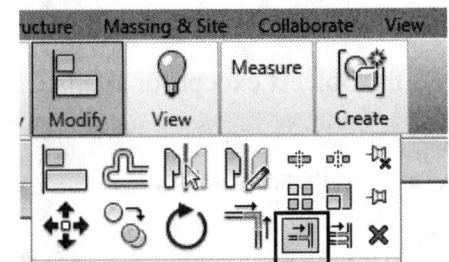

Select the **Extend Single Element** tool from the Modify panel.

To use this tool, select the face of the wall you want to extend TO first, then the wall you want to extend.

34.

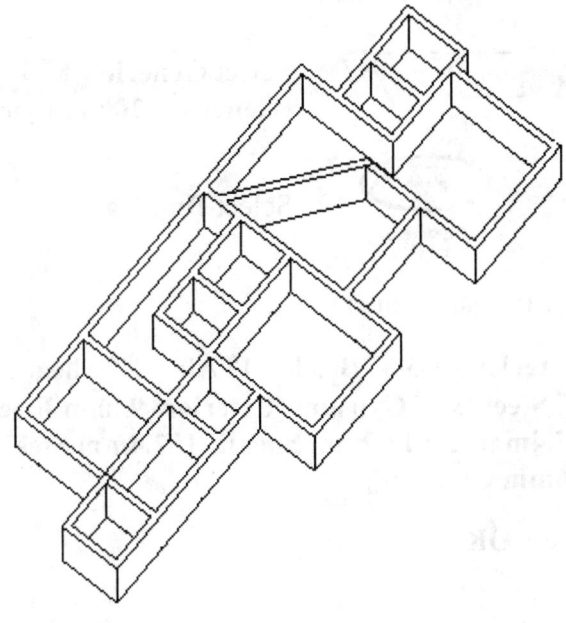

Orbit the model so you can see where to trim and extend walls.

35. Save as *ex3-3.rvt*.

Exercise 3-4
Wall Properties

Drawing Name: ex3-2.rvt
Estimated Time: 40 minutes

This exercise reinforces the following skills:

- ❑ Walls
- ❑ Filter
- ❑ Wall Properties
- ❑ Flip Orientation
- ❑ Join

[ ] brackets are used to indicate metric units or designations.

1. Open or continue working in *ex3-2.rvt*.

2. Select the exterior walls using **Filter**.
    Use crossing to select the floor plan.

3. ▽:25   Select the **Filter** tool.

4. Uncheck all the objects except for Walls.

    Press **OK**.
    This way, only walls are selected.

Filter	
Category:	Count:
☐ Dimensions	3
☑ Walls	22

5. ▾ ⊞ Edit Type   Select **Edit Type** in the Properties panel.

6. Select **Generic – 8″**
    [**Generic – 200 mm**] under
    Type.

    Select **Duplicate**.

Type Properties	X
Family:	System Family: Basic Wall ▾ Load...
Type:	Generic - 8" ▾ Duplicate...
	Rename...

7. For the name, enter:

    Exterior - 3-5/8″ Brick – 1″ Air – ½″ Sheath – 6″ Steel- 5/8″ Gypsum [Exterior- 92mm Brick-25.4mm Air-12.7mm Sheath-152.4mm Steel-16mm Gypsum].

    Press **OK**.

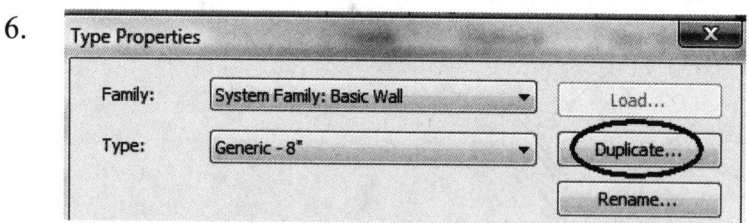

Name: Exterior -3-5/8″ Brick – 1″ Air – ½″ Sheatl

Name: m Sheath-152.4mm Steel-16mm Gypsum

8. 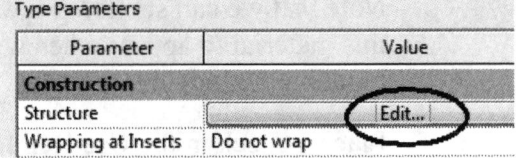　　Select **Edit** for Structure.

9. `<< Preview`　Enable the Preview button to expand the dialog so you can see the preview of the wall structure.

10. `Insert`　Select the **Insert** Button.

TIP: In the dialog, notice that the bottom of the list indicates toward the interior side and the top of the list indicates toward the exterior side of the wall.

11. 　Select the second line in the Function column.

Select **Finish 1 [4]** from the drop-down list.

12. 　Press the **Insert** button until you have seven layers total.

Arrange the layers as shown.

Assign the Functions as shown:
- Layer 1: Finish 1 [4]　　Layer 5: Structure [1]
- Layer 2: Thermal/Air Layer　　Layer 6: Core Boundary
- Layer 3: Substrate [2]　　Layer 7: Finish 2 [5]
- Layer 4: Core Boundary

13. Select the **Material** column for Layer 1.

14. 　　In the Materials search box, type **bri**.

15. 　Any materials with 'bri' as part of the name or description will be listed.

Highlight **Masonry-Brick** from the Name list.

16.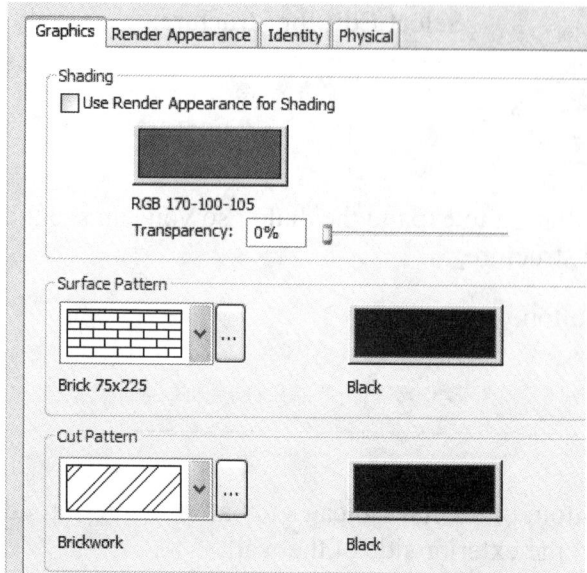

Note that we can set how we want this material to appear when we render and shade our model.

Place a check in the **Use Render Appearance for Shading**.

17. Select the Browse button next to the Surface Pattern field.

18. Note you can set how the surface pattern appears in drafting or model mode.

Press **OK**.

19. Select the **Render Appearance** tab.

Press the **Replace** button.

20. Select the Brick material you prefer.

21. Press **Apply** and **OK** to close the Material dialog.

22.

	Function	Material	Thickness
1	Finish 1 [4]	Masonry - Brick	0' 3 5/8"
2	Thermal/Air Lay	<By Category> ⊡	0' 0"
3	Substrate [2]	<By Category>	0' 0"

Change the Thickness to **3 5/8″ [92mm]**.

23.

	Function	Material
1	Finish 1 [4]	Masonry - Brick
2	Thermal/Air Lay	<By Category>
3	Substrate [2]	<By Category>

Locate Layer 2 and verify that it is set to Thermal/Air Layer.
Select the **Material** column.

24.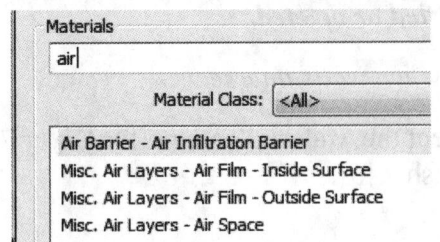

Type **air** in the search field.

Select **Air Barrier – Air Infiltration Barrier**.

Press **OK**.

25.

	Function	Material	Thickness
1	Finish 1 [4]	Masonry - Brick	0' 3 5/8"
2	Thermal/Air Lay	Air Barrier - Air I	0' 1"
3	Substrate [2]	<By Category>	0' 0"

Set the Thickness of **Layer 2** to **1″ [25.4]**.

	Function	Material	Thickness
1	Finish 1 [4]	Masonry - Brick	92.0
2	Thermal/Air Layer [3]	Air Barrier - Air Infiltration	25.4
3	Core Boundary	Layers Above Wrap	0.0
4	Structure [1]	<By Category>	200.0
5	Core Boundary	Layers Below Wrap	0.0

26.

	Function	Material	Thickne
1	Finish 1 [4]	Masonry - Brick	3' 0 5/8"
2	Thermal/Air La	Air Barrier - Air Infiltration Barr	0' 1"
3	Substrate [2]	Wood - Sheathing - plywood	0' 0 1/2"
4	Core Boundary	Layers Above Wrap	0' 0"
5	Structure [1]	Metal - Stud Layer	0' 6"
6	Core Boundary	Layers Below Wrap	0' 0"

Set Layer 3 to Substrate [2], **Material- Wood-Sheathing-plywood**, Thickness to ½″ [**17.2**].

	Function	Material	Thickness
1	Finish 1 [4]	Masonry - Brick	92.0
2	Thermal/Air Layer [3	Air Barrier - Air Infiltration	25.4
3	Substrate [2]	Wood - Sheathing - plywo	17.2
4	Core Boundary	Layers Above Wrap	0.0
5	Structure [1]	Metal - Stud Layer	152.4
6	Core Boundary	Layers Below Wrap	0.0
7	Structure [1]	<By Category>	0.0

27. Set the Material for Structure [1] to **Metal – Stud Layer**.

Press **OK**.

28. Set the Thickness for Layer 4 Structure [1] to **6″ [152.4]**.

	Function	Material	Thickness	Wr
1	Finish 1 [4]	Masonry - Brick	3' 0 5/8"	☑
2	Thermal/Air La	Air Barrier - Air Infilt	0' 1"	☑
3	**Core Boundary**	**Layers Above Wrap**	**0' 0"**	
4	Structure [1]	Metal - Stud Layer	6"	☐
5	**Core Boundary**	**Layers Below Wrap**	**0' 0"**	

The Core Boundary Layers may not be modified or deleted.

These layers control the location of the wrap when walls intersect.

29. Select the Material column for Layer 7: Finish 2 [5].

	Function	Material	Thickness
1	Finish 1 [4]	Masonry - Bric	0' 3 5/8"
2	Thermal/Air L	Air Barrier - Ai	0' 1"
3	Substrate [2]	Wood - Sheat	0' 0 1/2"
4	**Core Boundary**	**Layers Above W**	**0' 0"**
5	Structure [1]	Metal - Stud L	0' 6"
6	**Core Boundary**	**Layers Below W**	**0' 0"**
7	Finish 2 [5]	<By Category	0' 8"

30. Select **Paint [Drywall]** under Material Class.

31. Select Gypsum Wall Board [**Plasterboard**].

Press **OK**.

32.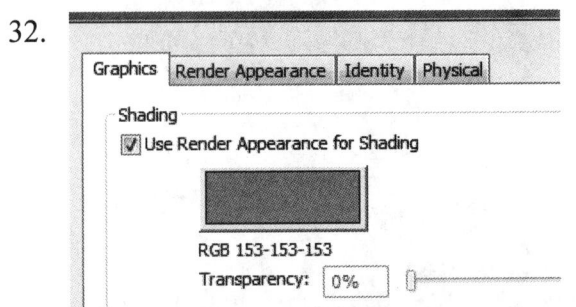

Place a check in the **Use Render Appearance** for Shading.

33.

Select the **Render Appearance** tab.

Select **Replace**.

34.

Select **Beige**.

If you prefer a different color, pick your choice!

Press **OK**.

35.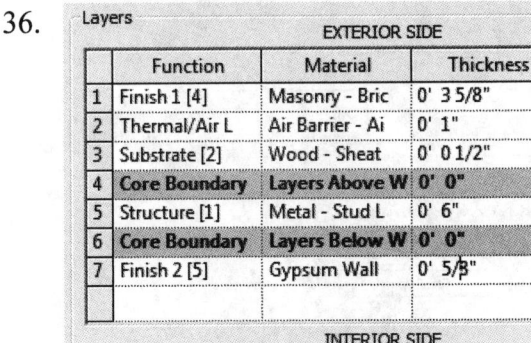

Note you can specify how the paint is applied as well as the finish.

Press **OK**.

36.

Set Layer 7 to **Finish 2 [5]**, **Material – Gypsum Wall Board** [**Material – Plasterboard**], Thickness to **5/8″** [**16mm**].

	Function	Material	Thickness
		EXTERIOR SIDE	
1	Finish 1 [4]	Masonry - Bric	0' 3 5/8"
2	Thermal/Air L	Air Barrier - Ai	0' 1"
3	Substrate [2]	Wood - Sheat	0' 0 1/2"
4	Core Boundary	Layers Above W	0' 0"
5	Structure [1]	Metal - Stud L	0' 6"
6	Core Boundary	Layers Below W	0' 0"
7	Finish 2 [5]	Gypsum Wall	0' 5/8"
		INTERIOR SIDE	

37.

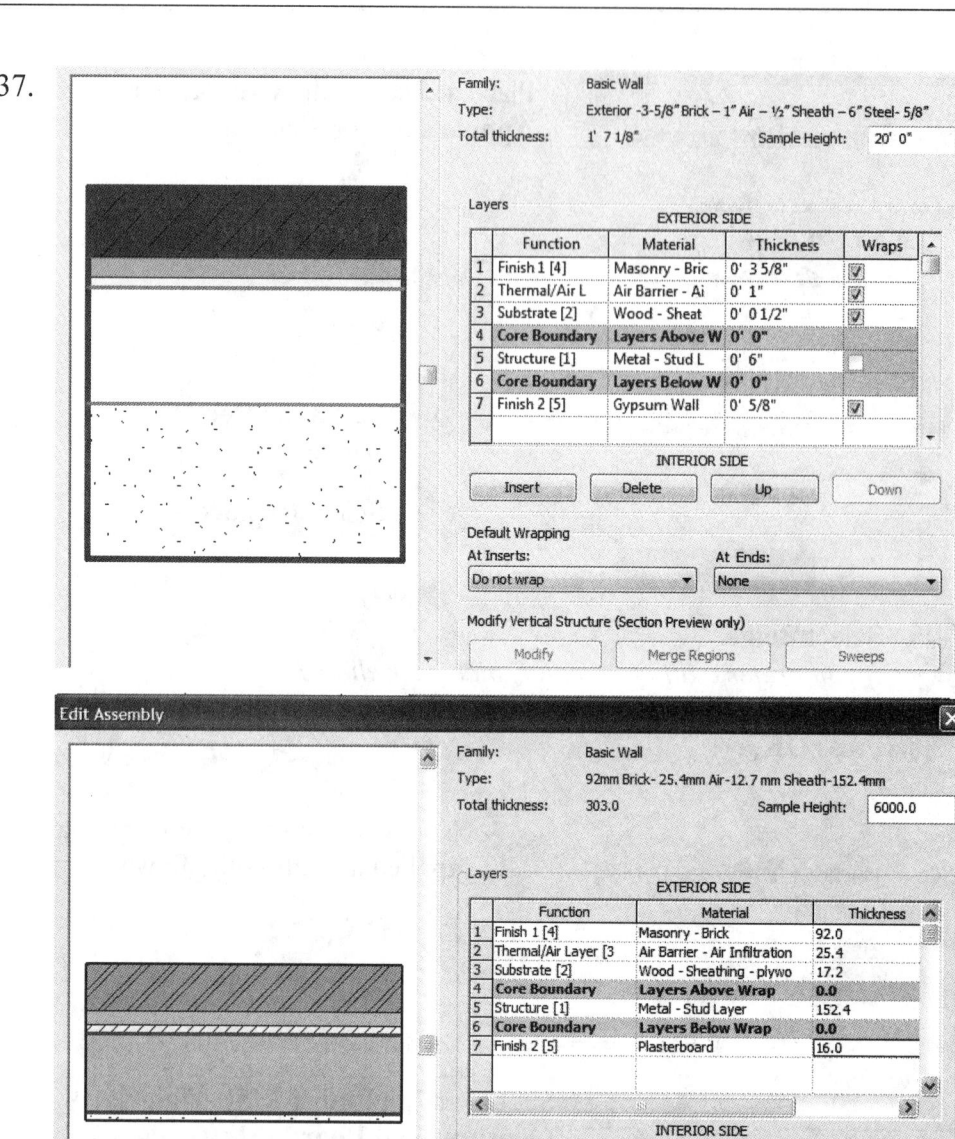

Set Layer 1 to Finish 1 [4], Masonry – Brick, Thickness: **3-5/8″ [92]**.
Set Layer 2 to Thermal/Air Layer, Air Barrier, Thickness: **1″ [25.4]**.
Set Layer 3 to Substrate [2], Wood-Sheathing-plywood, Thickness to **½″ [17.2]**.
Set Layer 4 to Core Boundary, Layers Above Wrap, Thickness to **0″**.
Set Layer 5 to Structure [1], Metal- Stud Layer, Thickness to **6″ [152.4]**.
Set Layer 6 to Core Boundary, Layers Below Wrap, Thickness to **0″**.
Set Layer 7 to Finish 2 [5], Plasterboard, Thickness to **5/8″ [16]**.
Press **OK** to exit the Edit Assembly dialog.

38. 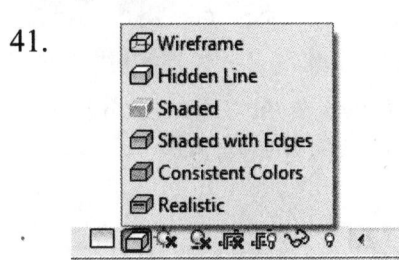 Set the Coarse Scale Fill Pattern to **Diagonal up**.

Set the Coarse Fill Color to **Blue**.

39. Press **OK** twice to exit the Properties dialog.
Because your walls were selected when you started defining the new wall style, your walls now appear with the new wall style.

40. If you zoom in, you will see that the coarse fill pattern is Diagonal Up and is Color Blue.

41.  Set the Model Graphics Style to **Wireframe** using the quick tool at the lower left of your display.

42. 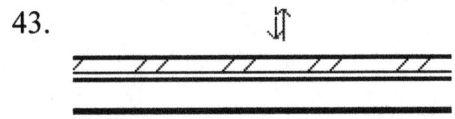 Set the Detail Level to **Medium**.
Press **OK**.

You will not see the hatching or any change in line width unless the Detail Level is set to Medium or Fine.

43. We now see the wall details, but the brick side is toward the interior and the gypsum board is towards the exterior. In other words, the walls need to be reversed or flipped.

How do we know the walls need to be flipped?

44. When we pick the walls, the orientation arrows are located adjacent to the exterior side of the wall.

The orientation arrows are the blue arrows that are activated when an object is selected.

45. Select the wall, right click and select **Change wall's Orientation** or just click the blue arrows.

46. Go around the building and flip the orientation of the walls so that the brick is on the outside.

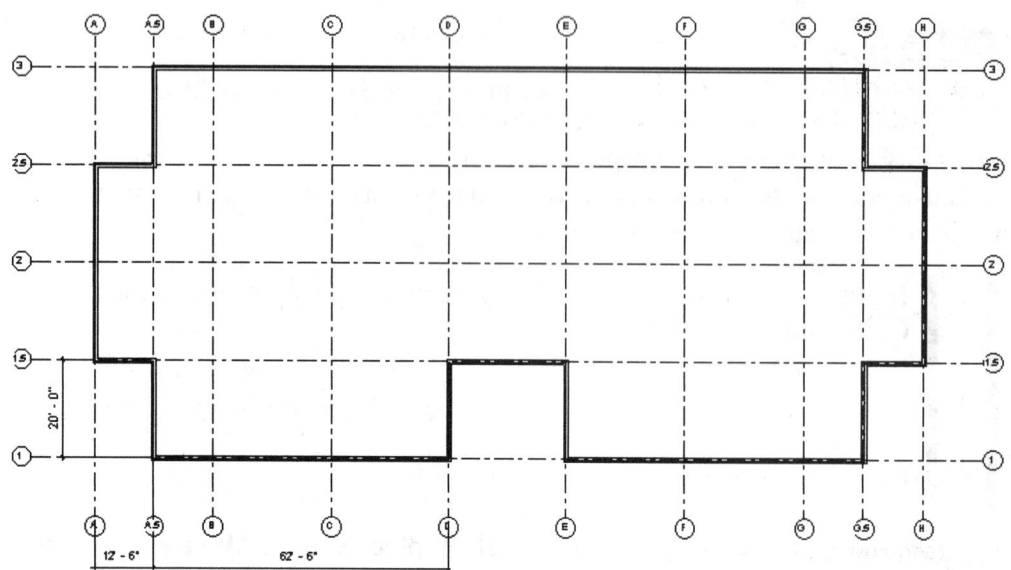

If you have problems selecting a wall instead of a grid line, use the TAB key to cycle through the selection.

47. Save the file *ex3-4.rvt.*

Exercise 3-5
Add Level 1 Interior Walls

Drawing Name: ex3-4.rvt
Estimated Time: 10 minutes

This exercise reinforces the following skills:

- Wall
- 3D View
- Visibility
- Wall Properties

1. Open or continue working in *ex3-4.rvt.*

2. Activate **Level 1**.

3. Select the **Wall** tool on the Build panel under the Home ribbon.

4. In the Properties panel, select
   Interior: 3 1/8″ Partition (1-hr)
   [Basic Wall: Interior - 138mm Partition (1-hr)].

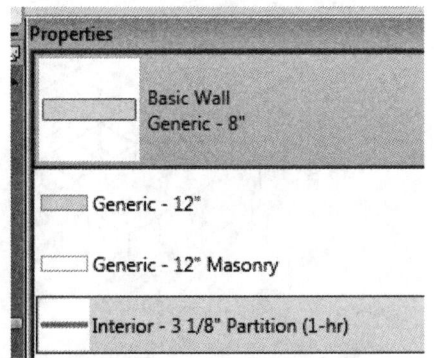

Basic Wall : Generic - 140mm Masonry
Basic Wall : Generic - 200mm
Basic Wall : Generic - 200mm - Filled
Basic Wall : Generic - 225mm Masonry
Basic Wall : Generic - 300mm
Basic Wall : Interior - 79mm Partition (1-hr)
Basic Wall : Interior - 135mm Partition (2-hr)
Basic Wall : Interior - 138mm Partition (1-hr)
Basic Wall : Interior - Blockwork 100
Basic Wall : Interior - Blockwork 140
Basic Wall : Interior - Blockwork 190
Basic Wall : Retaining - 300mm Concrete

5. Place interior walls as shown.

Imperial Units

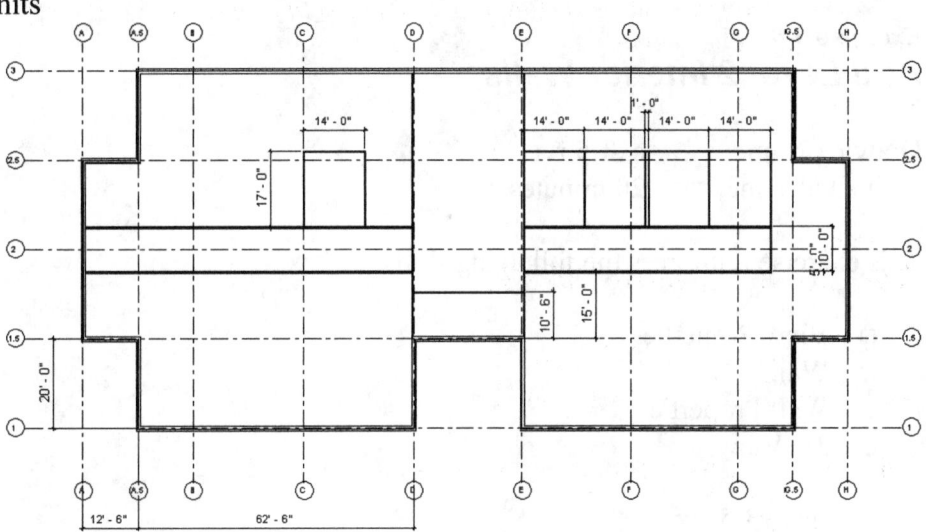

Metric Units (using centimeters)

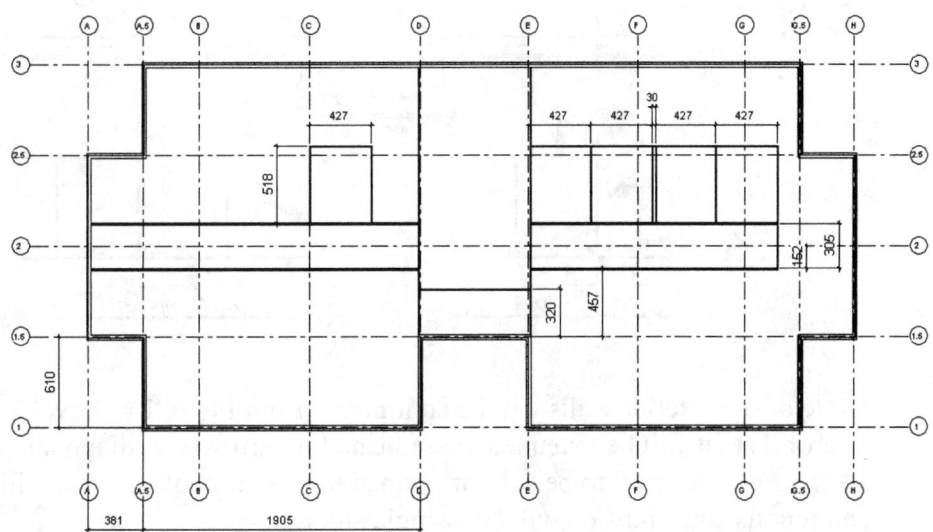

6.  Activate the View ribbon.
Select the **3D View** tool.

We see our first floor interior walls.

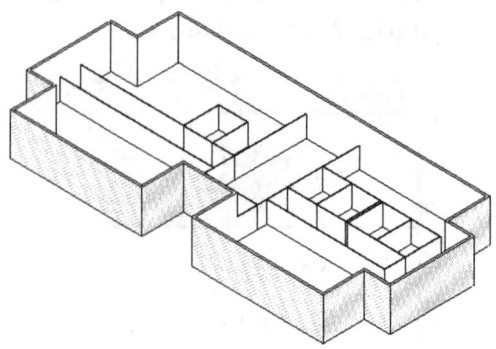

7. Save the file as *ex3-5.rvt*.

Exercise 3-6
Add Level 2 Interior Walls

Drawing Name: ex3-5.rvt
Estimated Time: 20 minutes

This exercise reinforces the following skills:

- ❑ View Properties
- ❑ Wall
- ❑ Wall Properties
- ❑ 3D View

1. Open *ex3-5.rvt*.

2.  Activate **3D View**.

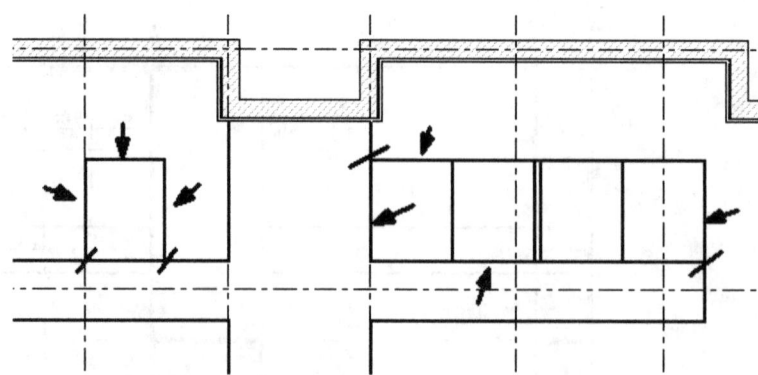

Some of our interior walls will be continuous from Level 1 to Level 2.
The walls that will be extended are indicated by arrows. A diagonal line indicates
where the walls need to be split or divided as a portion of the wall will be
continuous and a portion will be a single story.

3. ⌐──── Level 2
    ⊟─── Elevations (Building Elevation)
        ──── East
        ──── North
        ┃ South ┃
        ──── West

Switch view to a **South Elevation** view.

Double left click in the browser window on the South Elevation view

---

4.

    Cancel

    Repeat [Project Units]
    Recent Commands   ▶

    Drag End
    Go to Floor Plan
    Reset to Crop
    Reset to 3D Extents
    Maximize 3D Extents

Select the level line.

Right click and select **Maximize 3D Extents**.

This will stretch the level to cover the entire building.

Repeat for the other level.

5. Select the first grid line labeled **A**.

6. Select **Edit Group** under the Edit Group panel on the Modify/ Model Groups ribbon.

    This ribbon will only be visible if the gridline is selected.

7.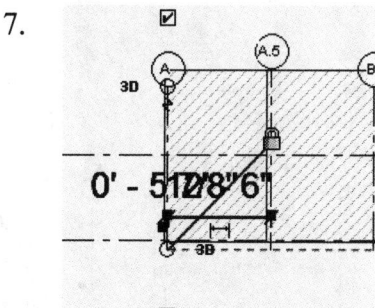

    0' - 5⅛"

Select the first grid line labeled **A** a second time.

8.

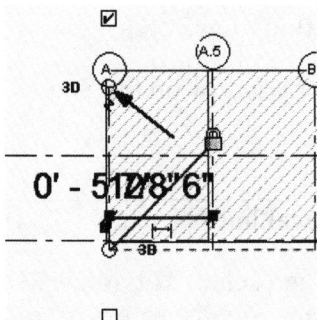

Use the grip indicated to drag the grid line above the building.

9.

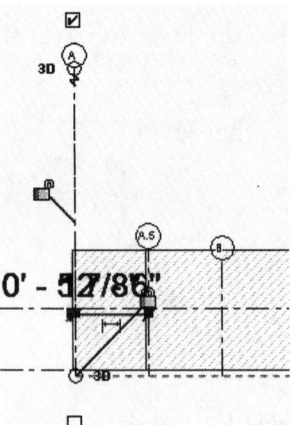

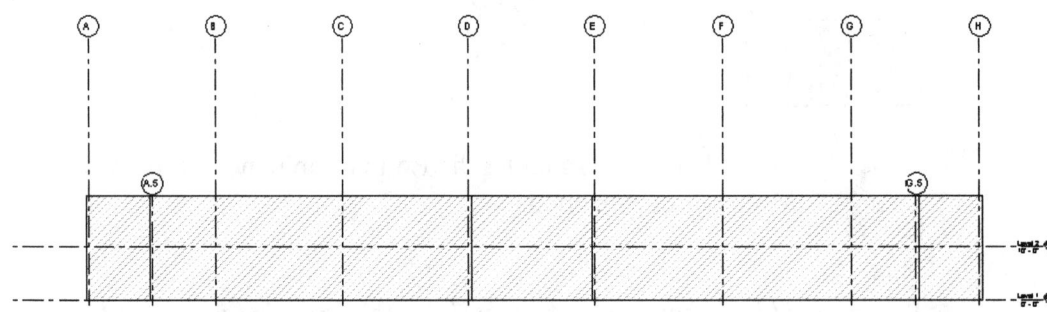

Select Finish on the **Edit Group** toolbar.

10. All the grid lines which were created as part of the array adjust.

11.

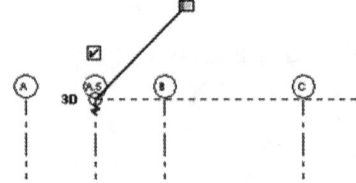

Use the grip to adjust the location of the remaining grid lines.

12.

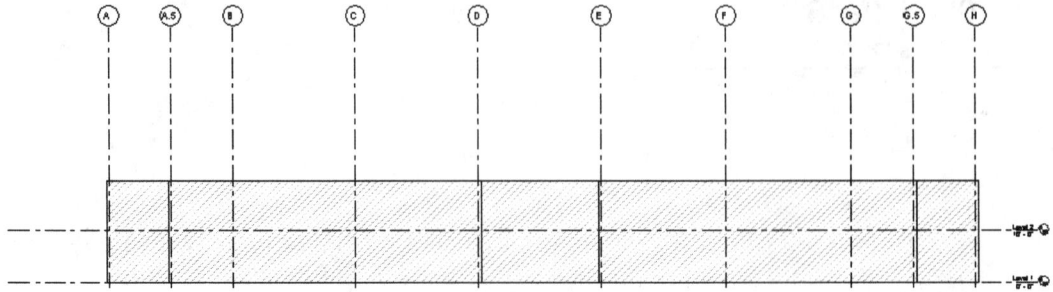

The current model has level lines for the ground plane and second floor, but not for the roof. We will add a level line for the roof to constrain the building's second level and establish a roof line.

13. 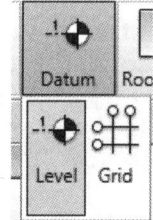   Select the **Level** tool on the Datum panel on the Home ribbon.

14. Draw a level line **10′ [4000** mm] above Level 2.

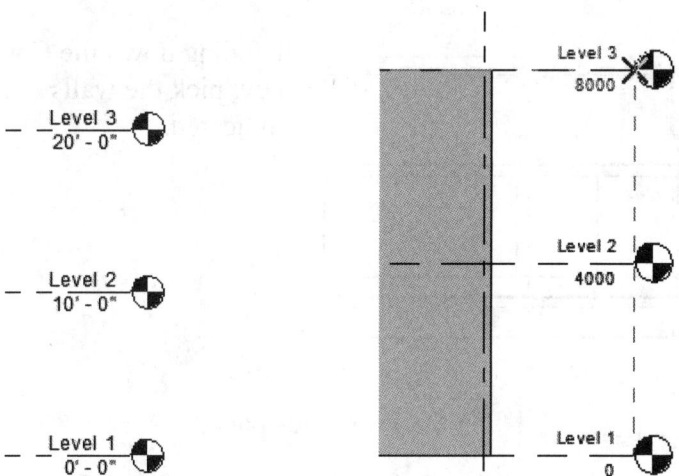

15. 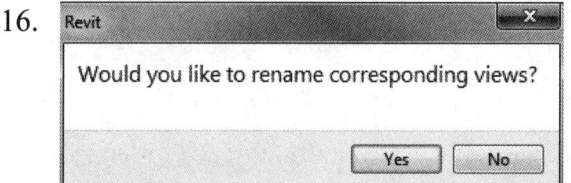   Rename Level 3 by double left clicking on the level name.
                    ☑ Rename to **Roof Line**.

16. 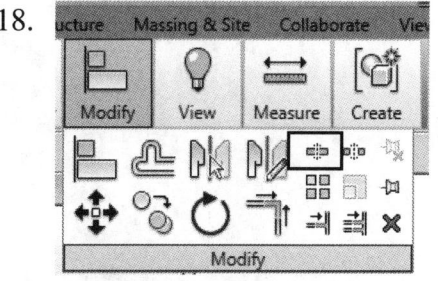   Press **Yes**.

           This renames the views in the Project Browser to Roof Line.

17. Switch back to the Level 1 Floor plan view.

18. 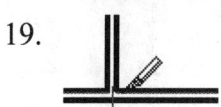   Activate the **Modify** ribbon.

           Select the **Split** tool.

19.   Split the walls where portions will remain only on level 1 and portions will be continuous up to the roof line.

20. Split the walls at the intersections indicated.

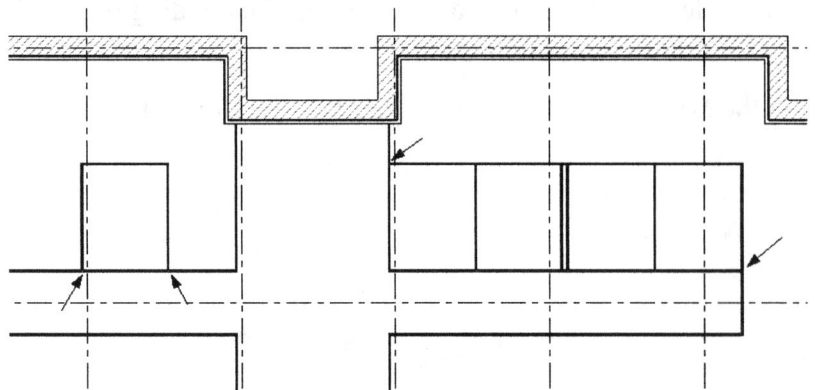

21. 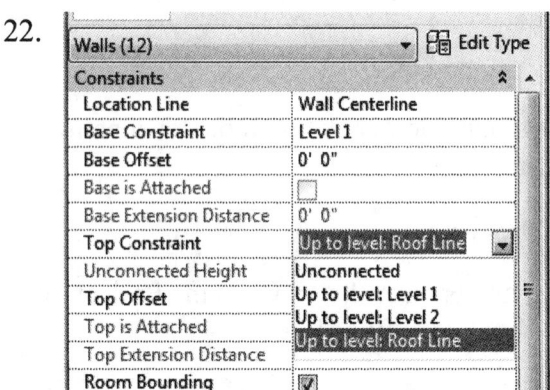 Holding down the Control key, pick the walls indicated.

22.

Walls (12)	▼	🔡 Edit Type
Constraints		☆ ▲
Location Line	Wall Centerline	
Base Constraint	Level 1	
Base Offset	0' 0"	
Base is Attached	☐	
Base Extension Distance	0' 0"	
Top Constraint	Up to level: Roof Line	▼
Unconnected Height	Unconnected	
Top Offset	Up to level: Level 1	≡
Top is Attached	Up to level: Level 2	
Top Extension Distance	Up to level: Roof Line	
Room Bounding	☑	

On the Properties pane:

Set the Top Constraint to **Up to Level: Roof line**.

Press **OK**.

By constraining walls to levels, it is easier to control their heights. Simply change the level dimension and all the walls constrained to that level will automatically update.

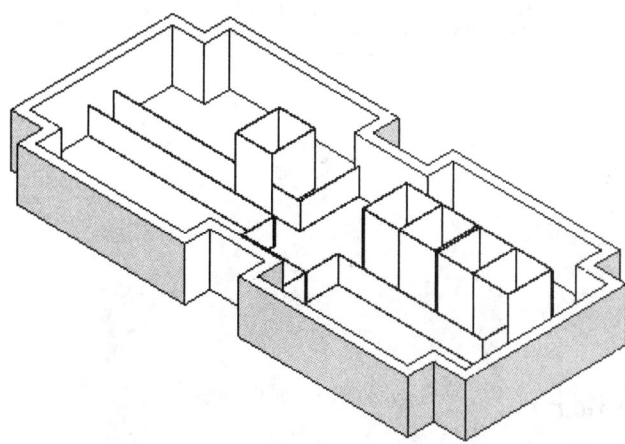

Walls that extend through multiple levels should be created out of just one wall, not walls stacked on top of each other. This improves model performance and minimizes mistakes from floor to floor. For a stair tower, create the wall on the first floor and set its top constraint to the highest level.

23.

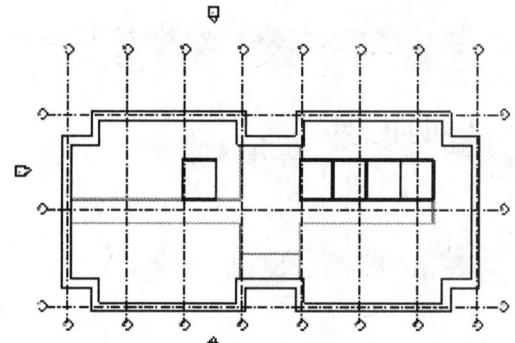

Activate the **Level 2** view.

It can be disconcerting to try to create elements on the second level (Level 2) when you can see the interior walls in the first level (Level 1).

24.

Visibility/Graphics Overr...	Edit...
Visual Style	Hidden Line
Graphic Display Options	Edit...
Underlay	Level 1
Underlay Orientation	None
Orientation	Level 1
Wall Join Display	Level 2
	Roof Line

On the Properties Pane:
Locate the Underlay parameter and select **None**.

This means that the user will only see what is visible on Level 2.

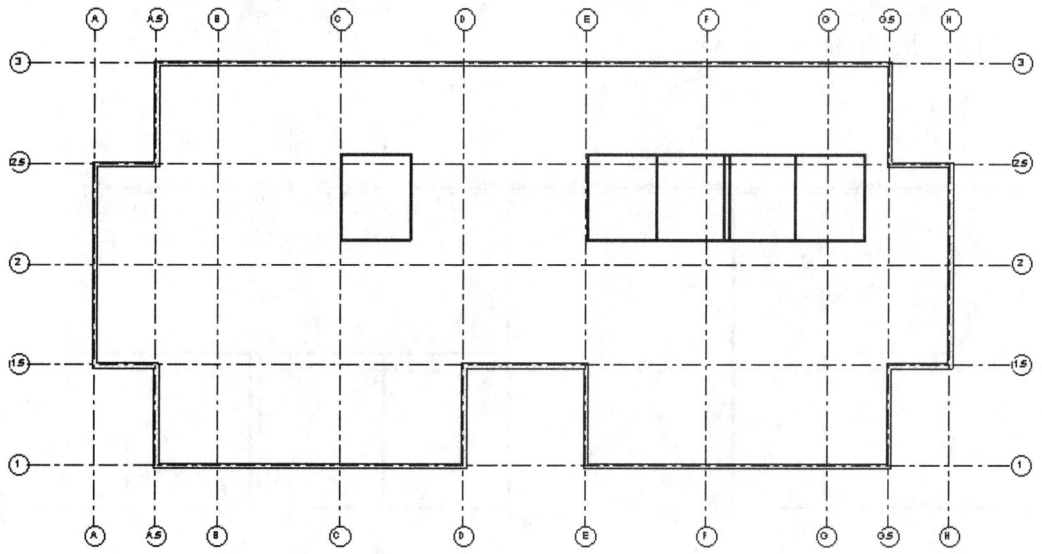

25. Save the file as *ex3-6.rvt*.

Exercise 3-7
Add Doors

Drawing Name: ex3-6.rvt
Estimated Time: 10 minutes

This exercise reinforces the following skills:

- ❑ Door
- ❑ Load From Library

1.   Open or continue working in *ex3-6.rvt*.

2.   Activate the **Level 1** view.

3.   [Home] Activate the **Home** ribbon.

4.   Select the **Door** tool from the Build panel.

5.   Select **Single-Flush 36″ x 84″ [M_Sgl Flush: 0915 × 2134mm]** from the drop-down.

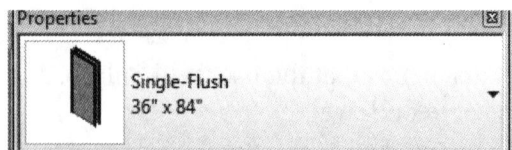

6.   Place the doors as shown.

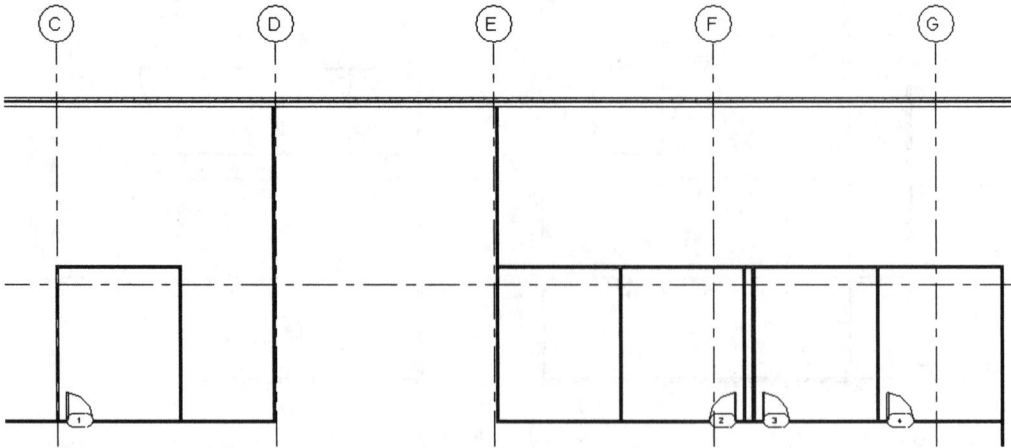

Use the arrows on the doors to flip their orientation.

To position a door, pick on it to activate the dimensions. Then, pick the dimension and enter the desired value.

7.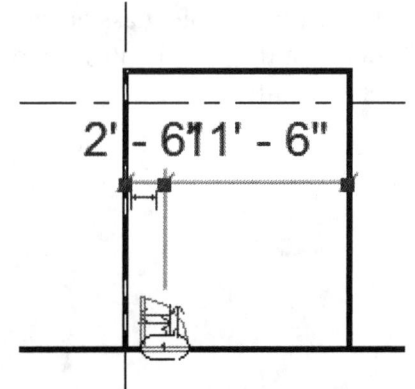

When you pick on a door, it will highlight. You will see a vertical set of arrows and a horizontal set of arrows. To flip a door along the Y-axis, select the vertical arrows. To flip a door orientation along the X-axis, select the horizontal arrows. To modify a door's placement, pick a temporary dimension and edit. The second dimension will automatically adjust accordingly.

TIP: Door numbers are often keyed to room numbers – 101A, etc. To edit the door tag, just click on the number and it will change to blue and you can renumber it. You can also change the door number from the Properties dialog box of the door or from the door schedule. A change in any of those locations will update automatically on all other views.

8. 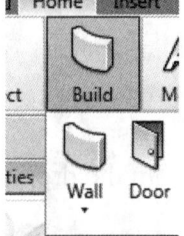 Select the **Door** tool.

9. 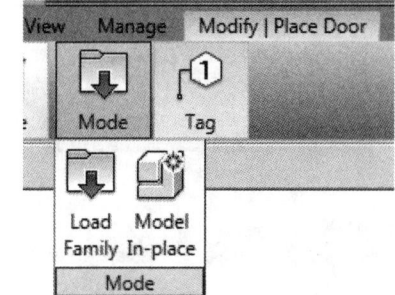 Select **Load Family** from the Mode panel.

10. Browse to the *Doors* folder.

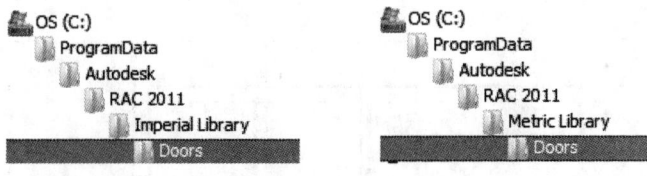

11. Locate the *Double-Glass 2. Rfa [M_Double-Glass 2.rfa]* file under the *Doors* folder and **Open**.

12.

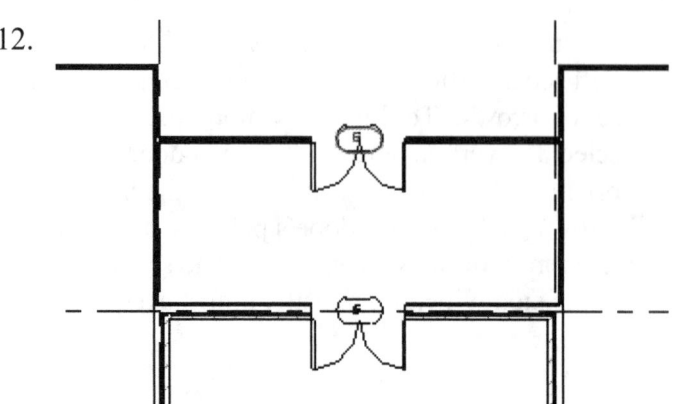

Place two double glass entry doors at the middle position of the entry walls.

The double doors should swing out in the path of egress for accuracy. The interior doors should typically swing into the room space not the hall.

13. Activate **Level 2**.

14. Home Activate the **Home** ribbon.

15. Select the **Door** tool from the Build panel.

16. Select **Single-Flush 36″ x 84″ [M_Sgl Flush: 0915 × 2134mm]** from the drop-down.

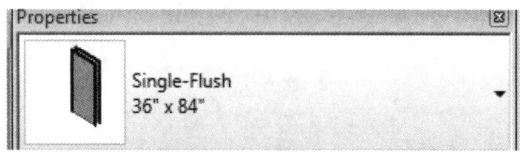

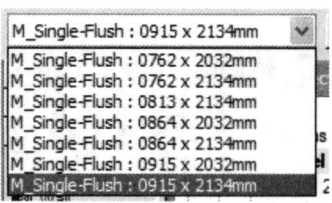

17. Place the doors as shown.

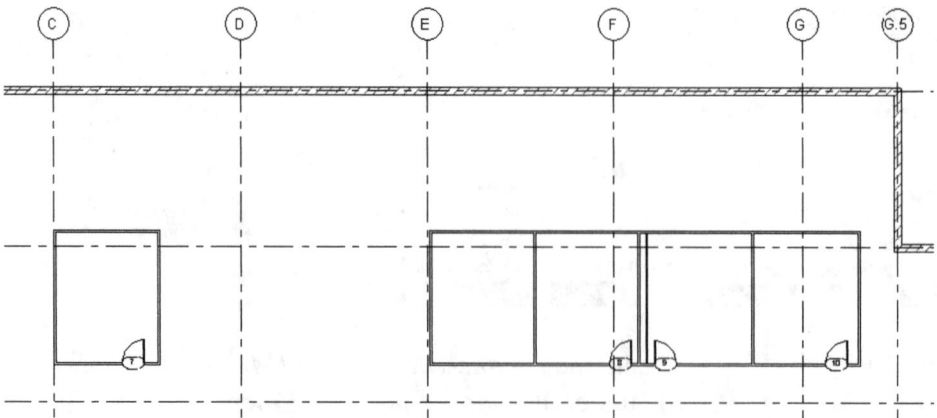

18. Save the file as *ex3-7.rvt*.

Exercise 3-8
Adding Stairs

Drawing Name: ex3-7.rvt
Estimated Time: 40 minutes

This exercise reinforces the following skills:

- ❑ Stairs
- ❑ Edit Sketch
- ❑ Activate Dimensions
- ❑ Stair Properties

A short video of this exercise is available on my website to help users with this exercise. Access at *www.mossdesigns.com/ex3-7-revit.zip*. This is a compressed or zipped file. You will need to extract/decompress the file before you will be able to view it.

1.   Open *ex3-7.rvt*.

2.   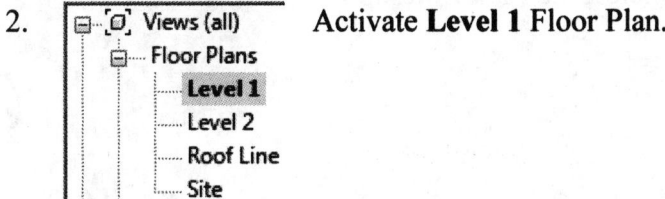   Activate **Level 1** Floor Plan.

3.   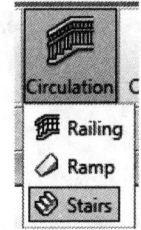   Select the **Stairs** tool under the Circulation panel on the Home ribbon.

When you are creating a stair, you need to define two boundary lines or curved arcs and the correct number of risers. Revit will automatically calculate the number of risers for you.

TIP: You can also pick the railing on the stair and select 'Edit sketch'. Then, add a line, this will make a continuous railing without adding a second piece.

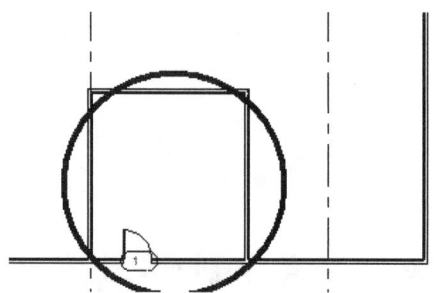
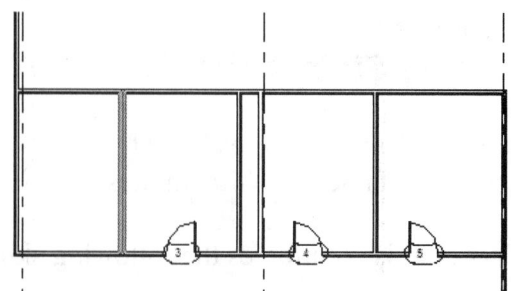

Our first set of stairs will be located in the room indicated by the circle.

4.

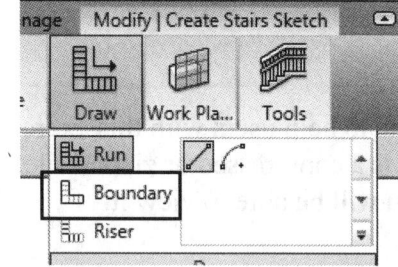

Select the **Boundary** tool.
This tool allows you to sketch the left and right sides of a stairs.

5.

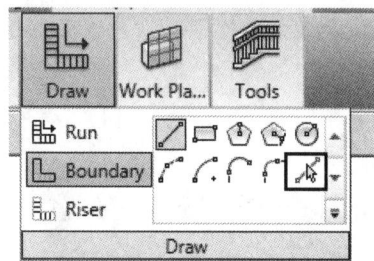

Select the **Pick Lines** tool.

6.

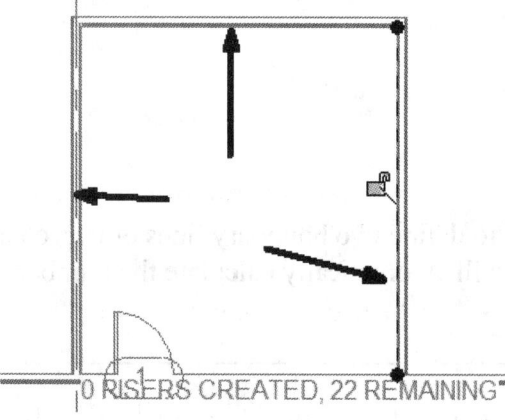

Pick the three interior walls.

"0 RISERS CREATED, 22 REMAINING"

7. Offset: 3' 0" ☐ Lock   Set the Offset to **3'** [**1060 mm**].

8.

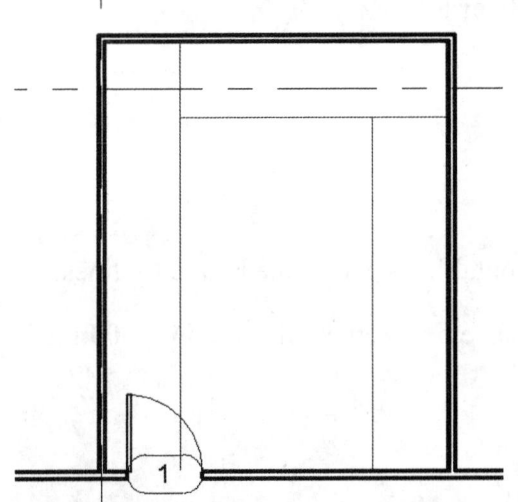

Offset the three lines you just placed.

9.

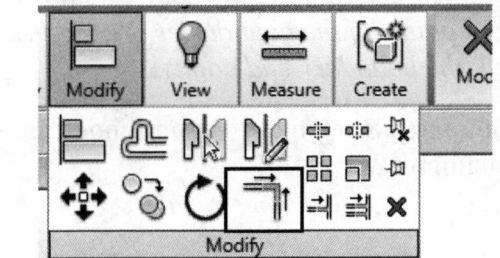

Select the **Trim** tool.

10.

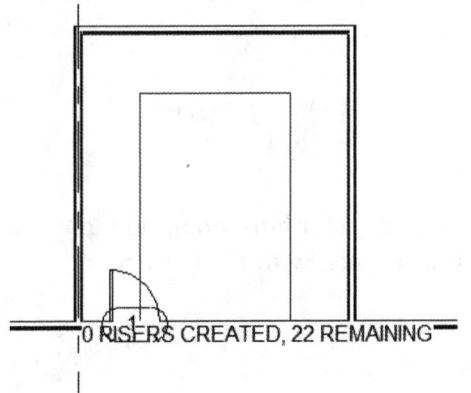

Trim the inner lines as shown.

Select the line sections you want to keep when using the Trim tool.

11.

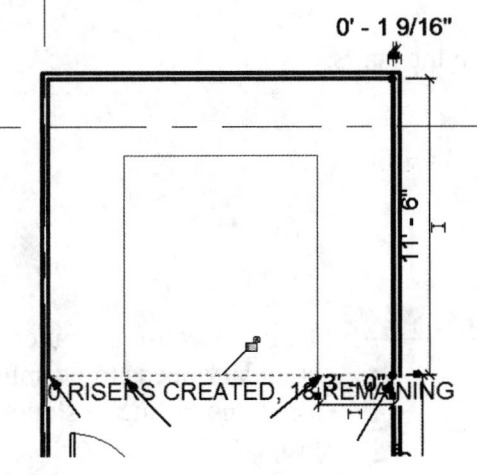

Select each vertical line to activate the grips.

Adjust the end point of each vertical line to bring it into the room.

12. 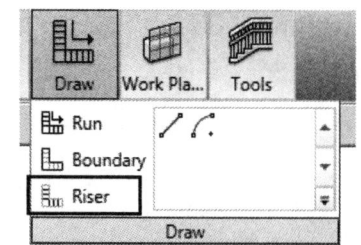 Select the **Riser** tool.

13. 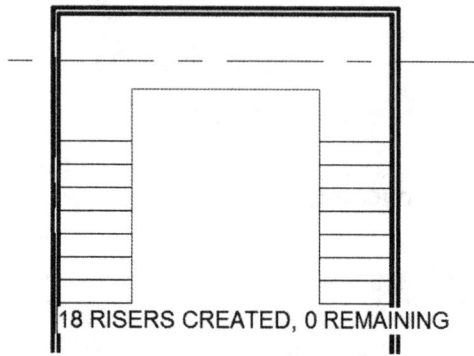 Draw horizontal lines across the boundary lines.

Set the distance between the lines at **11″** [**300mm**].

Note that as you add the risers, Revit updates the riser count required. If you don't see the riser count, check to see where the end points of the boundaries are located. The riser count text is located coincident with the boundary end points.

14. 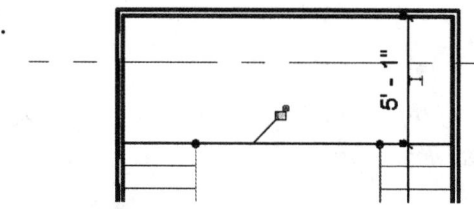 Continue placing the risers until none are remaining.

15. Adjust the inner horizontal boundary line so it is aligned with the top risers.

16. 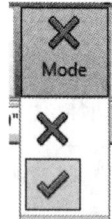 Under Mode:
Select the **Green Check** to finish the stairs.

17. An error dialog may appear.

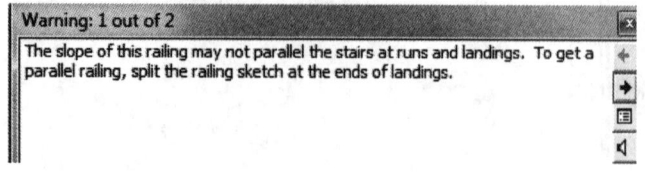

This is because the outer boundary needs to be split to allow the railing to slope properly.

18.

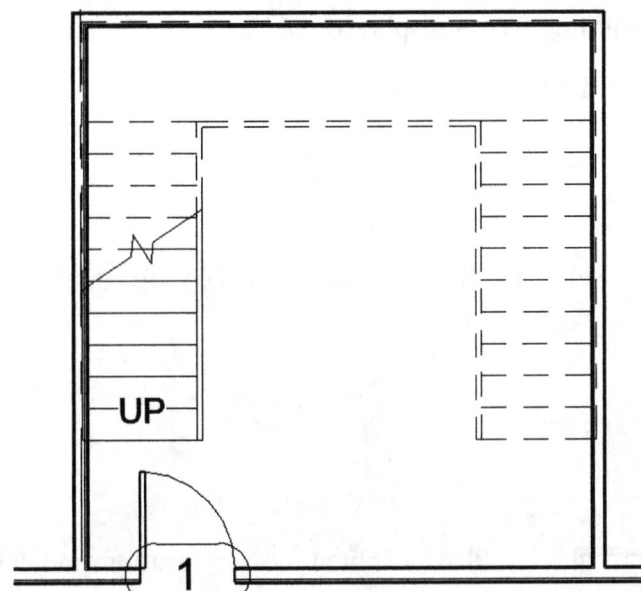

The stairs are completed.

19. 3D Views {3D} Activate the **3D View**.

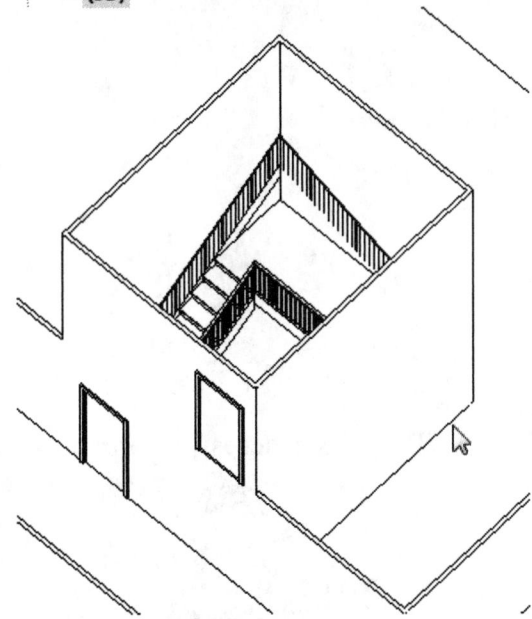

In the 3D View, we see that the railing does not align properly with the landing.

We will correct this.

20. Floor Plans
    Level 1
    Level 2
    Roof Line
    Site

Activate **Level 1**.

21.

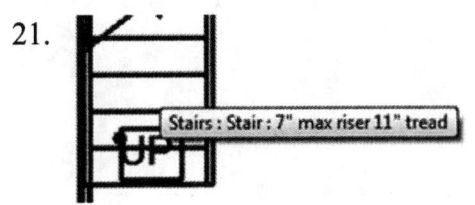

Hover your mouse over the stairs. You should see a tool tip indicating the stairs.

Left click to select the stairs.

22. 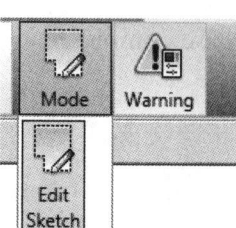 A small warning tool is displayed on the ribbon.

Select the **Edit Sketch** tool under Mode.

23. 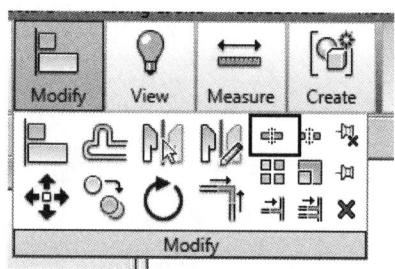 Select the **Split** tool under the Modify panel.

24. 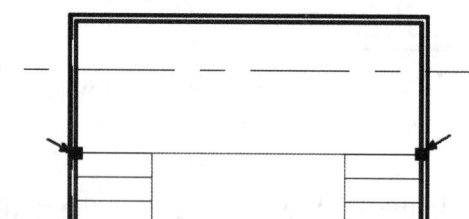 Place a split at the two locations indicated.

25.  Under Mode:
Select the **Green Check** to finish the stairs.

26. Activate **3D View**.

27. 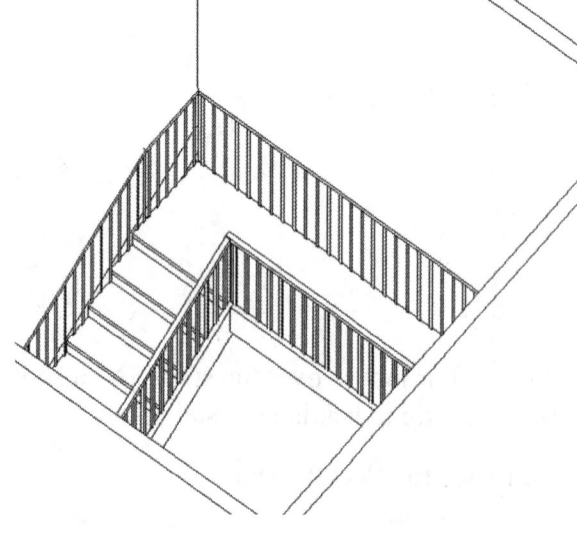 Press F8 to access the orbit tool.

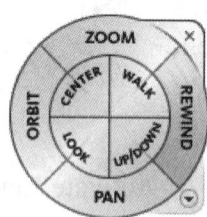

28. Save as *ex3-8.rvt*.

Exercise 3-9
Creating a Handrail on a Wall

Drawing Name: ex3-8.rvt
Estimated Time: 20 minutes

This exercise reinforces the following skills:

- ❑ Railings
- ❑ Railing Types

1. Open *ex3-8.rvt*.

2. 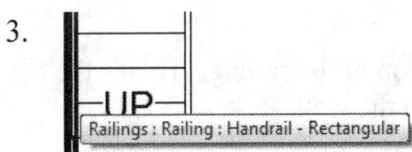 Activate **Level 1**.

3. 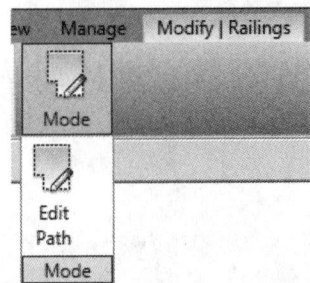 Hover your mouse over the Railing on the left side of the stairs.

    Left click to select the railing.

If you have difficulty selecting the railing, use the TAB key to cycle the selection or use the FILTER tool.

4. 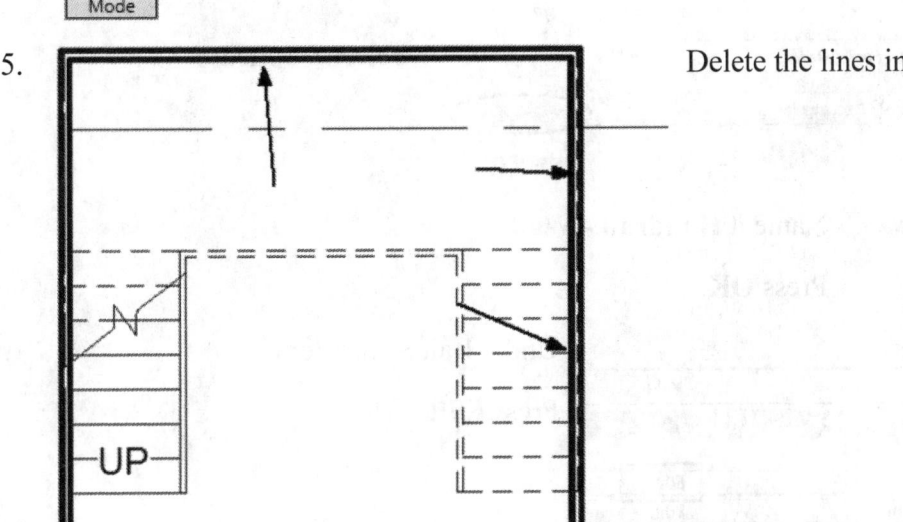 Select **Edit Path** under the Mode panel.

5. Delete the lines indicated.

6. Move the two remaining lines away from the wall.

Adjust the top vertical line so it is about 1′ 6″ above the top riser.

7. Select the **LINE** tool from the Draw panel.

8. Add a short horizontal line at the top of the railing. This is the bar that of the handrail that attaches to the wall.

Add a vertical line going below the bottom riser and another horizontal line that attaches to the wall at the bottom of the railing.

9. Select **Edit Type** from the Properties pane.

10. Family: System Family: Railing   Type: Handrail - Rectangular   Select **Duplicate**.

11. Name: Handrail - Wall   Name it **Handrail - Wall**.

Press **OK**.

12. Under Rail Structure:

Press **Edit**.

Parameter	Value
Construction	
Railing Height	3′ 0″
Rail Structure	Edit...
Baluster Placement	Edit...
Baluster Offset	-0′ 1″

13.

	Name	Height	Offset	Profile	Material
1	Rail 1	3' 0"	-0' 1"	Rectangular Handrail : 2"	<By Category>

Rails

Click in the **Material** column.

14. Select the **New** material button on the bottom left of the dialog.

15. Material Class: Wood
Name: Wood - Oak

Name it **Wood - Oak**.

Press **OK**.

16. Shading
☑ Use Render Appearance for Shading
RGB 114-082-052

Press a check on **Use Render Appearance for Shading**.

17.
Graphics | Render Appearance | Identity | Physical
Render Appearance Based On:
Birch - Solid Stained Dark No Gloss   Replace...

Select the Render Appearance tab.

Press **Replace**.

18. oak ☒

Type **oak** in the search field in the upper right of the dialog.

19. Red Oak - ...
Red Oak - Honey

Select **Red Oak - Honey**.

If you prefer to use a different material, select it.

Press **OK**.

20. Press **OK** to close the dialog.

21. Rails

	Height	Offset	Profile	Material
1	3' 0"	-0' 1"	Rectangular Handrail : 2" x	Wood - Oak

Press **OK**.

22.
Rail Structure   Edit...
Baluster Placement   Edit...
Baluster Offset   -0' 1"

Press **Edit** next to Baluster Placement.

23.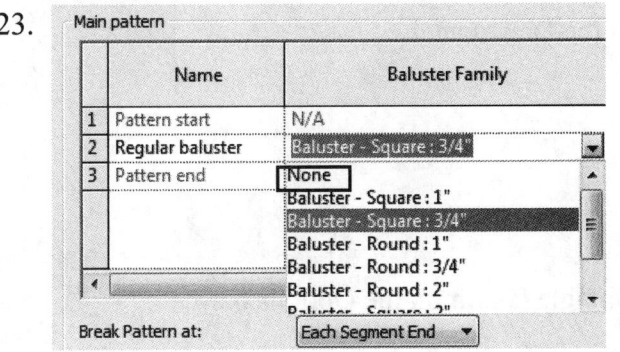
Main pattern

	Name	Baluster Family
1	Pattern start	N/A
2	Regular baluster	Baluster - Square : 3/4"
3	Pattern end	None

None
Baluster - Square : 1"
Baluster - Square : 3/4"
Baluster - Round : 1"
Baluster - Round : 3/4"
Baluster - Round : 2"

Break Pattern at: Each Segment End ▼

On Row 2 of the Main Pattern table, set the Regular baluster to **None**.

24.  In the Posts table, set all the posts to **None**.

Press **OK** twice to exit all dialogs.

	Name	Baluster Family	
1	Start Post	None	Hc
2	Corner Post	None	Hc
3	End Post	None	Hc

25. Select the **Green Check** under Mode to exit Edit Mode.

If you get an error message, check the sketch. It must be a single open path. All line segments must be connected with no gaps and no intersecting lines or overlying lines.

26. Switch to a 3D view.

27. 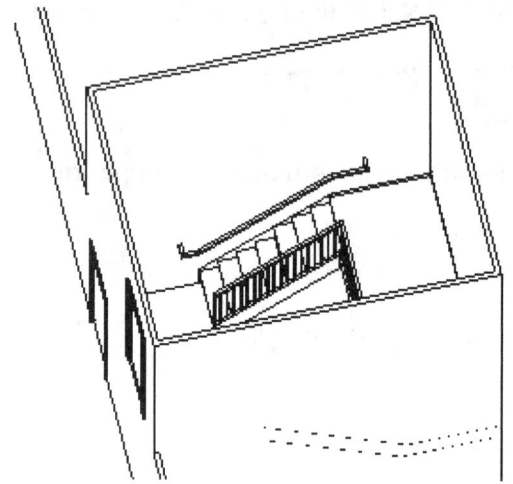 Inspect the railing.

28. Activate **Level 1**.

Floor Plans
Level 1
Level 2
Roof Line
Site

29. Activate the Home ribbon.

Select **Railing** from the Circulation panel.

30. 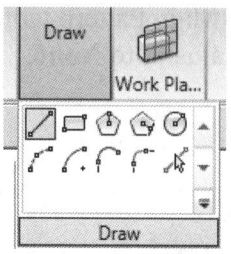 Select **Line** from the Draw panel.

31. Enable **Chain** on the Options bar.

☑ Chain   Offset: 0' 0"   ☐ Radius: 1' 0"

32. 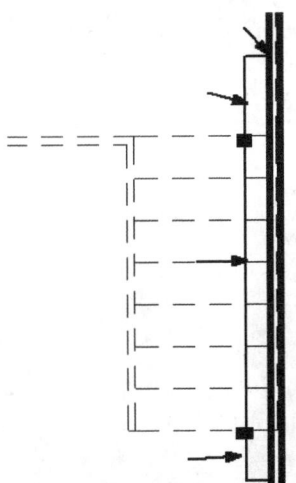 Draw the rail path in five segments.

By creating separate segments, you allow the rail to remain parallel to the floor, landing, and stairs.

33. 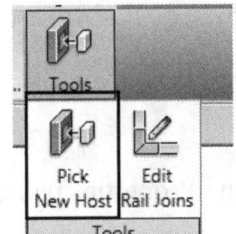 Select **Pick New Host** under Tools.

Then, select the stairs.

By assigning a host, you instruct the railing to slope parallel to the stairs.

34. 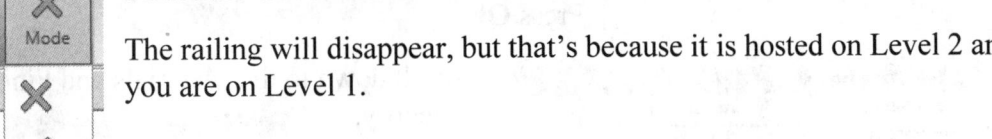 Select **Edit Type** on the Properties pane.

35. Type: Handrail - Wall Verify that the type is set to **Handrail- Wall**.

Press **OK**.

36. Select the **Green Check** under Mode.

The railing will disappear, but that's because it is hosted on Level 2 and you are on Level 1.

37. Switch to a 3D view.

38. 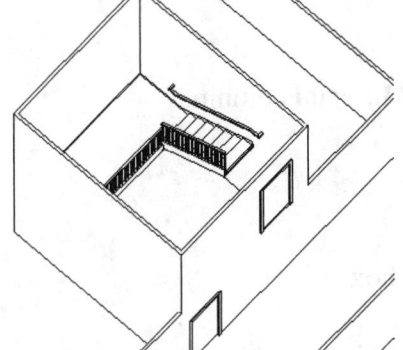 Inspect the railing.

39. Save as *ex3-9.rvt*.

Exercise 3-10
Creating a Stairs Type

Drawing Name: ex3-8.rvt
Estimated Time: 20 minutes

This exercise reinforces the following skills:

- ❑ Floor
- ❑ Floor Properties

1. Open *ex3-9.rvt*.

2. 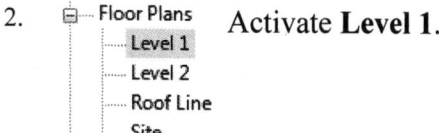 Activate **Level 1**.

3. 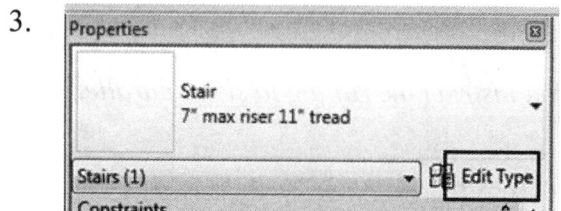 Select the stairs.

   Select **Edit Type** on the Properties pane.

4. Duplicate...   Select **Duplicate**.

5. Name: Stairs - Oak Tread with Painted Riser   Type **Stairs - Oak Tread with Painted Riser**.

   Press **OK**.

6. 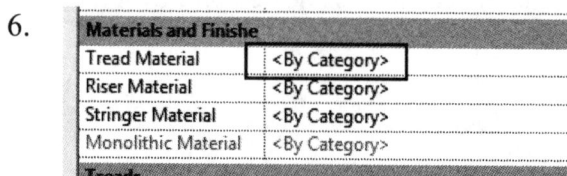 Scroll down to the Materials and Finishes category.

   Select the **Tread Material** column.

7. Wood - Oak   Select the **Wood - Oak** material.

   Press **OK**.

8.
Materials and Finishe	
Tread Material	Wood - Oak
Riser Material	<By Category>
Stringer Material	<By Category>
Monolithic Material	<By Category>

   Select the **Riser Material** column.

9.
   Metal - Paint Finish - Dark Gr
   Paint
   Paints and Coatings
   Parking Stripe
   Roofing - Generic

   Type Paint in the search text box.

   Highlight **Paint**.

10. Select the **New Material** tool.

11. Name: Paint - White | Type **Paint - White**.

    Press **OK**.

12. Shading
    ☑ Use Render Appearance for Shading
    RGB 216-216-204

    Place a check on **Use Render Appearance for Shading**.

13.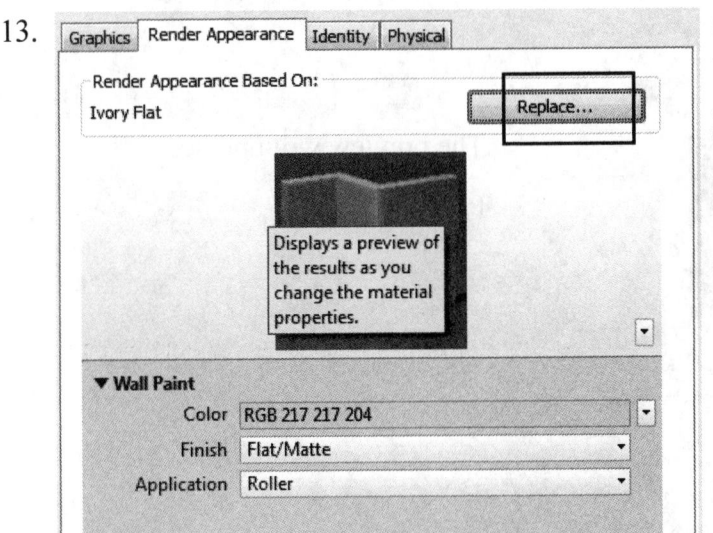

    Select the Render Appearance tab.

    Press the **Replace** button.

14. Select the **Flat - Antique White** color.

    Press **OK**.

15. You can adjust the color using RGB.

    ▼ Wall Paint
    Color   RGB 255 255 255
    Finish   Flat/Matte
    Application   Roller

    I use ColorSchemer (www.colorschemer.com) to determine the RGB code for custom colors.

    Select the **Edit Color** button.

16. 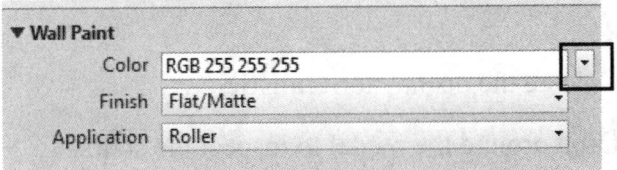 Select **Define Custom Colors**.

17. 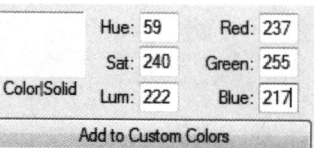 In the Red field, enter **237**.
In the Green field, enter **255**.
In the Blue field, enter **217**.

Press **Add to Custom Colors**.

This matches Sherwin William's Buckram Binding, SW0036.

18. 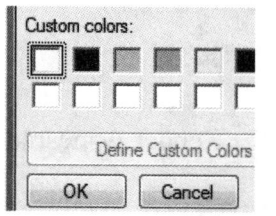 Select the color swatch.

Press **OK**.

19. 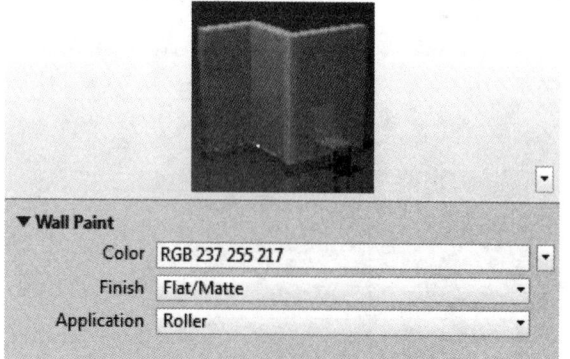 The preview will update.

Press **OK**.

20. 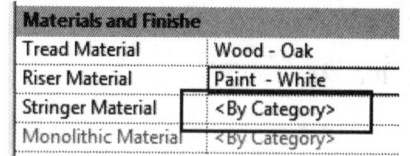 Select the **Stringer Material** column.

21. Wood - Oak   Select the **Wood - Oak** material.

Press **OK**.

22. Press **OK** to close the dialog.

23. 🏠 ▾ Switch to a **3D** view.

24. 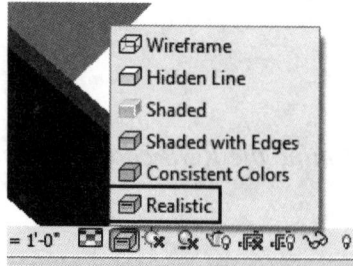 Change the display to **Realistic**.

Orbit around the model to inspect the stairs.

25.

Observe how the assigned materials affect the stairs' appearance.

26. If you want the boards to be oriented horizontally instead of vertically on the treads:

Select the stairs.
Edit Type.
Select the Tread Material.
Select the Render Appearance tab.
Next to the image picture, select Edit Image from the drop down list.
Expand the Transform area.
Set the Rotation to 90 degree.
Press Done.

27. Save as *ex3-10.rvt*.

Exercise 3-11
Adding a Floor Landing

Drawing Name: ex3-10.rvt
Estimated Time: 20 minutes

This exercise reinforces the following skills:

- ❑ Floor
- ❑ Floor Properties

1. Open *ex3-10.rvt.*

2. 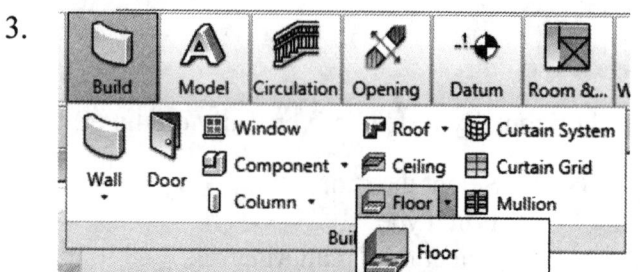 Activate **Level 2**.

3. 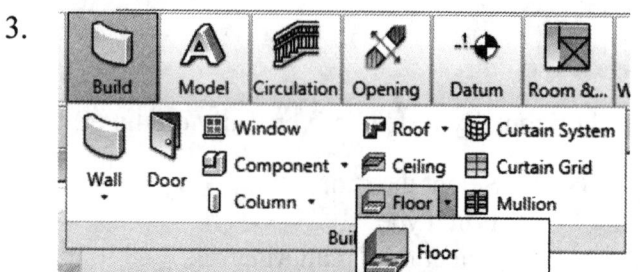 Select the **Floor** tool from the Build panel on the Home ribbon.

4. 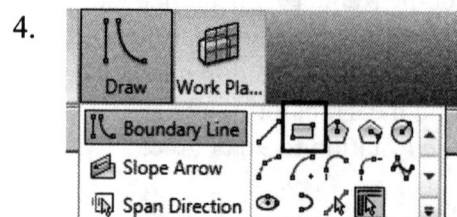 Select the **Rectangle** tool from the Draw panel of the Modify/Create Floor Boundary ribbon.

5. 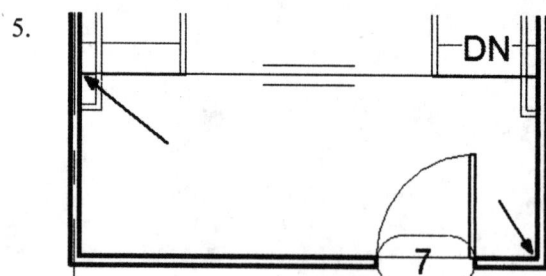 Draw a rectangle from the top of the stair to the corner of the stairwell.

   Right click and select **Cancel** twice to exit the command.

6. Edit Type   Select **Edit Type** from the Properties pane.

7. Duplicate...   Select **Duplicate**.

8. Name: Landing - Concrete on Metal Deck   Name the floor style **Landing - Concrete on Metal Deck**.
   Press **OK**.

9.

Parameter	Value
Constructio	
Structure	Edit...
Default Thick	150.0

Select **Edit** next to Structure.

10. Insert   Select **Insert** to add an additional structure.

11.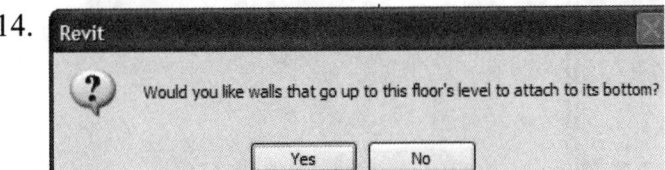

Layers

	Function	Material	Thickness	Wrap
1	**Core Boundary**	**Layers Above Wrap**	0.0	
2	Structure [1]	Concrete - Cast In Situ	100.0	
3	Structure [1]	Metal - Decking	3.0	
4	**Core Boundary**	**Layers Below Wrap**	0.0	

Layers

	Function	Material	Thickne
1	**Core Boundary**	**Layers Above Wrap**	0' 0"
2	Structure [1]	Concrete - Cast-in-Place Concrete	0' 6"
3	Structure [1]	Metal - Deck	1"
4	**Core Boundary**	**Layers Below Wrap**	0' 0"

Set Layer 2 to **Structure [1], Concrete - Cast In Place, 6″ [100 mm]**.

Set Layer 3 to **Structure [1], Metal - Decking - 1″ [3 mm]**.

12. Press **OK** to exit the dialog.

13. 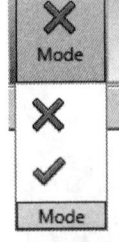 Select the **Green Check** under Mode to finish the floor.

14.

Revit

? Would you like walls that go up to this floor's level to attach to its bottom?

Yes   No

You may see a dialog asking if you want walls extending from your floor.

Select '**No**'.

If you select Yes, then walls will be added and you will have walls inserted on top of walls...this will create an error.

15. 3D Views {3D} Activate **3D View**.

16. 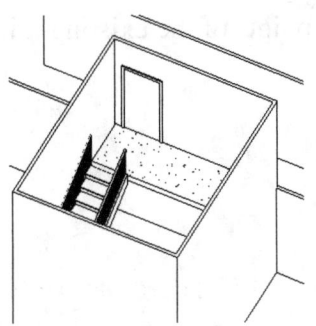 The landing should look pretty good, but we need to add some rails to prevent an accident.

To orbit the view, press down on the mouse scroll wheel and press the Shift key at the same time.

17. Save as *ex3-11.rvt*.

Exercise 3-12
Adding a Railing

Drawing Name: ex3-11.rvt
Estimated Time: 15 minutes

This exercise reinforces the following skills:

- ❑ Railing
- ❑ Railing Properties

1. Open *ex3-11.rvt.*

2. 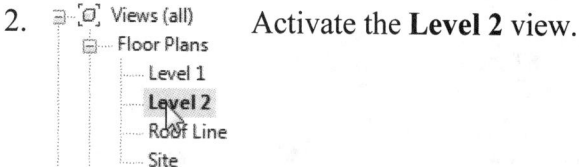 Activate the **Level 2** view.

3. Select the **Railing** tool under the Circulation panel on the Home ribbon.

4.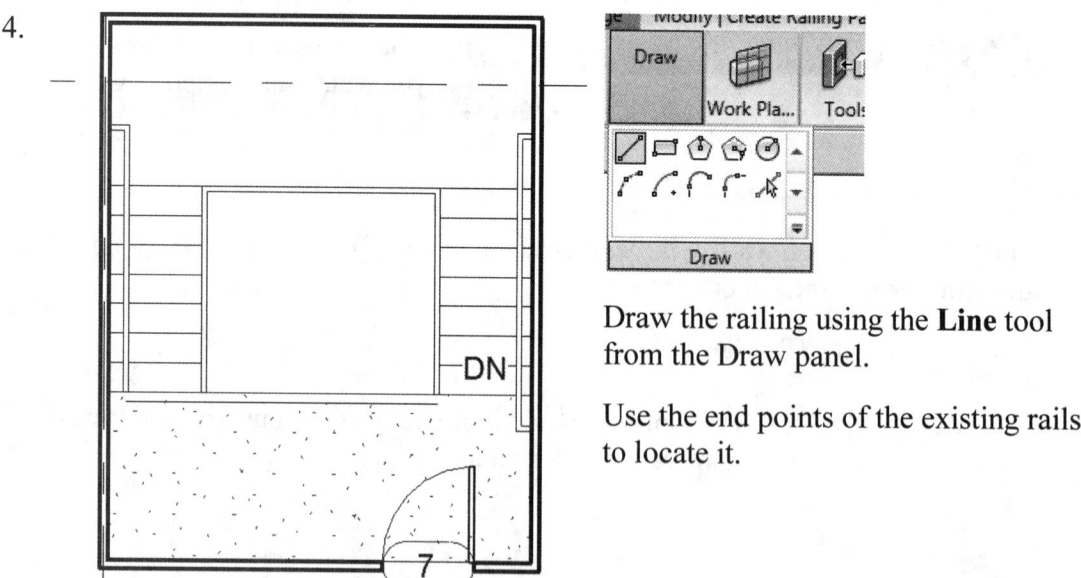

   Draw the railing using the **Line** tool from the Draw panel.

   Use the end points of the existing rails to locate it.

5. Select **Edit Type** from the Properties pane.

6. Select **Duplicate**.

7.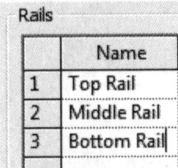

Name the new railing style – **Guardrail-Landing**.

Press **OK**.

8.

Parameter	Value
Construction	
Railing Height	3' 0"
Rail Structure	Edit...
Baluster Placement	Edit...
Baluster Offset	0' 0"

Select the **Edit** button next to Rail Structure.

9. Add two rails.

	Name
1	Top Rail
2	Middle Rail
3	Bottom Rail

Name the three rails.
Set Rail 1 to **Top Rail**.
Set Rail 2 to **Middle Rail**.
Set Rail 3 to **Bottom Rail**.

10.

	Name	Height	Offset	Profile	Material
1	Top Rail	3' 0"	-0' 1"	Circular Handrail : 1"	Metal - Aluminum
2	Middle Rail	1' 6"	0' 0"	Circular Handrail : 1"	Metal - Aluminum
3	Bottom Rail	0' 6"	0' 0"	Circular Handrail : 1"	Metal - Aluminum

Set the rail heights to **3' [1100]**, **1'-6" [600]**, and **6" [150 mm]**.
Set the profiles to **Circular Handrail: 1" [M_Circular Handrail: 30 m]**.
Set the material to **Metal - Aluminum**.
Press **OK**.

11.

Parameter	Value
Construction	
Railing Height	3' 0"
Rail Structure	Edit...
Baluster Placement	Edit...
Baluster Offset	0' 0"

Select **Edit** next to Baluster Placement.

12.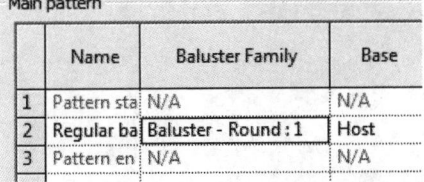

Main pattern

	Name	Baluster Family	Base
1	Pattern sta	N/A	N/A
2	Regular ba	Baluster - Round : 1	Host
3	Pattern en	N/A	N/A

Under Main Pattern:

Set the Baluster Family to **Baluster - Round 1"**.

13.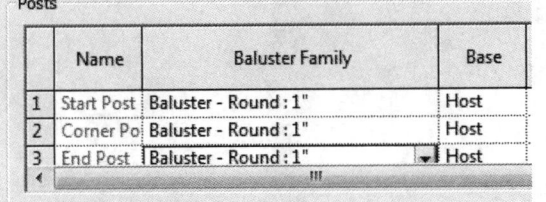

Posts

	Name	Baluster Family	Base
1	Start Post	Baluster - Round : 1"	Host
2	Corner Po	Baluster - Round : 1"	Host
3	End Post	Baluster - Round : 1"	Host

Under Posts:

Set the Baluster Family to **Baluster - Round 1"**.

14. 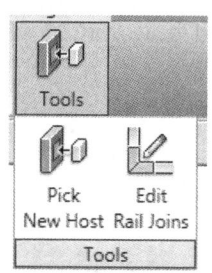 In the Dist. from previous column, set the distance to **4" [150]**. Press **OK**.

Close the dialog.

15.  Select **Pick New Host** under the Tools panel.

Select the floor landing as the host.

16. Select the **Green Check** under Mode to finish the railing.

17. Switch to a 3D view to inspect the railing.

18. Save the file as *ex3-12.rvt*.

Exercise 3-13
Modifying the Floor Plan- Skills Review

Drawing Name: ex3-12.rvt
Estimated Time: 30 minutes

This exercise reinforces the following skills:

- ❑ 3D View
- ❑ Copy
- ❑ Align
- ❑ Floor
- ❑ Railing

1.   Open *ex3-12.rvt*.

2.   Activate the **North** Elevation.

3.   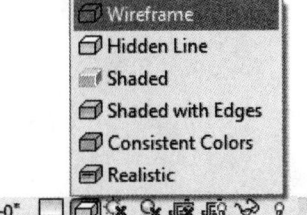 Set View Properties to **Wireframe**.

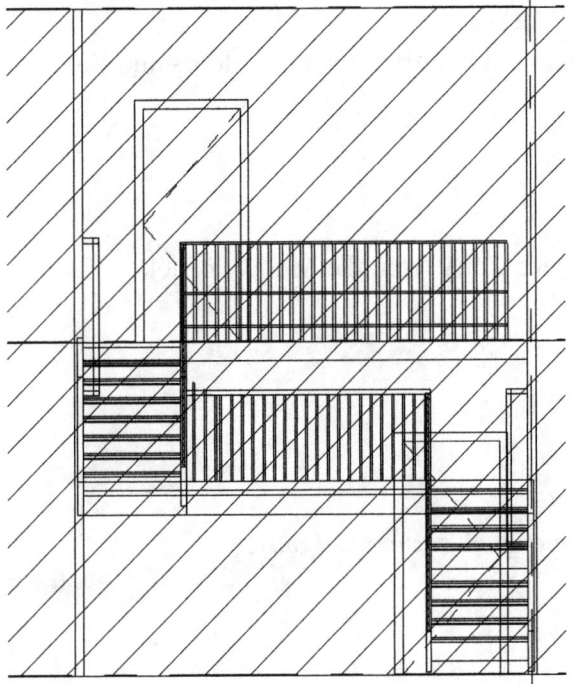 We see that our stairs in elevation look pretty good.

4.   Activate **Level 2**.

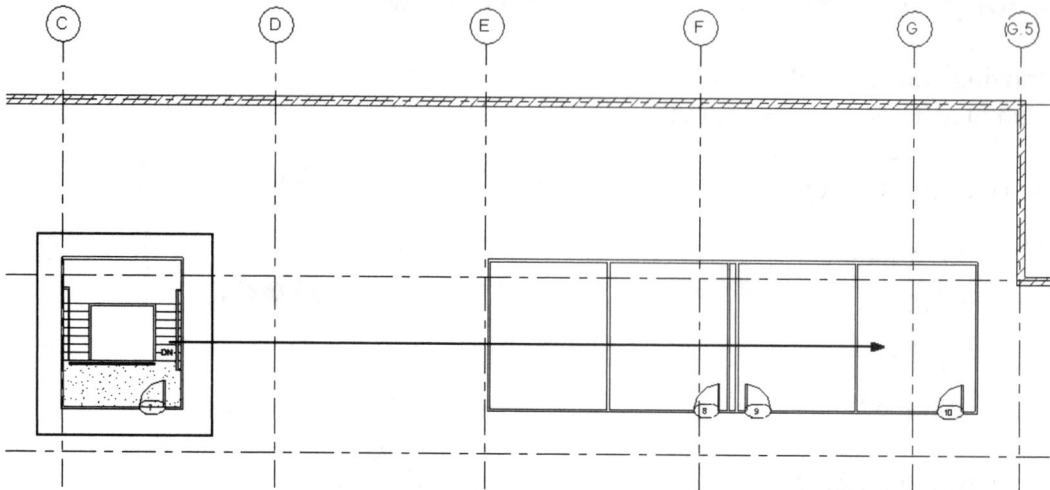

We want to copy the stairs, railings, and landing to the stairwell indicated.

5.   Window around the walls, stair and railings.

6.   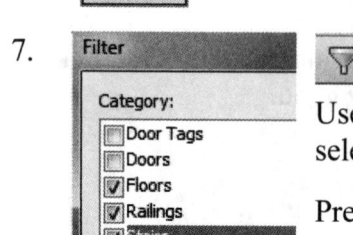   Select the **Filter** tool.

7.   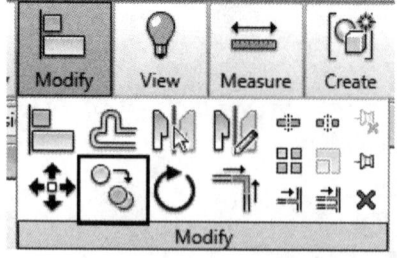   Use **Filter** to ensure that only the Stairs, Floors and Railings are selected.

Press **OK**.

8.   Select **Copy** from the Modify panel.

Copy can be used to copy on the same work plane/level only.

9.

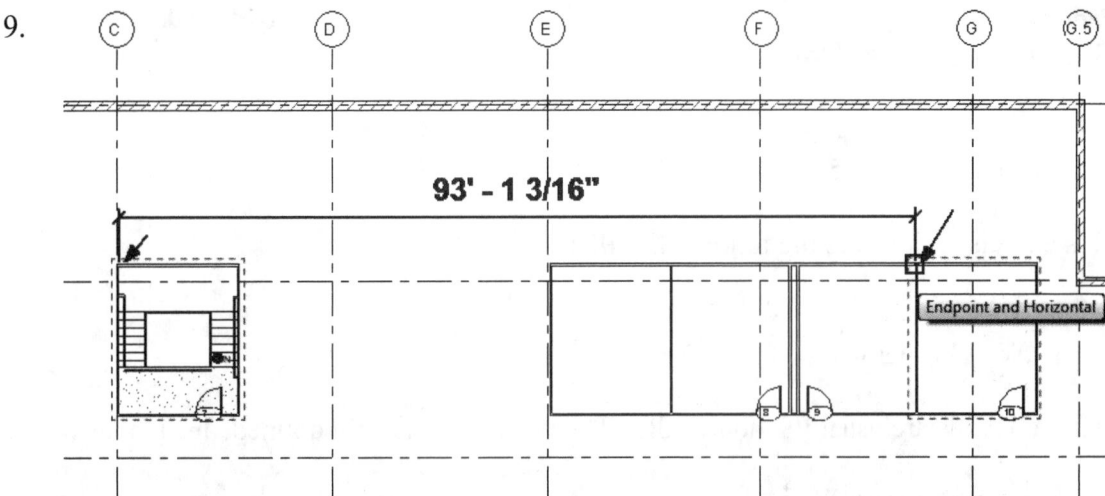

93' - 1 3/16"

Endpoint and Horizontal

Select the top left corner of the existing stairwell as the basepoint.

Select the top left corner of the target stairwell as the target location.

(Instead of copying the stair, you can also repeat the process we used before to create a stair from scratch.)

10. 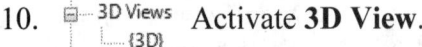 Activate **3D View**.

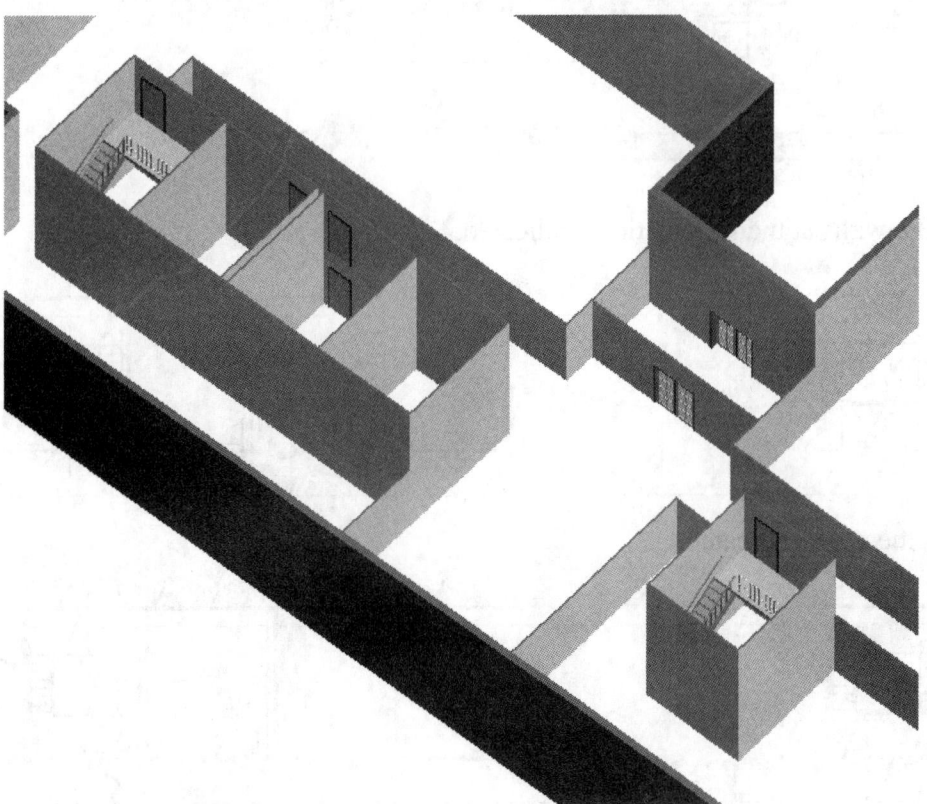

You should see a complete stairs with landing and railing in both stairwells.

11. Save as *ex3-13.rvt*.

Exercise 3-14
Defining a 2-hr Wall

Drawing Name: ex3-13.rvt
Estimated Time: 5 minutes

This exercise reinforces the following skills:

- ❑ Split
- ❑ Wall Properties

Stairwell walls are usually 2-hour walls. The walls, as currently defined, are 1-hour walls.

1.   Open *ex3-13.rvt*.

2.   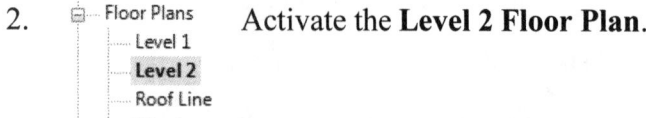   Activate the **Level 2 Floor Plan**.

3.   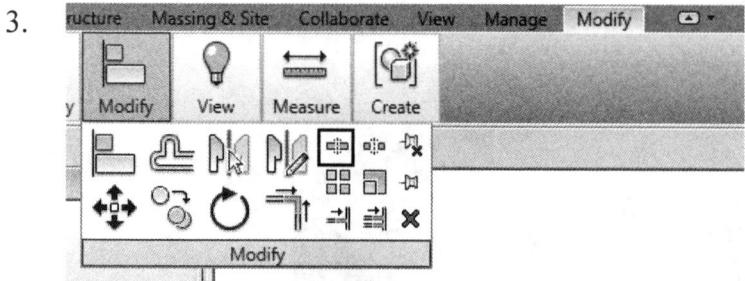   Select the **Split** tool from the Modify panel on the Modify ribbon.

4.   Split the walls at the intersections indicated.

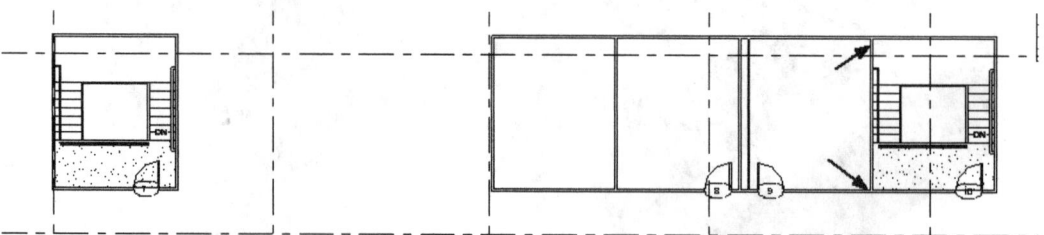

5.   Select the walls indicated.

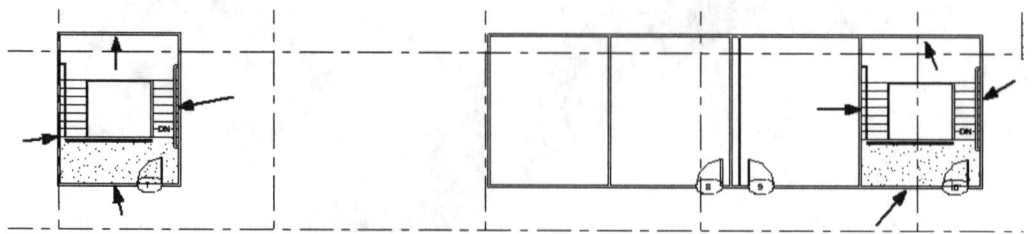

These walls will be defined as 2-hr walls.

6.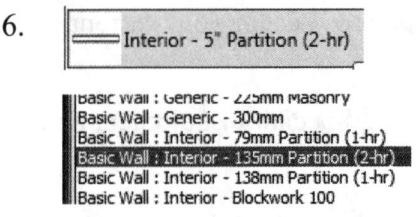

On the Properties pane, select the **Interior - 5″ Partition (2-hr)** [**Basic Wall: Interior - 135mm Partition (2-hr)**] from the Type Selector drop down list.

7. Save the file as *ex3-14.rvt*.

Exercise 3-15
Adding an Elevator

Drawing Name: ex3-14.rvt
Estimated Time: 40 minutes

This exercise reinforces the following skills:

- Autodesk Seek
- 3D View
- Delete
- Wall Properties
- Families

I haven't found an elevator I am really happy with from Autodesk. The elevator provided on the CD that comes with the text was developed and created by the author using student input.

1. Open *ex3-14.rvt*.

2. Floor Plans
   ‐‐‐ Level 1
   ‐‐‐ Level 2
   ‐‐‐ Roof Line
   ‐‐‐ Site

   Activate the **Level 1 Floor Plan**.

3. Insert Annotate Structure M
   ink Import Load fro... Autodes...
   Load Family Load as Group
   Load from Library

   Activate the **Insert** ribbon.

   Select **Load Family** from the Load from Library panel.

4. File name: Elevator_Two Level
   Files of type: All Supported Files (*.rfa, *.adsk)

   Locate the Elevator_ Two Level on the CD included with the text.

   Press **Open**.

5. Specialty Equipment
   Elevator_Two Level
   SPF-21
   SPF-25
   SPF-30
   SPF-35

   The elevator is now available in the browser for your current project.

   To locate it, look for the folder called Specialty Equipment and expand that folder.

6. Elevator_Cab-Traction_Ree
   SPF-21
   SPF-25
   SPF-30
   SPF-35

   Select the SPF-35 model.
   Hold down the left mouse button and drag into the display window.

7.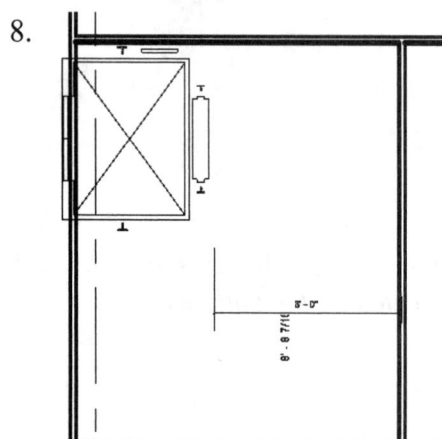

   Select **Place on Work Plane** from the Placement panel.

8.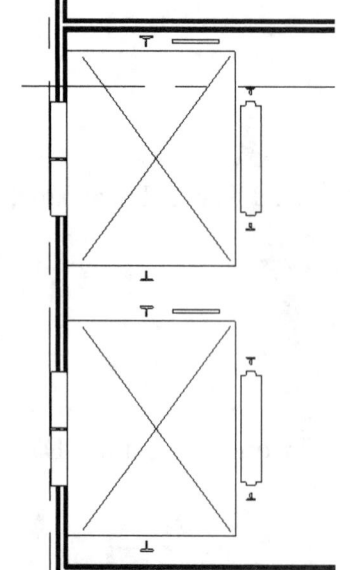

   The elevator will appear on the cursor.
   Press the SPACE bar to rotate the elevator to orient it properly.

   Left pick to place.

9. Place two elevators.

   Right click and select CANCEL to exit the command.

10.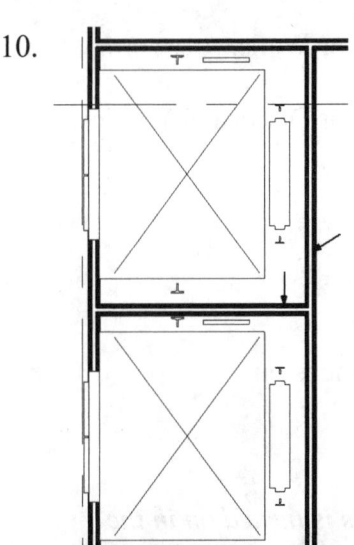

Add a wall behind and to the right of the two elevators as shown.

Add a wall between the two elevator shafts. Use the midpoint of the wall behind the elevators to locate the wall.

Constrain both walls to the Roof Line level.

Base Extension Distance	0.0
Top Constraint	Up to level: Roof Line
Unconnected Height	8000.0

11. Manage   Activate the **Manage** ribbon.

12.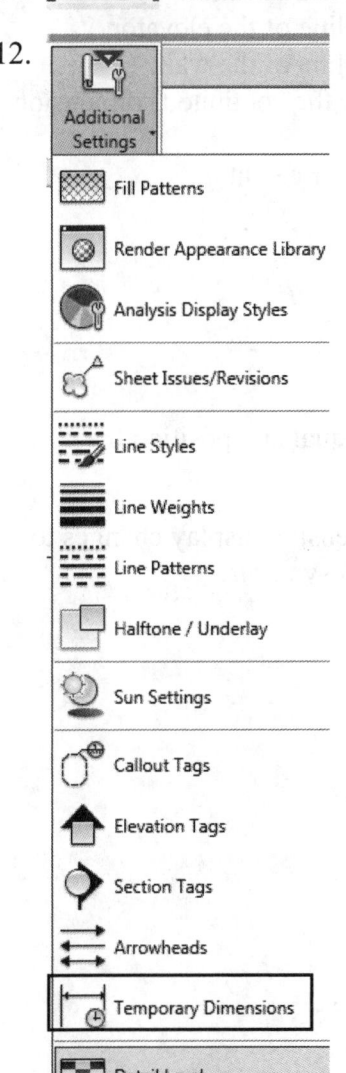

Go to **Settings→Additional Settings→Temporary Dimensions**.

13.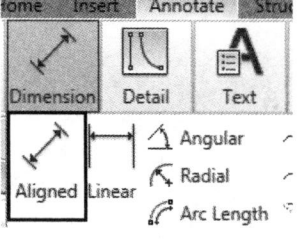

Enable **Centerlines** for Walls.

Enable **Centerlines** for Doors and Windows.

Press **OK**.

14. | Annotate | Activate the **Annotate** ribbon.

15. Select the **Aligned** tool under Dimension.

Make sure visibility of dimensions is turned on in the Visibility/Graphics dialog.

16.

Select the center of the wall.
Select the center line of the elevator.
Select the center line of the wall.
Left pick to place the continuous dimension.

Repeat for the other elevator.

17. Left click on the EQ symbol to set the dimensions equal and position the elevator centered in the space.

18.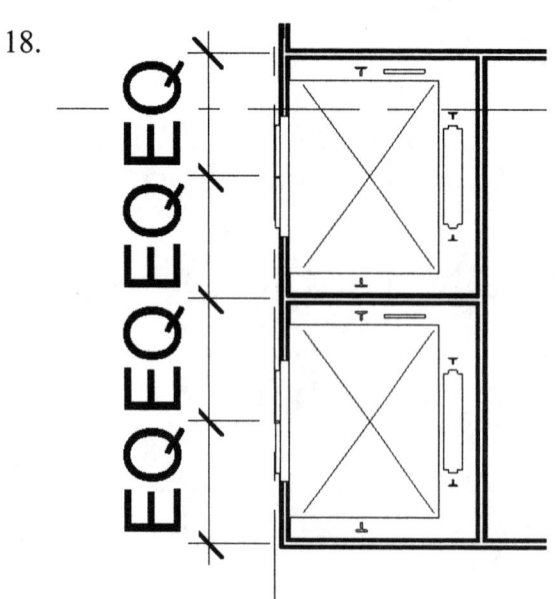

The dimension display changes to show EQ symbols.

19.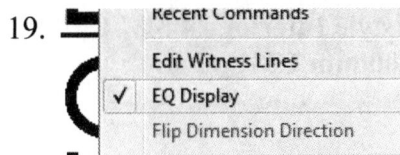

To display dimensions:
Select the extension line of the dimension.

Uncheck the EQ Display to show dimensions.

20.

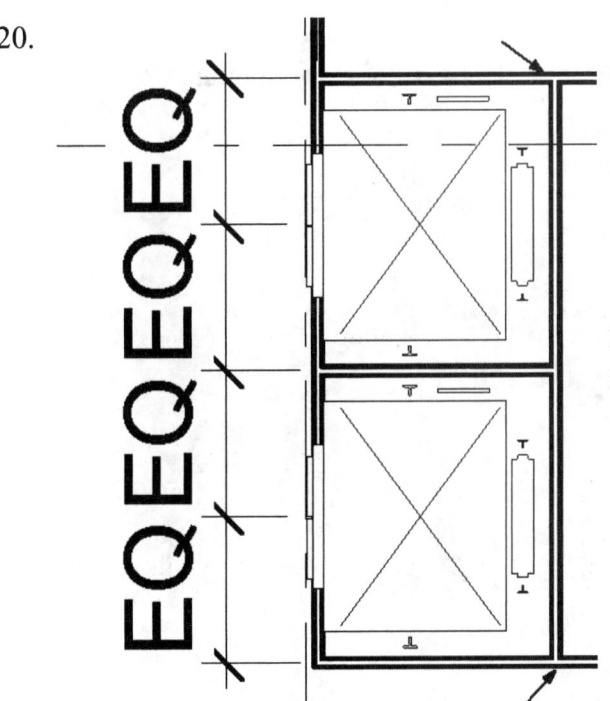

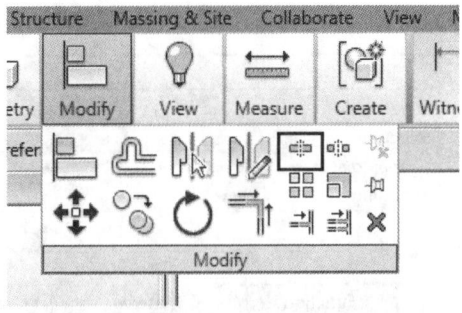

Activate the **Modify** ribbon.
Use the **SPLIT** tool and split the walls
at the intersections shown.

21.

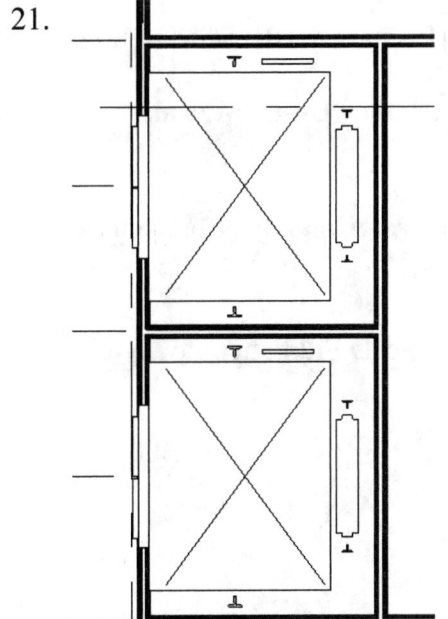

Elevator shaft walls are 2-hour, usually CMU.

Select the elevator shaft walls.

Use the **Filter** tool to ensure only the walls are
selected.

22. Select **Edit Type** from the Properties pane.

23. Select the **Duplicate** button.

24. 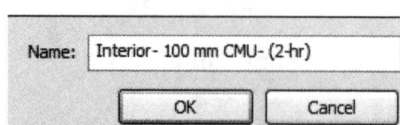 Name the new wall style **Interior - 4 3/8″ CMU (2-hr)** [**Interior - 100 mm CMU (2-hr)**].

Press **OK**.

25. Select **Edit** next to Structure.

Parameter	Value
Construction	
Structure	Edit...
Wrapping at Inserts	Do not wrap
Wrapping at Ends	None

26.

Layers

EXTERIOR SIDE

	Function	Material	Thickness
1	Finish 2 [5]	Gypsum Wall Board	0' 0 5/8"
2	**Core Boundary**	**Layers Above Wrap**	**0' 0"**
3	Structure [1]	Masonry - Concrete	0' 3 1/8"
4	**Core Boundary**	**Layers Below Wrap**	**0' 0"**
5	Finish 2 [5]	Gypsum Wall Board	0' 0 5/8"

Layers

EXTERIOR SIDE

	Function	Material	Thickness
1	Finish 2 [5]	Plasterboard	16.0
2	**Core Boundary**	**Layers Above Wrap**	**0.0**
3	Structure [1]	Masonry - Concrete Block	70.0
4	**Core Boundary**	**Layers Below Wrap**	**0.0**
5	Finish 2 [5]	Plasterboard	16.0

Set Layer 1 to Finish 2 [5], **Gypsum Wall Board [Plasterboard], 5/8″ [16 mm]**.
Set Layer 2 to Core Boundary.
Set Layer 3 to Structure [1], **Masonry-Concrete Masonry Units [Masonry - Concrete Block], 3 1/8″ [70 mm]**.
Set Layer 4 to Core Boundary.
Set Layer 5 to Finish 2 [5], **Gypsum Wall Board [Plasterboard], 5/8″ [16 mm]**.

Press **OK**.

27. Set the Coarse Scale Fill Pattern to **Gypsum-Plaster**.

Graphics	
Coarse Scale Fill Pattern	Gypsum-Plaster
Coarse Scale Fill Color	Black

Press **OK**.

28. 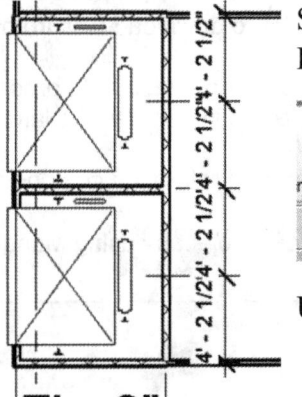 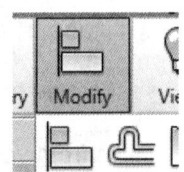 Set the properties of the elevator shaft walls to the new style: **Interior - 4 3/8″ CMU [Interior-100 mm CMU].**

Use **Modify→ALIGN** to adjust the walls.

29. Prefer: Wall faces ▼ Set the Option bar to **Prefer Wall faces**.

30. 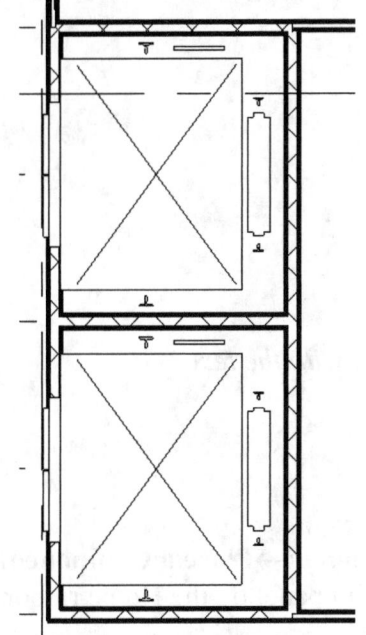 Use the ALIGN tool to adjust the walls so the faces are flush.

31. ⊟ 3D Views
      └ {3D} Switch to a 3D view.

Verify that all the walls appear properly, with walls for the second floor constrained as needed. Perform any clean-up.

32. Save the file as *ex3-15.rvt.*

➢ You must have access to the Internet in order to download files from Autodesk Seek.
➢ The Snap Settings you use are based on your Zoom factor. In order to use the smaller increment snap distances, zoom in. To use the larger increment snap distances, zoom out.
➢ When placing a component, use the spacebar to rotate the component before placing.
➢ You can purge any unused families from your project by using Manage→ Settings→Purge Unused.

Exercise 3-16
Load Family

Drawing Name: ex3-15.rvt
Estimated Time: 15 minutes

This exercise reinforces the following skills:

❑ Load Family
❑ Space Planning

All of the content required is on the CD that comes with the text

1. Open or continue working in *ex3-15.rvt*.

2. Activate **Level 1**.

3. 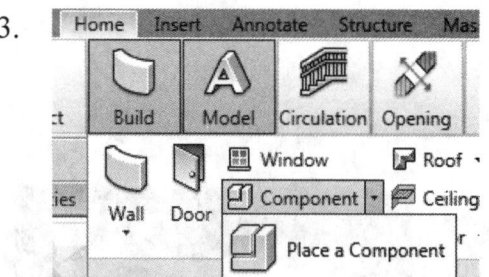   Select the **Component→Place a Component** tool from the Build panel on the Home ribbon.

4. 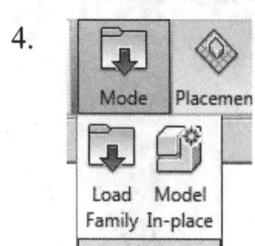   Select **Load Family** from the Mode panel.

5.

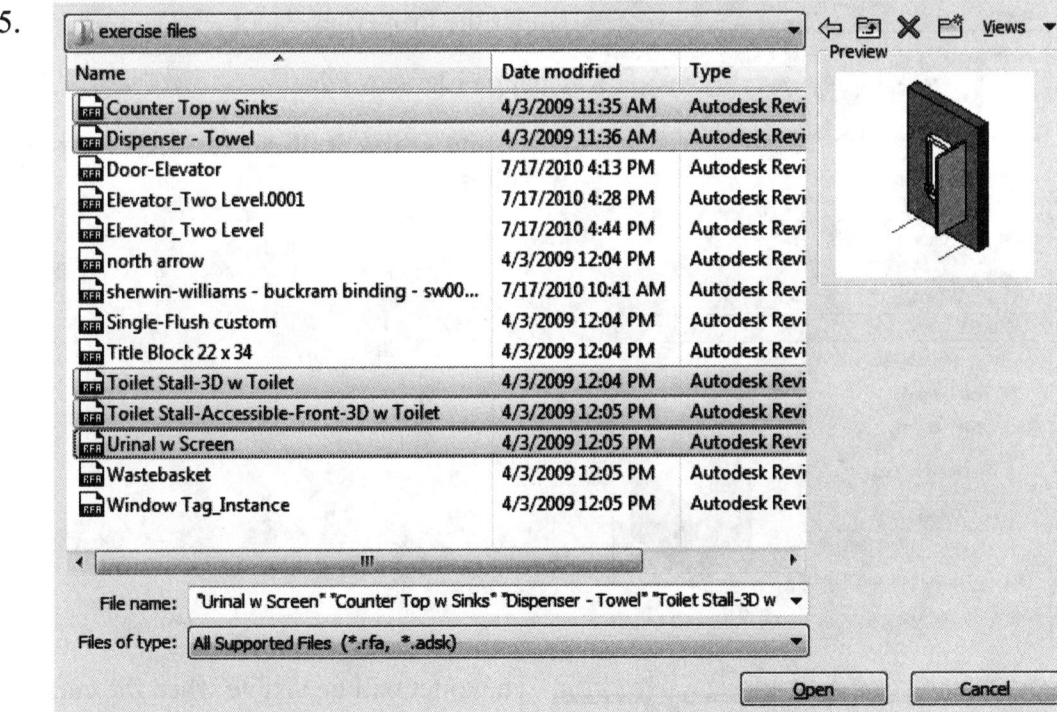

Locate the following files on the CD provided with the text.

- Urinal w Screen
- Counter Top w Sinks
- Dispenser - Paper Towel
- Toilet Stall - 3D w Toilet
- Toilet Stall - Accessible - Front - 3D w Toilet
- Mirror
- Trash Receptacle

You can select more than one file by holding down the CONTROL key.
Press **Open**.

6.

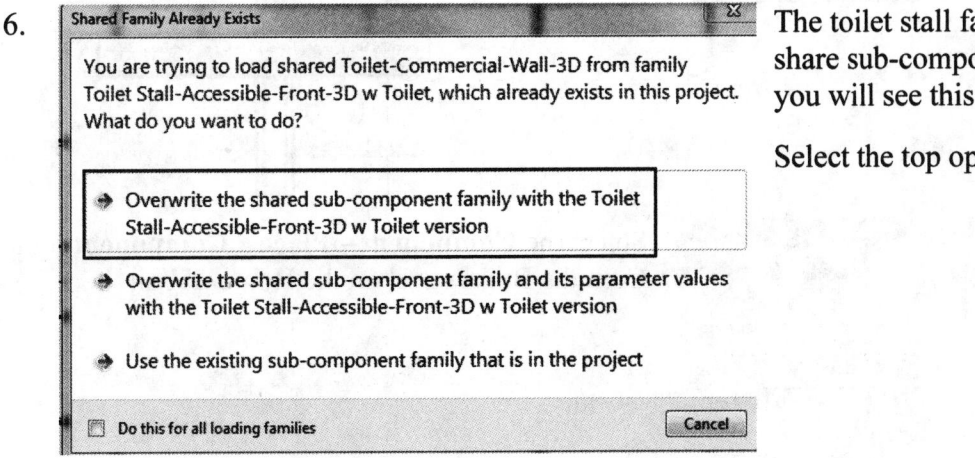

The toilet stall families share sub-components, so you will see this message.

Select the top option.

7.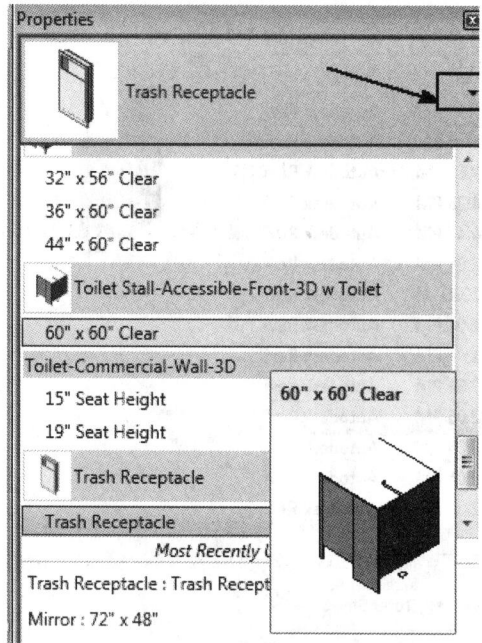

Under the Properties Pane:

Change Element Type:

Select the **Toilet Stall-Accessible-Front- 3D w Toilet**.

8.

The toilet will be visible when the cursor is over a wall.
Click to place. Do not try to place it exactly.
Simply place it on the wall.

Use the SPACE bar to orient the family.

9.

Use the ALIGN tool from the Modify **ribbon** to align the cubicle with the wall.

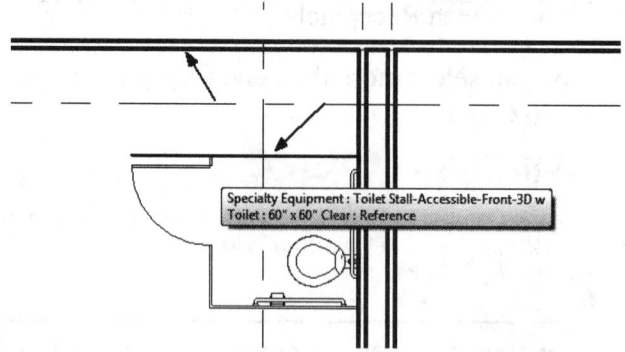

10.

Select the **Component→Place a Component** tool from the Build panel on the Home ribbon.

11.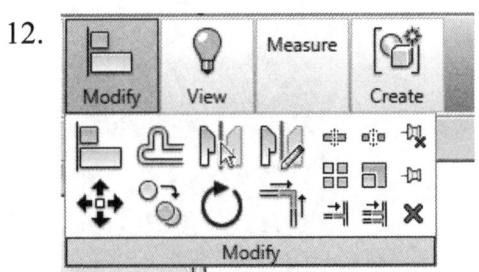

Select the **Toilet Stall - 3D w Toilet 36″ x 60″ Clear** from the Type drop down list on the Properties pane.

Place two toilet stalls.
Use the SPACE bar to orient the family.

12.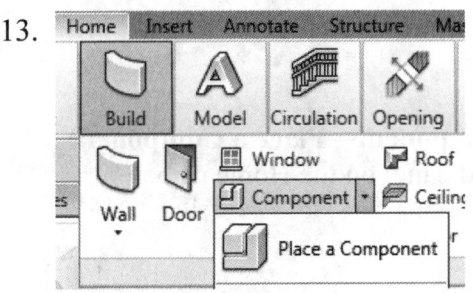

Use the ALIGN tool from the Modify **ribbon** to align the cubicle with the wall.

13.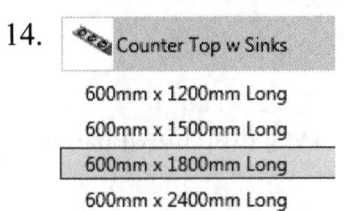

Select the **Component→Place a Component** tool from the Build panel on the Home ribbon.

14.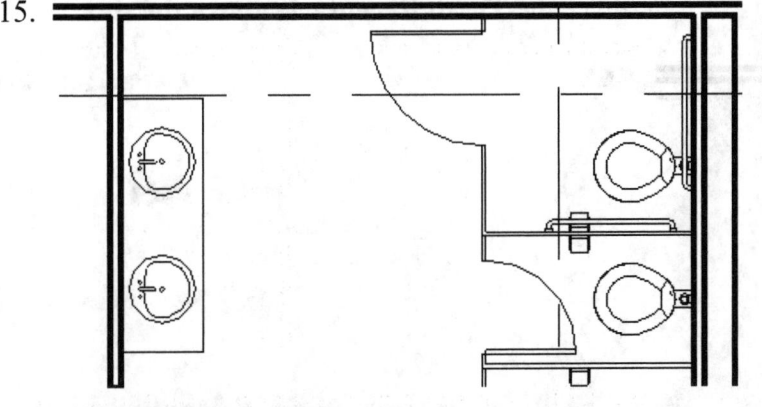

Select the **Counter Top w Sinks 600 mm x 1800 mm Long** from the Type drop down list on the Properties pane.

15.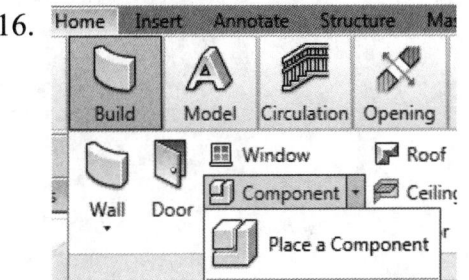

Place the **Counter Top w Sinks 600 mm x 1800 mm Long** in the lavatory.

16.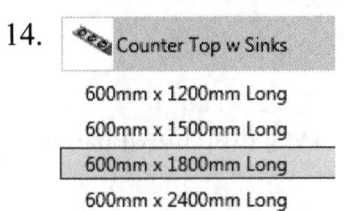

Select the **Component→Place a Component** tool from the Build panel on the Home ribbon.

3-73

17. Dispenser - Towel

Dispenser - Towel

Select the **Dispenser - Towel** from the Type drop down list on the Properties pane.

18. Place the **Dispenser - Towel** next to the sink.

19.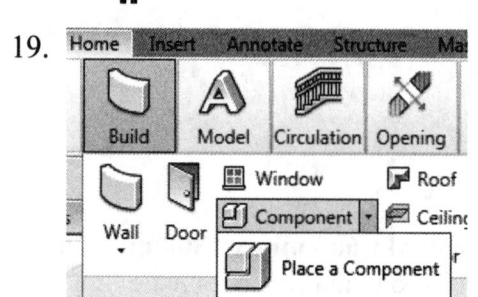

Select the **Component→Place a Component** tool from the Build panel on the Home ribbon.

20. Trash Receptacle

Trash Receptacle

Select the **Trash Receptacle** from the Type drop down list on the Properties pane.

21. Place the **Trash Receptacle above the sink**.

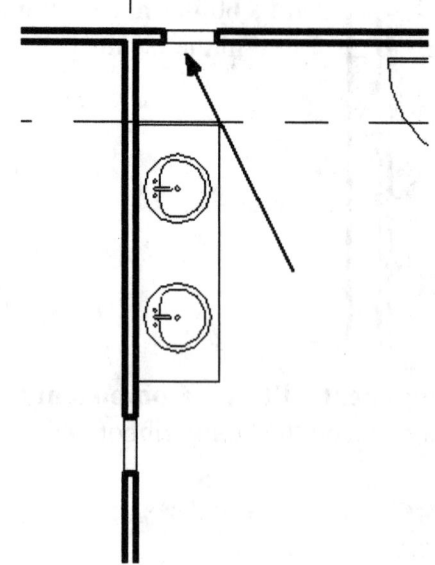

22. Select the **Component→Place a Component** tool from the Build panel on the Home ribbon.

23. Select the **Mirror: 72″ x 48″** from the Type drop down list on the Properties pane.

36" x 96"
72" x 48"
96" x 48"

24. Place the mirror above the sink.

25.

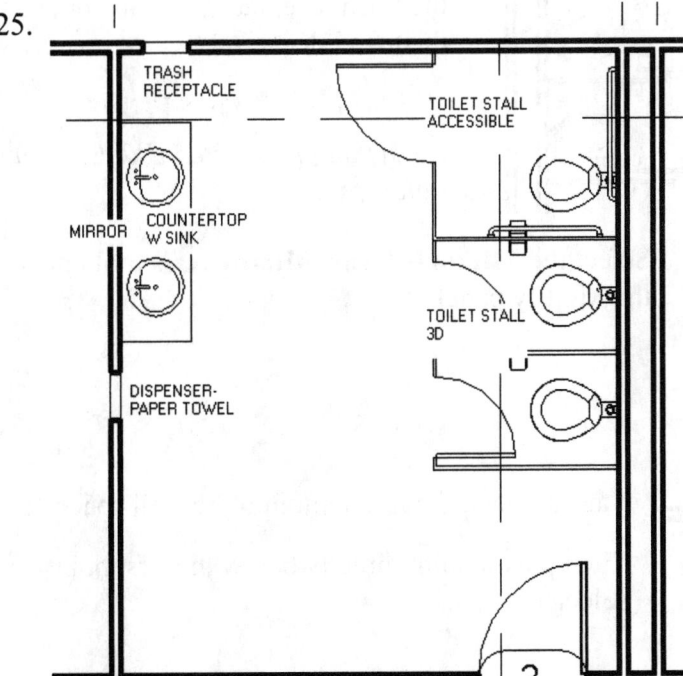

Place the components as shown.

You can place components by selecting them from the drop down list on the Option bar or by dragging and dropping from the browser.

You can flip the orientation of the component by pressing the SPACE bar before you pick to place it.

26. Save the file as *ex3-16.rvt*.

Exercise 3-17
Mirror Components

Drawing Name: ex3-16.rvt
Estimated Time: 10 minutes

This exercise reinforces the following skills:

- ❏ Modifying a Revit Family
- ❏ Family Types

*In order for the Mirror to work properly, the rooms need to be identical sizes.
This is a challenging exercise for many students. It takes practice to draw a mirror axis
six inches from the end point of the wall. If you have difficulty, draw a detail line six
inches between the 1´ gap used for plumbing and use the Pick Axis method for Mirror.*

1. Open or continue working in *ex3-16.rvt*.

2. Activate **Level 1**.

3.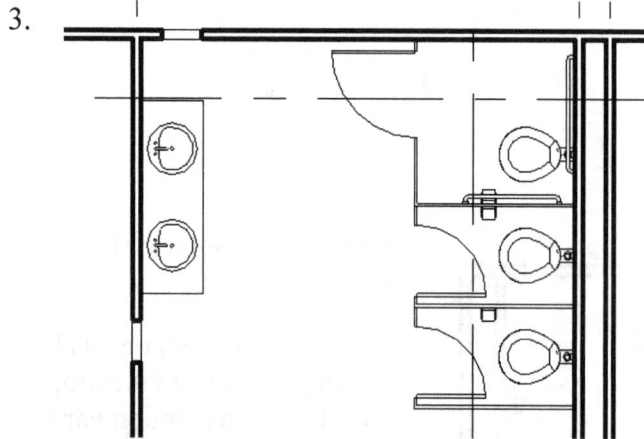
   Hold down the Control key and select the top two stalls or just window around them.

   They should highlight in red. Select the countertop with sinks, the trash receptacle, the mirror and the towel dispenser.

   Everything is selected EXCEPT one toilet stall.

4.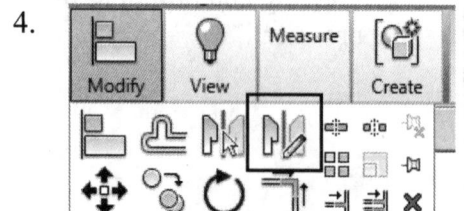
   Select the **Mirror→Draw Mirror Axis** tool under the Modify panel.

5.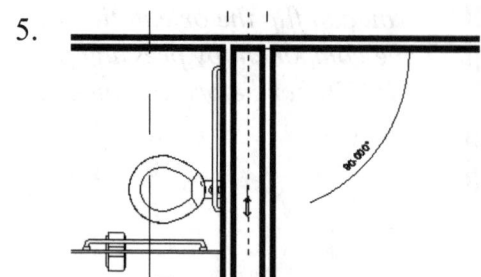
   Start a line at the midpoint into the wall space.

   Then pick a point directly below the first point selected.

6.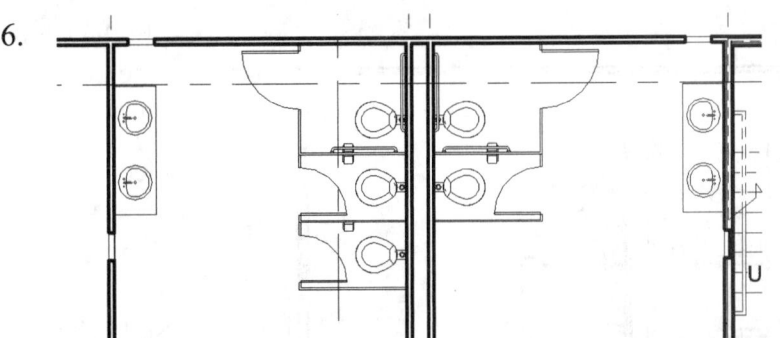
The stalls are mirrored.

7. Plumbing Fixtures
      Sink - Vanity - Round
      Toilet-Commercial-Wall-3D
      Urinal (1)
      Urinal w Screen
         Urinal w Screen

   You should have loaded the *Urinal w Screen* into your project browser from the *plumbing fixtures* folder.

8.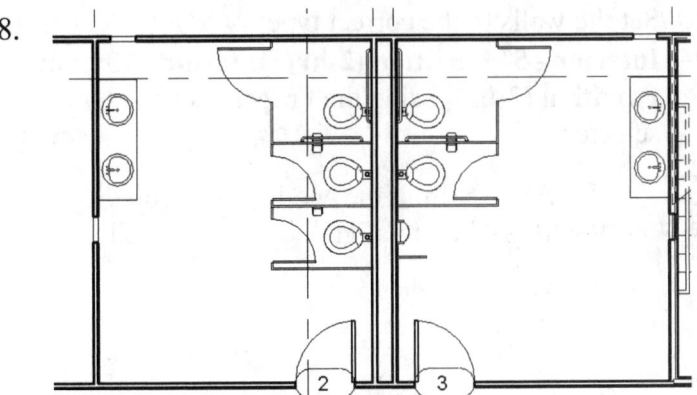
Drag and drop into the men's lavatory.

You can use the orientation flip arrows to flip the orientation of the privacy screen.

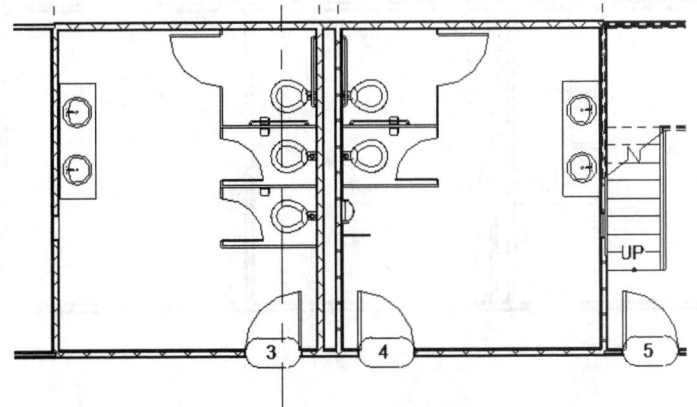
The walls surrounding both lavatories should be set to the correct wall type - **Interior - 5″ Partition (2-hr) [Interior - 135mm Partition (2-hr)]**.

9.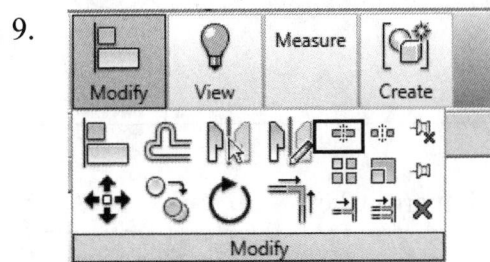
Select the **Split** tool from the Modify panel on the Modify ribbon.

10.

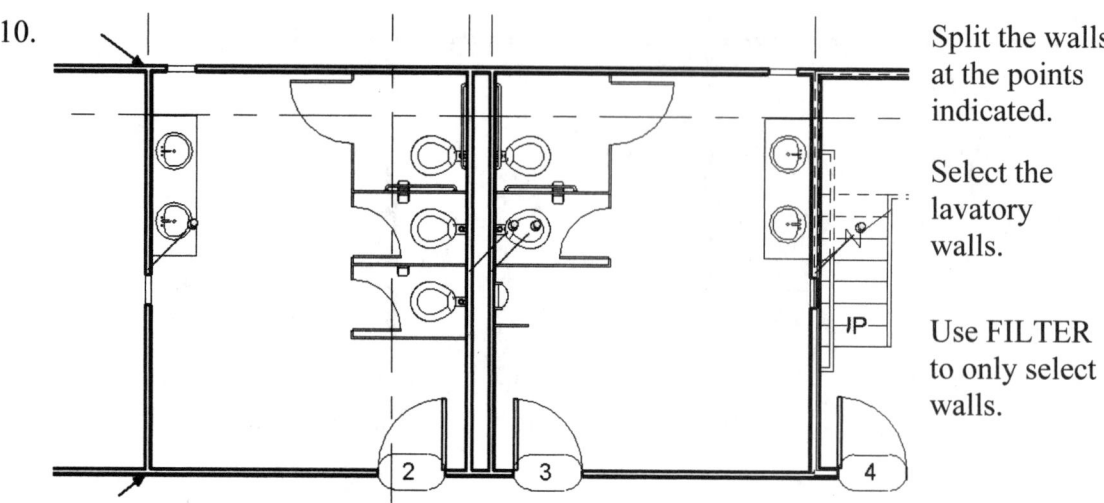

Split the walls at the points indicated.

Select the lavatory walls.

Use FILTER to only select walls.

11.

Interior - 5" Partition (2-hr)

Set the walls to the correct type: **Interior - 5″ Partition (2-hr) [Interior - 135mm Partition (2-hr)]** using the Properties pane type selector.

12.

Use ALIGN from the Modify panel on the Modify ribbon to align the lavatory walls.

13.

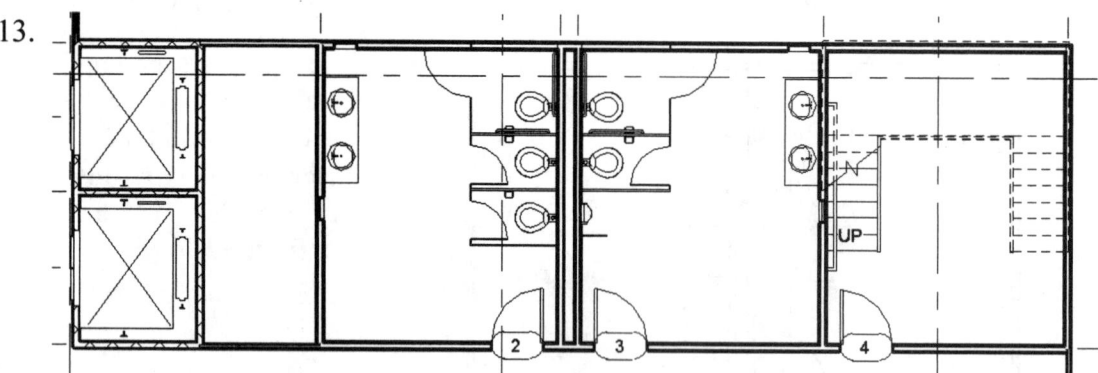

14. Save the file as *ex3-17.rvt.*

TIP: To re-select the previous selection set, hit the left arrow key.

Exercise 3-18
Copying Lavatory Layouts

Drawing Name: ex3-17.rvt
Estimated Time: 15 minutes

This exercise reinforces the following skills:

- ❑ 3D view
- ❑ Section Box
- ❑ Group
- ❑ Copy Aligned

1. Open *ex3-17.rvt*.

2. 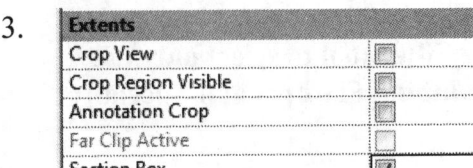 Switch to a **3D view**.

3.

Extents	
Crop View	☐
Crop Region Visible	☐
Annotation Crop	☐
Far Clip Active	☐
Section Box	☑

Scroll down the Properties pane.

Enable **Section Box**.

Press **OK**.

4.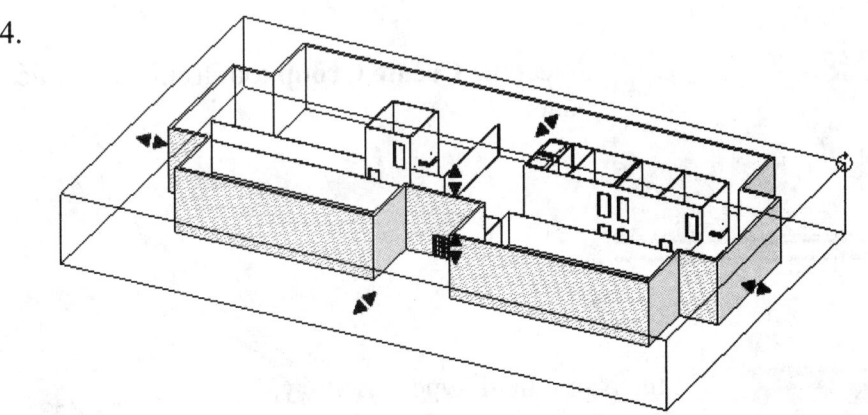

A clear box appears around the model. Left click to select the box.

There are grips indicated by arrows on the box.

5.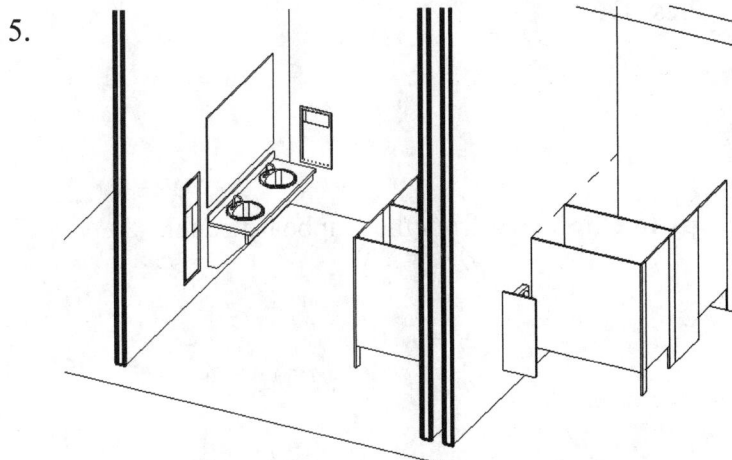

Select the grips and reduce the size of the box, so only the lavatories are shown.

Use the **SPIN** tool to rotate your view so you can inspect the lavatories.

If you hold down the SHIFT key and middle mouse button at the same time, you can orbit the model.

6. Activate **Level 1**.

7. Select the lavatory layout.

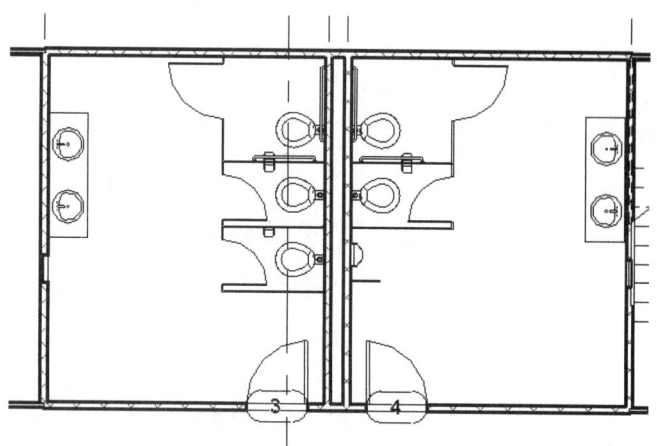

8.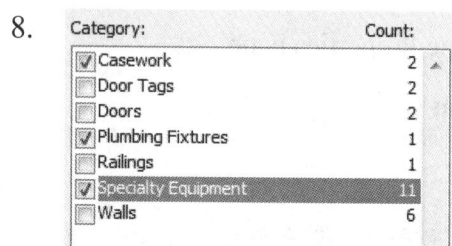

Hint: **Use the Filter tool to select only the Casework, Plumbing Fixtures and Specialty Equipment.**

9. Select the **Create Group** tool from the Create panel.

10. In the Name field, type **Lavatory**.

Press **OK**.

11.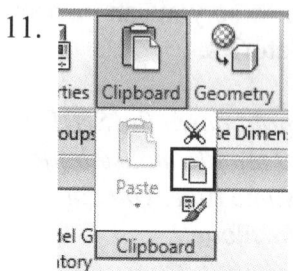

Select **Copy to Clipboard** from the Clipboard panel.

12. 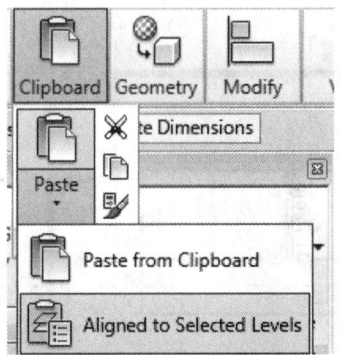 Select **Paste→Aligned to Selected Levels** from the Clipboard panel.

13. Select **Level 2**.

Press **OK**.

14. Switch to **Level 2**.

The lavatory should be placed.

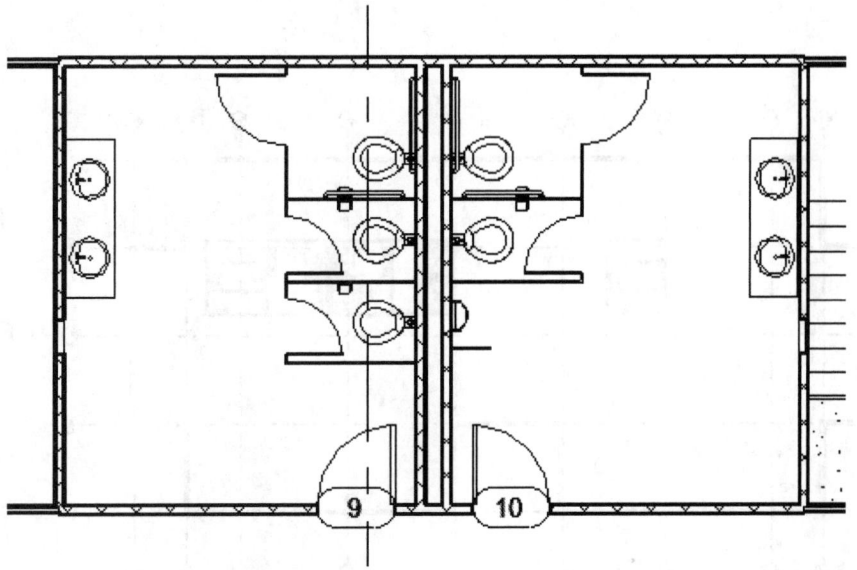

15. Save the file as *ex3-18.rvt*.

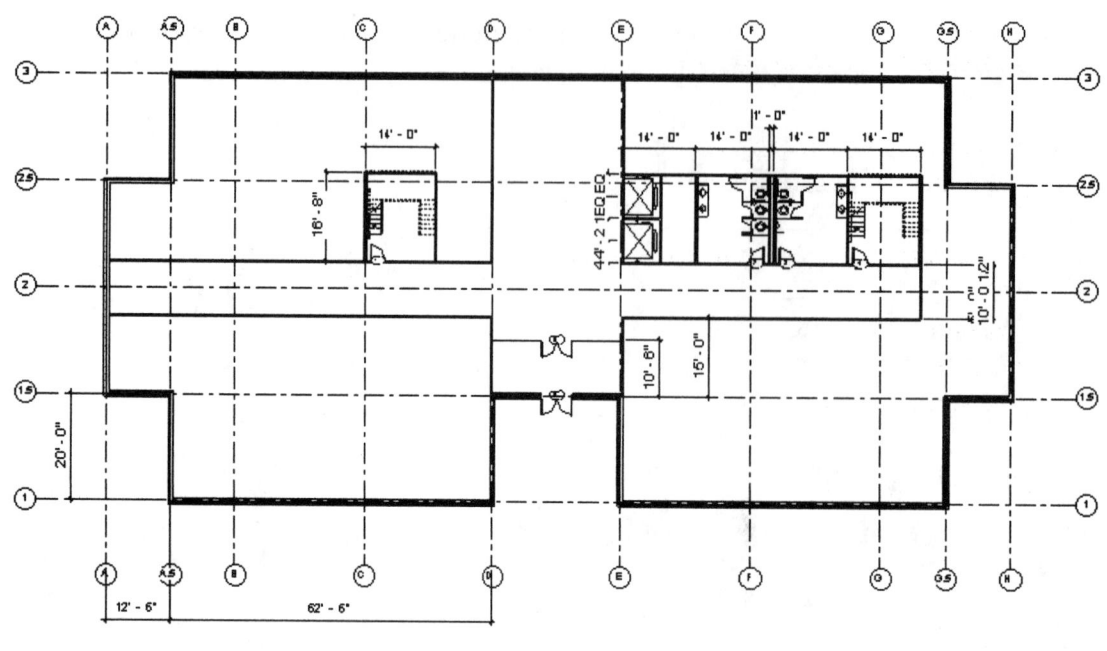

Level 1

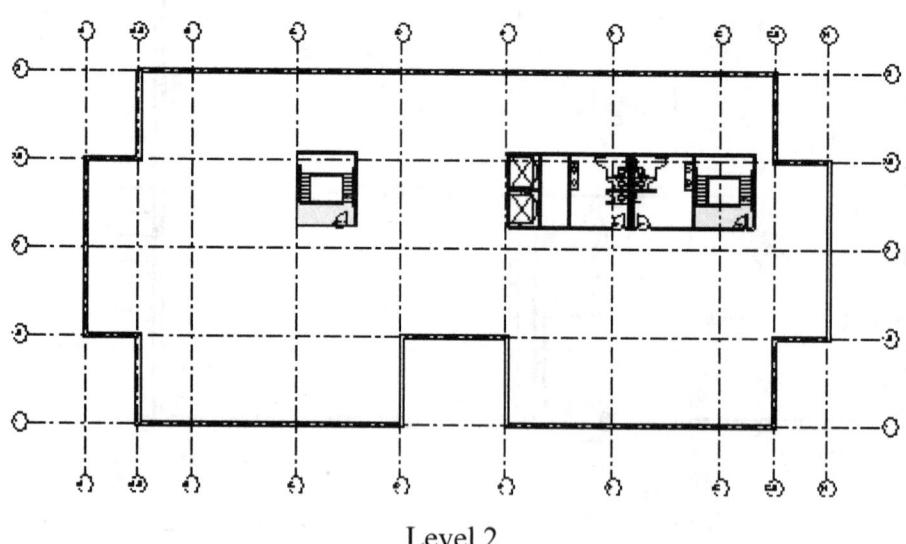

Level 2

Exercise 3-19
Add a Door to a Curtain Wall

Drawing Name: ex3-18.rvt
Estimated Time: 50 minutes

This exercise reinforces the following skills:

- Curtain Wall
- Modify Wall Curtain Wall
- Elevations

1. Open *ex3-18.rvt*.

2. Views (all)
   Floor Plans
   Level 1
      Activate **Level 1** Floor Plan.

3.   Select the East Wall.

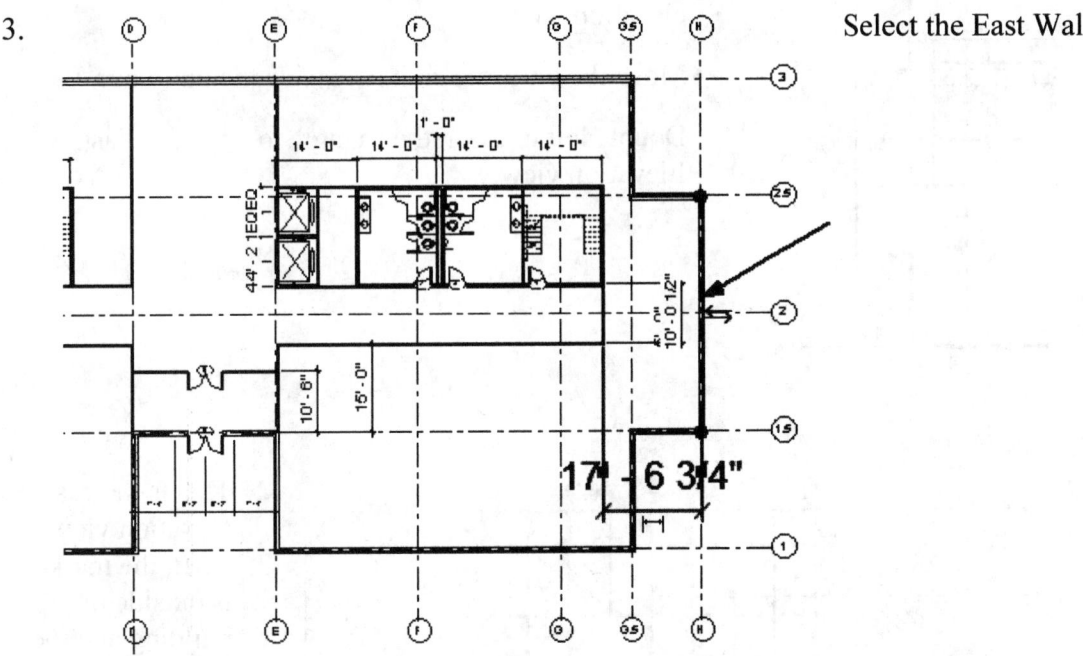

Use the TAB key to cycle your selection.

4. Curtain Wall

   Curtain Wall 1

   Exterior Glazing

   Storefront
      Select the **Storefront** Curtain Wall using the Properties pane.

5.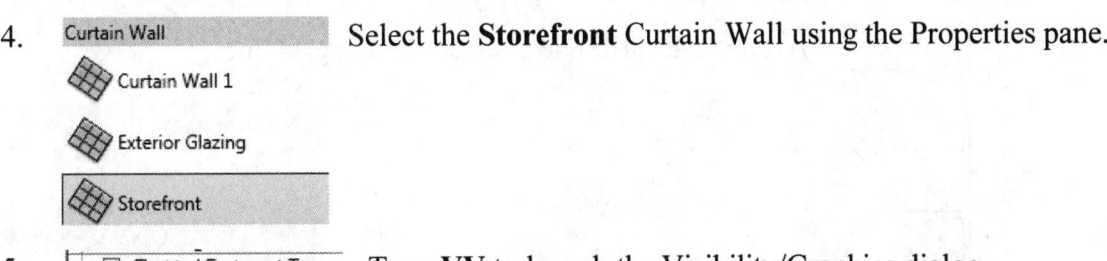
   ☑ Electrical Equipment Tags
   ☑ Electrical Fixture Tags
   ☑ Elevations
   ☑ Floor Tags
      Type **VV** to launch the Visibility/Graphics dialog.
   Enable **Elevations**.

6.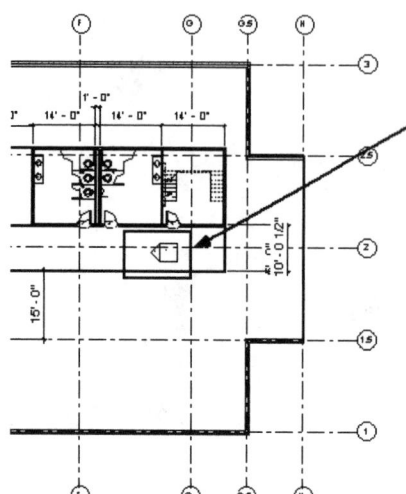

Locate your East Elevation marker.
In this case the marker is inside the building.
Drag the marker so it is outside the building.

7.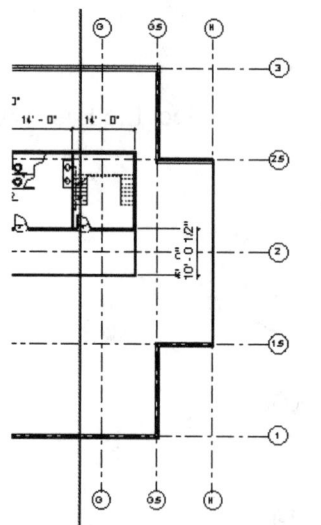

Left click on the triangle part of the elevation.
A blue line will appear to indicate the depth of the elevation view.

Move the blue line so it is outside the building.

Double left click on the triangle to open the East Elevation view.

8.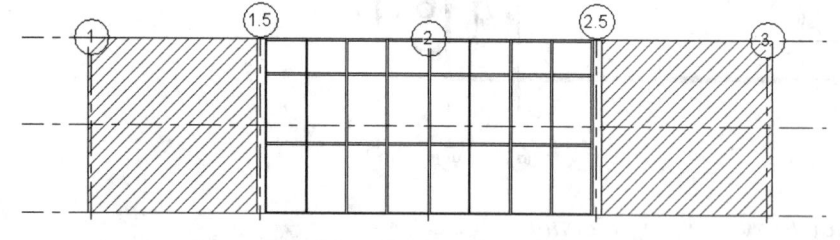

This is the east elevation view when the marker is outside the building and the depth is outside the building.

9.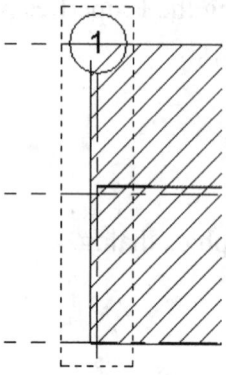

To adjust the grid lines, select the first grid line.

10.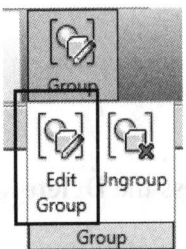

Select **Edit Group**.

11.

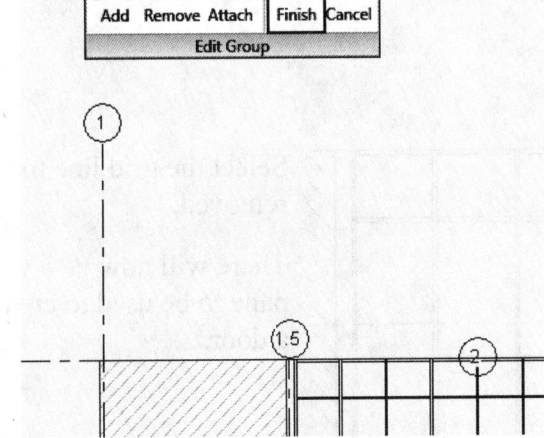

Select the grid line again.

Drag the bubble using the small circle above the building model.

12.

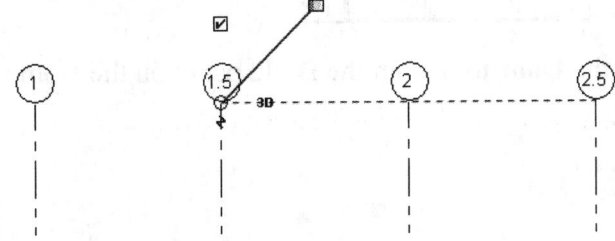

Select **Finish**.

13.

The group will adjust.

Drag the remaining gridlines so the bubbles are aligned with the grid line group.

14.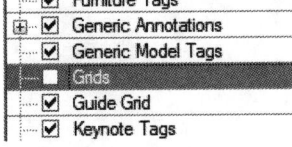

Type VV to launch the Visibility/Graphics dialog.
Turn off visibility of grids.

15. 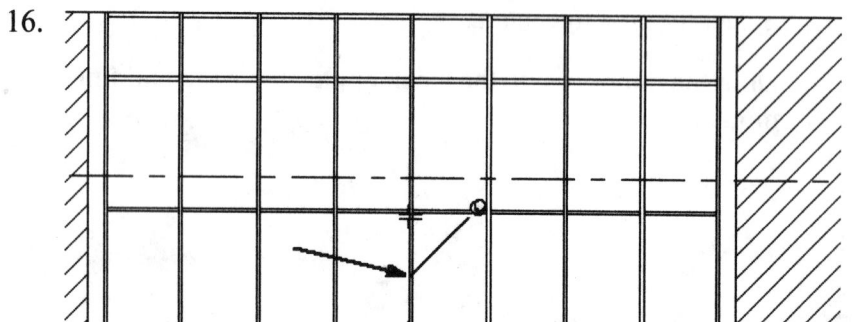 Select the center mullion.
Use the TAB key to cycle select.

Unpin the selection.

Right click and select **Delete** or press the **Delete** key on your keyboard to delete.

16. 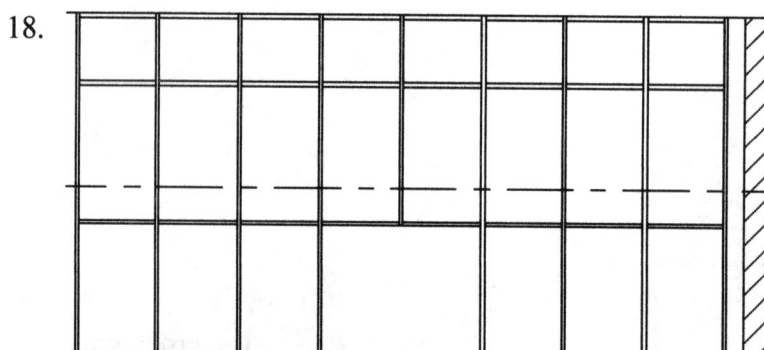 Select the grid line.

17. 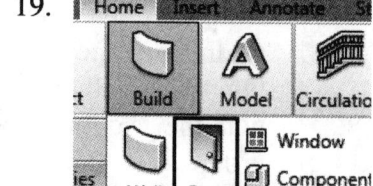 Select the **Add/Remove Segments** tool from the ribbon.

18. Select the grid line to be removed.

There will now be a wide pane to be used to create a door.

19. Select the **Door** tool from the Build panel on the Home ribbon.

20. 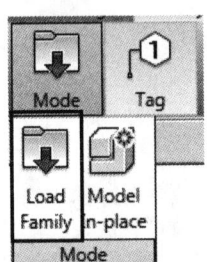 Select the **Load Family** tool from the Mode panel.

21. 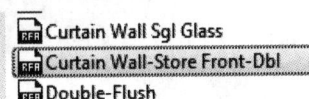 Locate the **Curtain Wall Dbl Glass** family from the *Doors* folder.
Press **Open**.

Exit the Door command.

22. 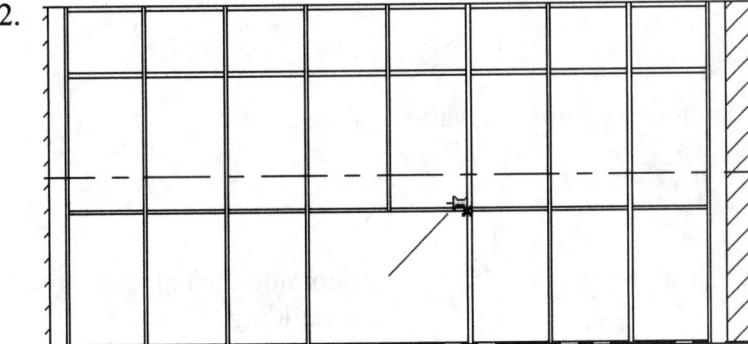 Using the TAB key, select the single panel where the door will be placed.

Unpin the glazing.

23. 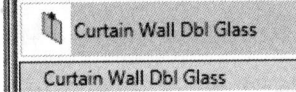 From the Properties pane:
Assign the Curtain Wall Dbl Glass door to the selected element.

Left click to place.

24. You will now see a door in your curtain wall.

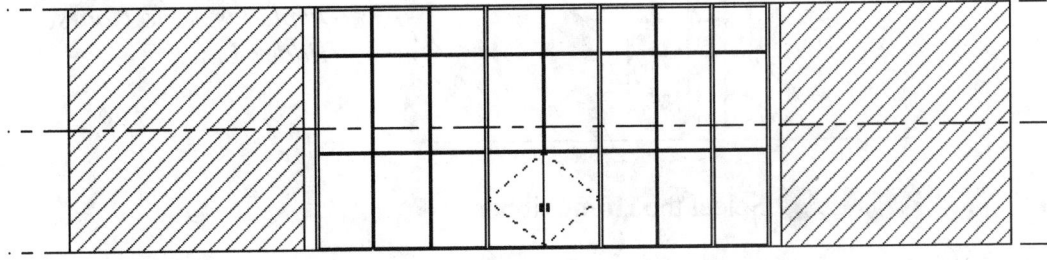

25. Save as *ex3-19.rvt*.

Exercise 3-20
Adding Windows

Drawing Name: ex3-19.rvt
Estimated Time: 50 minutes

This exercise reinforces the following skills:

- ❑   Window
- ❑   Window Properties
- ❑   Array
- ❑   Mirror
- ❑   Copy-Move

1.   Open *ex3-19.rvt.*

2.   Elevations (Building Elevation)   Switch to a **South** elevation view.
        East
        North
        South
        West

3.      Zoom into the entrance area of the building.

Display is set to Coarse, Hidden Line.

4.   Home Insert Anno   Select the **Home** ribbon.
        Build   Model

5.   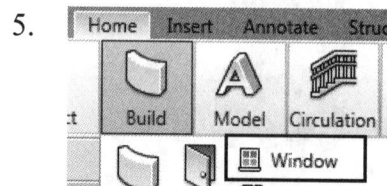   Select the **Window** tool from the Build panel.

6. 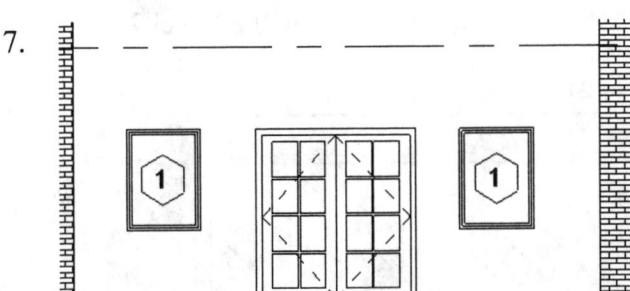 Set the Window Type to **Fixed: 36″ x 48″** [**Fixed: 0915 x 1220mm**].

7. Place two windows **5′ 2″** [**1927 mm**] from the door's midpoint.

8. In plan view, the windows will be located as shown.

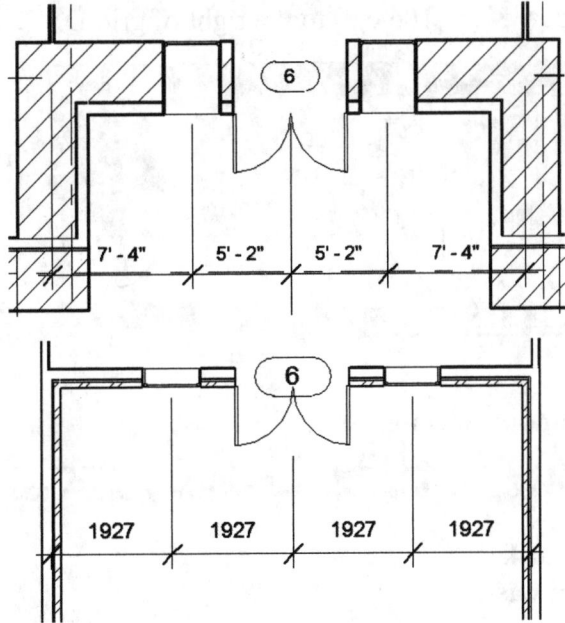

9. Activate the **South** Elevation.

10. Zoom into the entrance area.

11. Use the **ALIGN** tool to align the top of the windows with the top of the door.

12. Select the **Align** tool on the Modify panel on the Modify ribbon.

13. 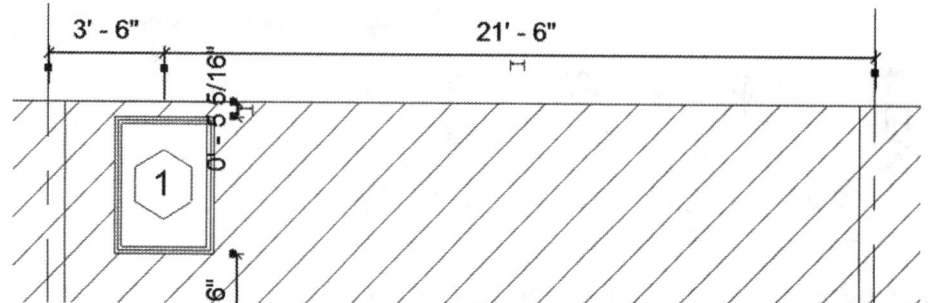 Enable **Multiple Alignment** on the Options bar.

14. Select the door, then a window. Repeat for the second window.

15. Place a **Fixed: 36″ x 48″** [**Fixed: 0915 x 1220mm**] window on the Level 2 wall.

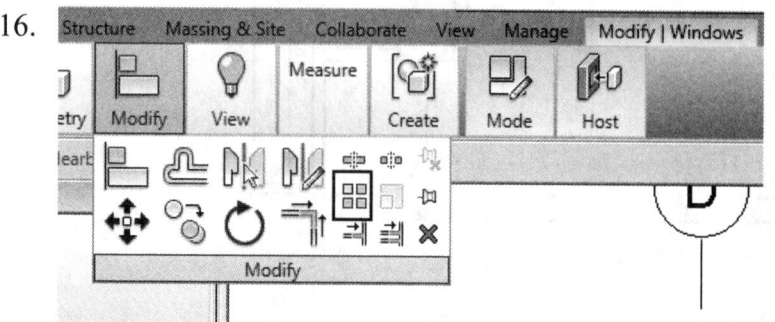

Locate the window 3′ 6″ [106 cm] to the right of grid D.

16. 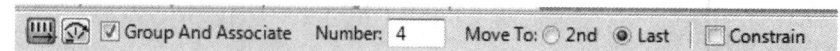 Select the window.
Select the **Array** tool from the Modify panel.

17. Enable **Group and Associate**.

Set the Number to **4**.
Enable Move to: **Last**.

18. 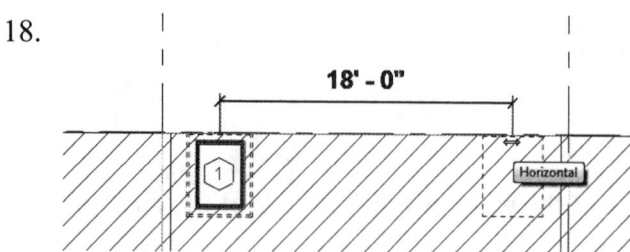 Pick the midpoint of the top of the window as the base points.

Move the cursor 18′ [584.64 cm] towards the right.
Pick to place.

19. 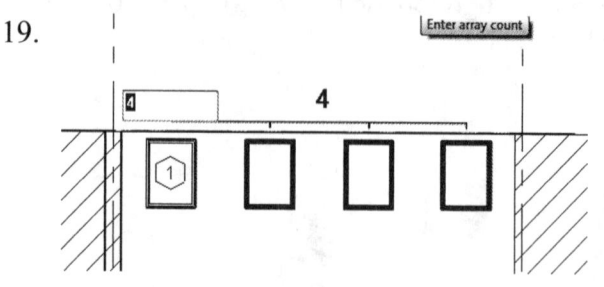 Press ENTER to accept the preview.

20.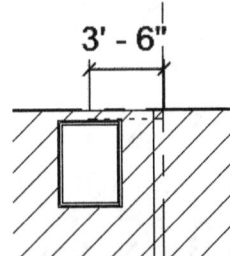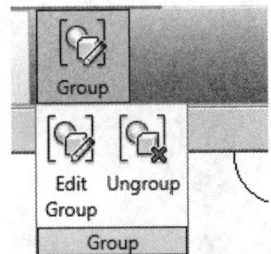

Use the **Measure** tool from the Quick Access tool bar to verify that the last window is 3′ 6″ [106 cm] from grid E.

Verify that the four windows are equally spaced using the Measure tool.

21.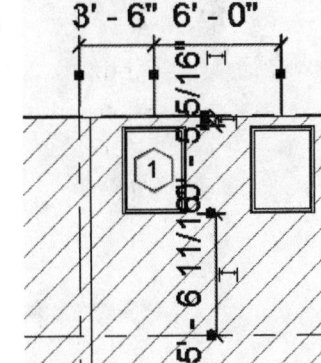

Select the window group.

Select **Edit Group** from the Group panel.

22.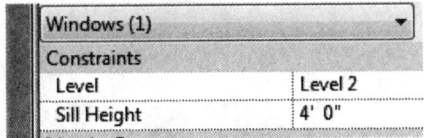

Select the window.

23.

In the Properties pane:
Set the Sill Height to **4′ 0″ [1219.2 mm]**.

24.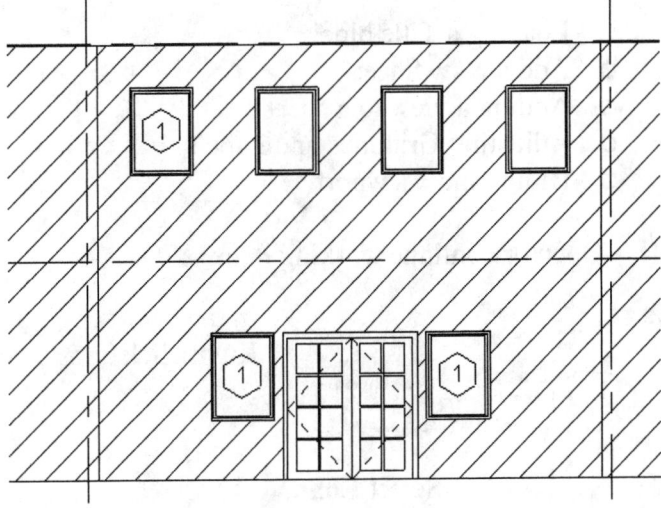

Select **Finish** from the Edit group toolbar.

25. You may add additional windows to complete the project.
    Use the MIRROR and ARRAY tools to place windows.

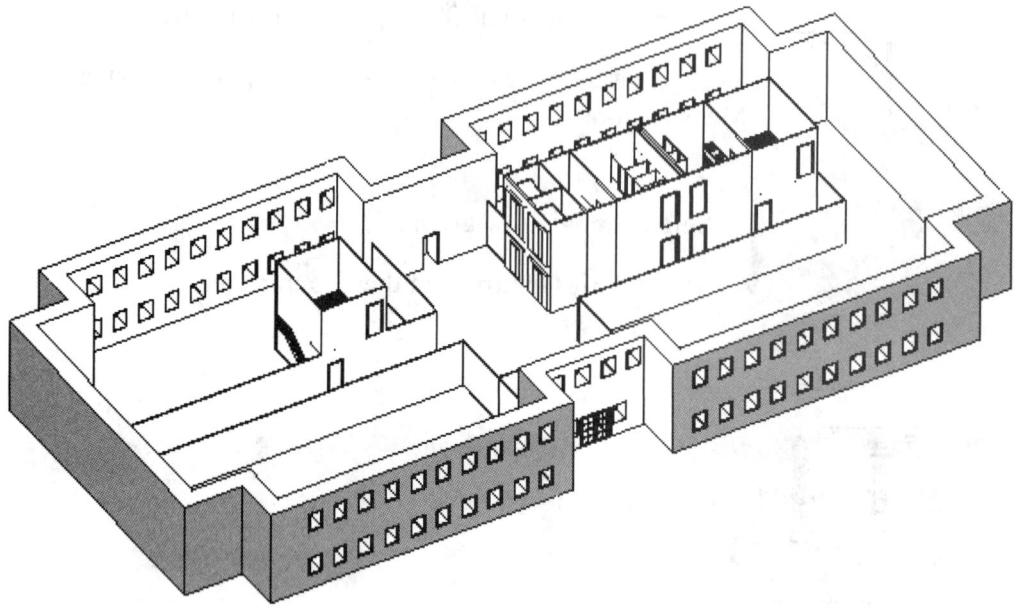

Elements can only be arrayed on the same work face.

26. Save the file as *ex3-20.rvt*.

Exercise 3-21:
Floor Plan Layout

Drawing Name: ex3-20.rvt
Estimated Time: 20 minutes

This exercise reinforces the following skills:

    ❑ Loading a Title block
    ❑ Add a New Sheet
    ❑ Adding a view to a sheet
    ❑ Adjusting Gridlines and Labels
    ❑ Hiding the Viewport

1. Open or continue working in *ex3-20.rvt*.

2. 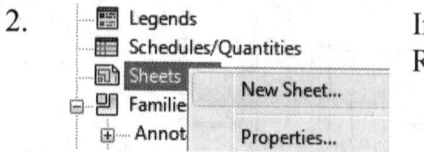 In the browser, highlight **Sheets**.
   Right click and select **New Sheet**.

3. [Load...]   Select **Load**.

4. 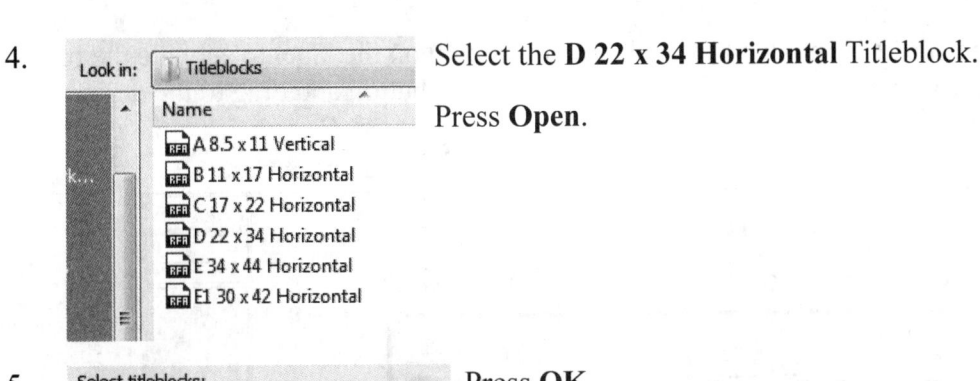 Select the **D 22 x 34 Horizontal** Titleblock.

Press **Open**.

5. 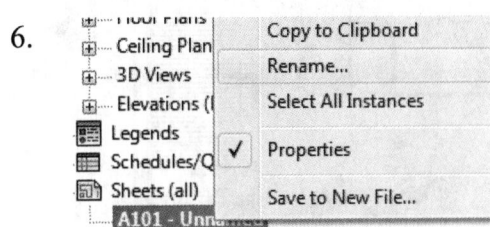 Press **OK**.

6. 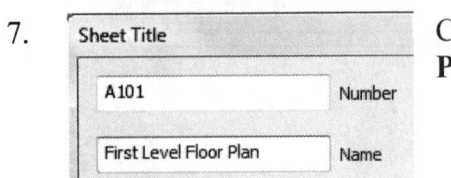 Highlight **A101-Unnamed** in the browser.
Right click and select **Rename**.

7. Change the Name of the Sheet to **First Level Floor Plan** and then press **OK**.

8. Drag and drop the Level 1 Floor Plan from the browser into the sheet.

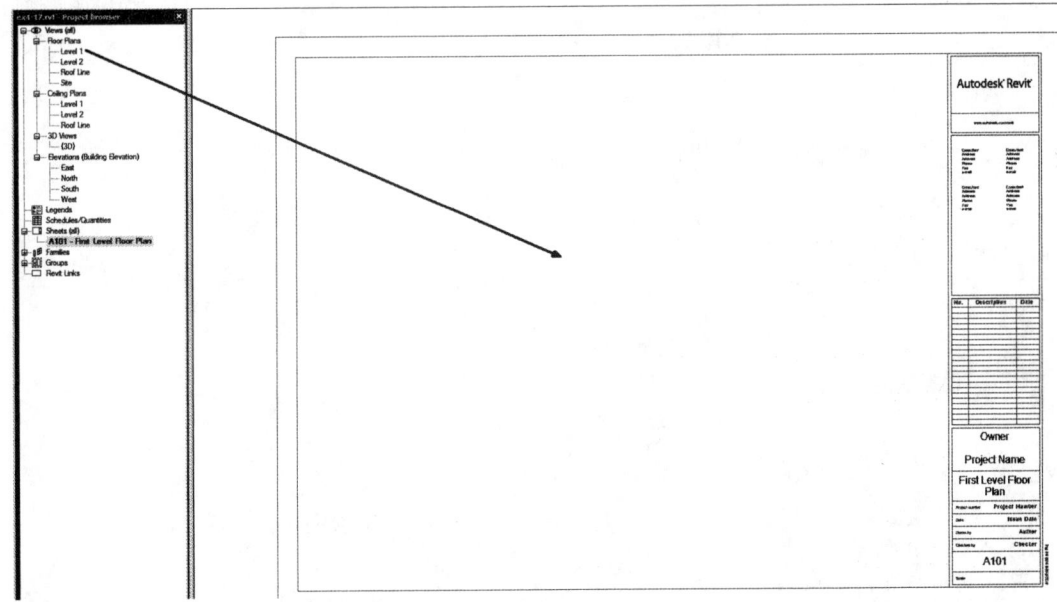

9. **Level 1**
1 —————————
1/8" = 1'-0"

If you zoom into the View label, you see the scale is set to *1/8″ = 1′-0″*.

You can adjust the position of the label, by picking on the label to activate the blue grip. Then hold the grip down with the left mouse button and drag to the desired location.

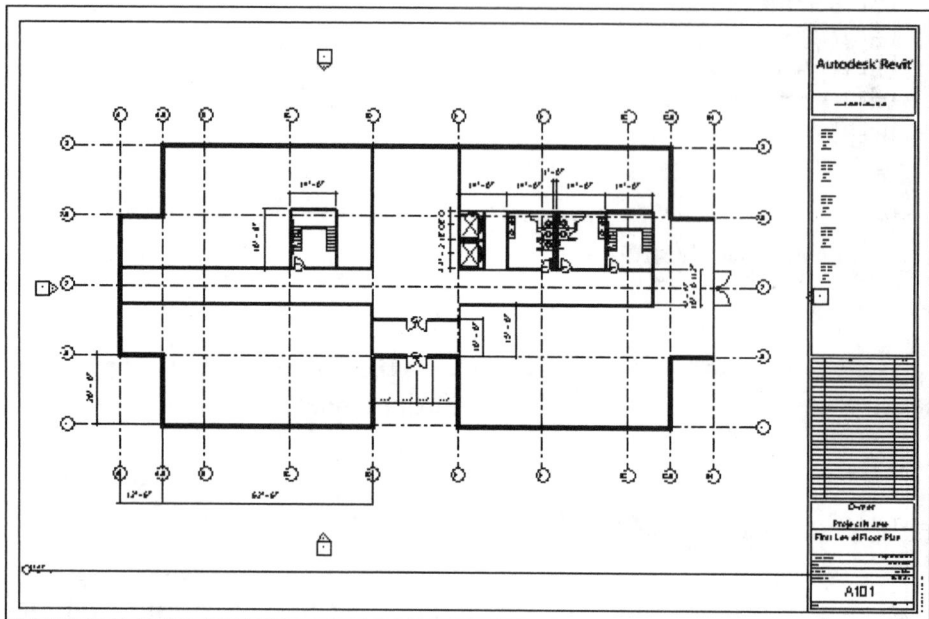

10. Save as *ex3-21.rvt*.

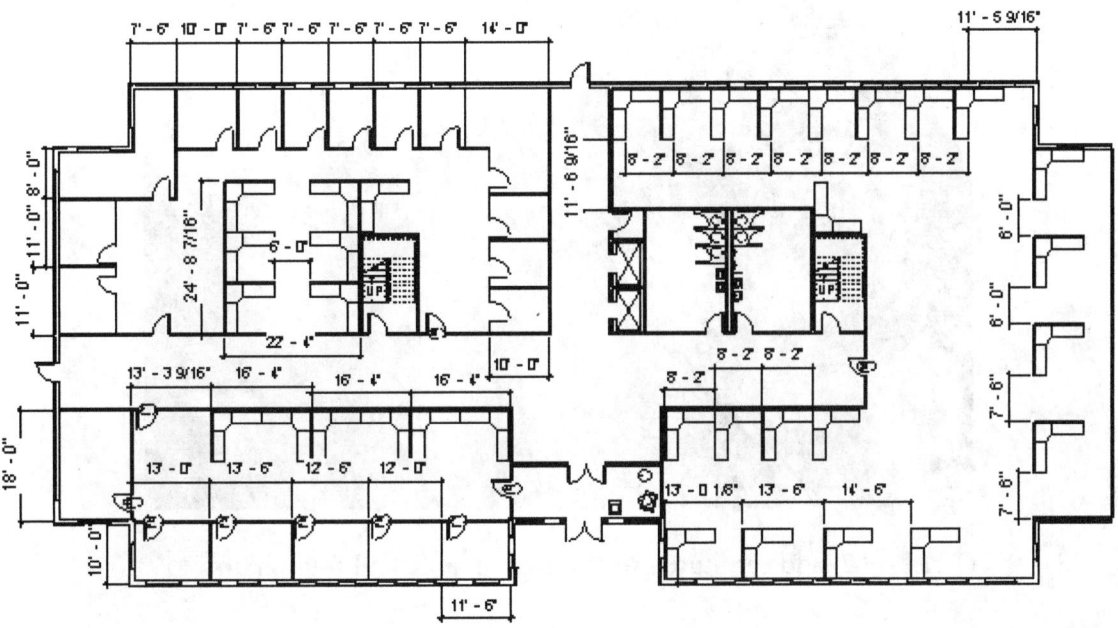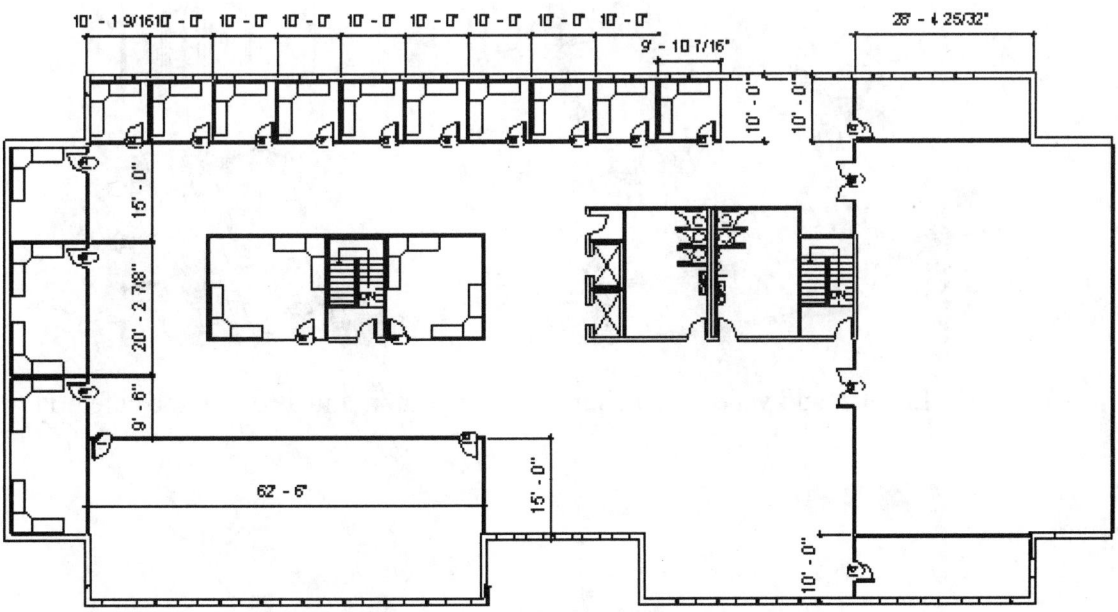

Additional Projects

1) Copy the Level 1 Floor plan and create the office layout shown.
Cubicles are Work Station Cubicle 96″ × 96″.

2) Copy the Level 2 Floor plan and create the office layout shown.

3)   On Level 2, add furniture groups using a table and four chairs.

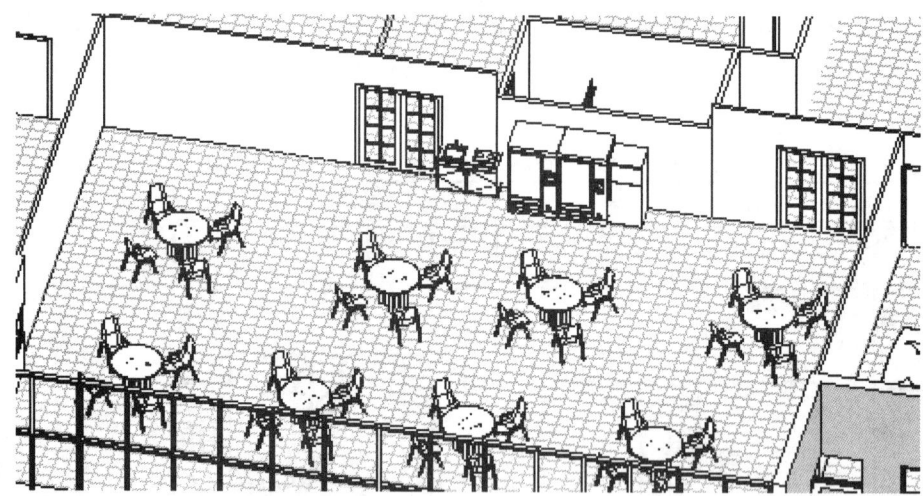

4)   On Level 2, add vending machines, a refrigerator, and a sink in the cafeteria area.

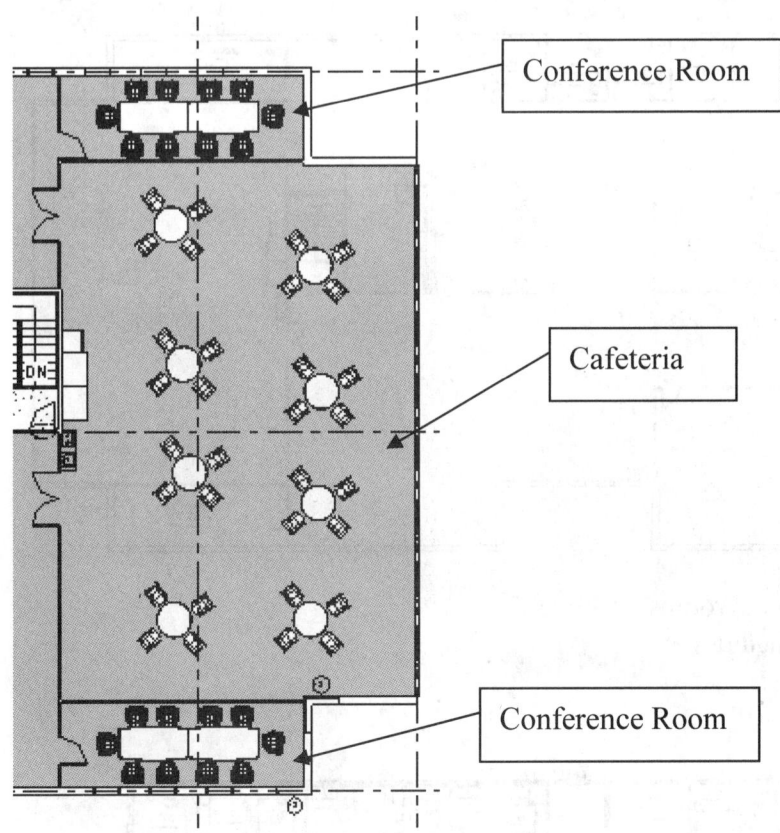

Add tables and chairs to the two conference room areas.

Use Group to create furniture combinations that you can easily copy and move.

5)   Furnish the two conference rooms on Level 2.

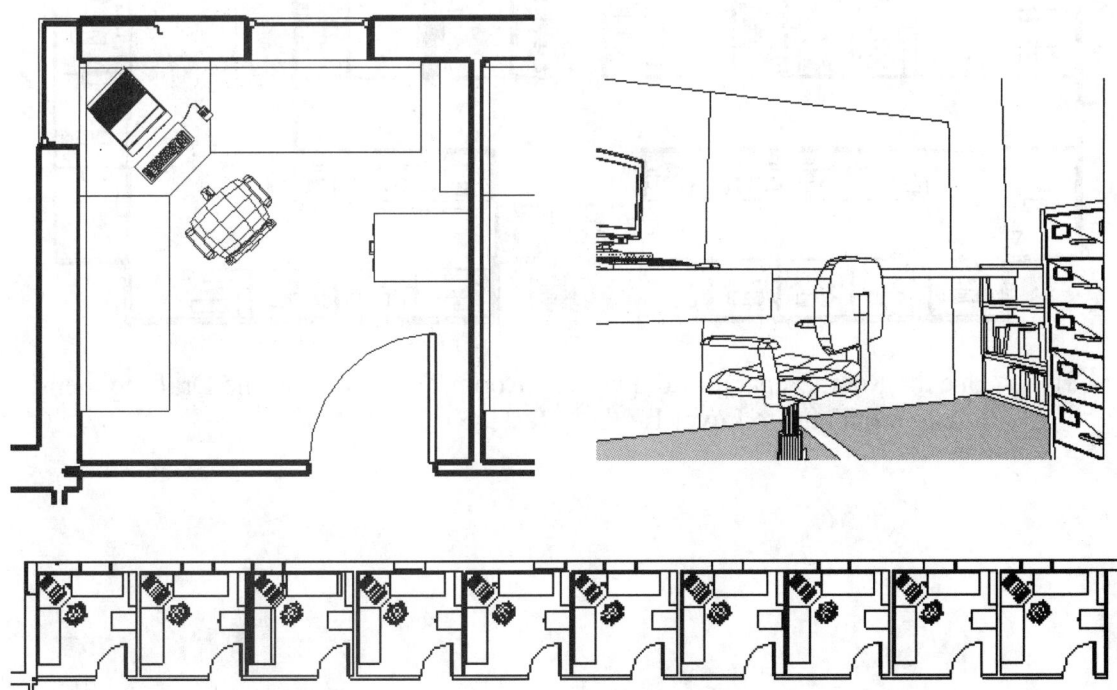

6)   Furnish the office cubicles with a file cabinet, bookcase, chair, and workstation.

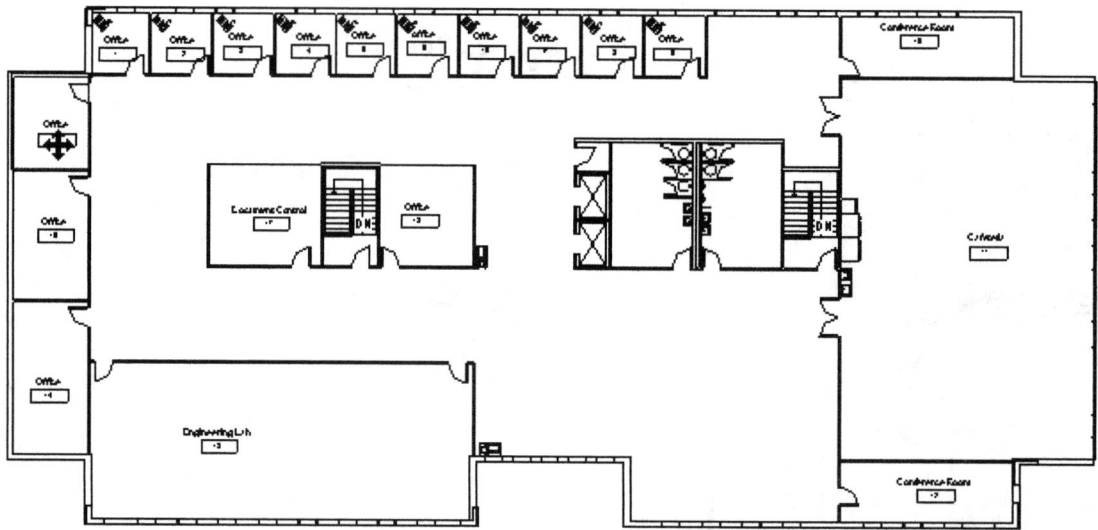

7)   Add room tags to the rooms on Level 2.
         Create a room schedule

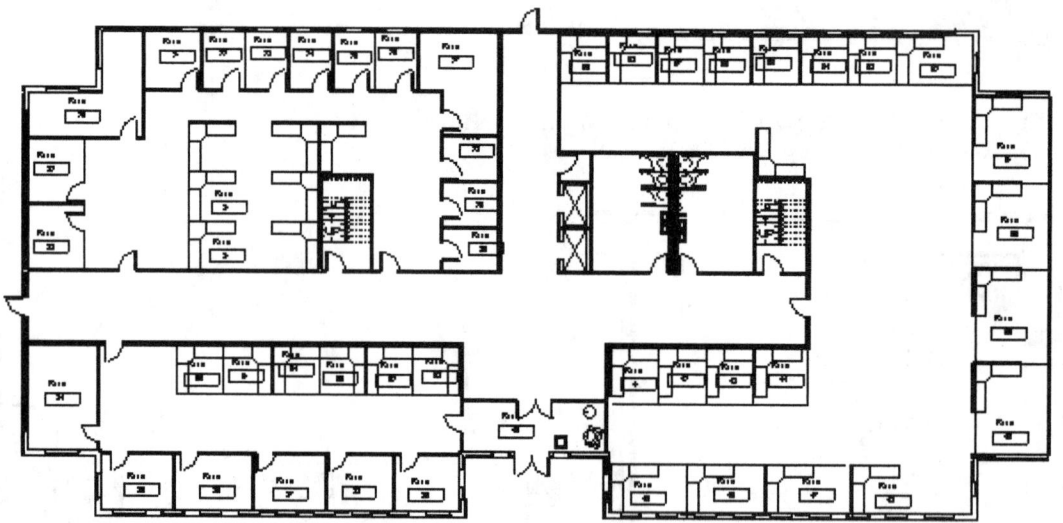

8)   Use the Room Separator tool and the Room Tag tool from the Drafting menu
         to add room tags to Level 1.

Lesson 3 Quiz

True or False

1. Changes in the settings for one view do not affect other views.

Multiple Choice

2. When placing doors, which key is pressed to flip orientation?
   Choose one answer.

   A. Ctl+S
   B. H
   C. Spacebar
   D. F
   E. L or R

3. Which of the following is NOT an example of bidirectional associativity?
   Choose one answer.

   A. Draw a wall in plan and it appears in all other views
   B. Add an annotation in a view
   C. Change a door type in a schedule and all the views update
   D. Flip a section line and all views update

4. Curtain Grids can be defined using all of the following except:
   Choose one answer.

   A. Vertical line
   B. Angled line
   C. Horizontal line
   D. Partial line

5. Which of the following are part of the sketch when you create custom stairs?
   Choose two answers.

   A. Run
   B. Railing
   C. Riser
   D. Boundary
   E. Tread width

6. Which command is used to place a free-standing element, such as furniture?
   Choose one answer.

       A. Detail Component
       B. Load Family
       C. Repeating Detail
       D. Model In Place
       E. Place a Component

7. Select the TWO which are Type properties of a wall:
   Choose at least two answers.

       A. FUNCTION
       B. COARSE FILL PATTERN
       C. BASE CONSTRAINT
       D. OP CONSTRAINT
       E. LOCATION LINE

8. Which is NOT true about placing windows?
   Choose one answer.

       A. Windows require a wall as a host
       B. Windows cut an opening in the wall when placed
       C. The location of the exterior side of the window can be selected
       D. Sill height is adjustable in plan view

ANSWERS:
  1) T; 2) C; 3) B; 4) B; 5) A & B; 6) E; 7) A & B; 8) D

Lesson 4
Floors and Ceilings

Ceiling Plans are used to let the contractor how the ceiling is supposed to look.

When drafting a reflected ceiling plan, imagine that you are looking down on the floor, which is acting as a mirror showing a reflection of the ceiling. You want to locate lighting, vents, sprinkler heads, and soffits.

We start by placing the floors that are going to reflect the ceilings. (Reflected ceiling plans look down, not up. They are the mirror image of what you would see looking up, as if the ceiling were reflected in the floor.)

We start by placing the floors we are going to lie on to look up at the ceilings.

Exercise 4-1
Creating Floors

Drawing Name: ex3-21.rvt
Estimated Time: 35 minutes

This exercise reinforces the following skills:

- ❑ Floors
- ❑ Floor Properties
- ❑ Materials

1. Open *ex3-21.rvt*.

2. Activate **Level 1**.

3.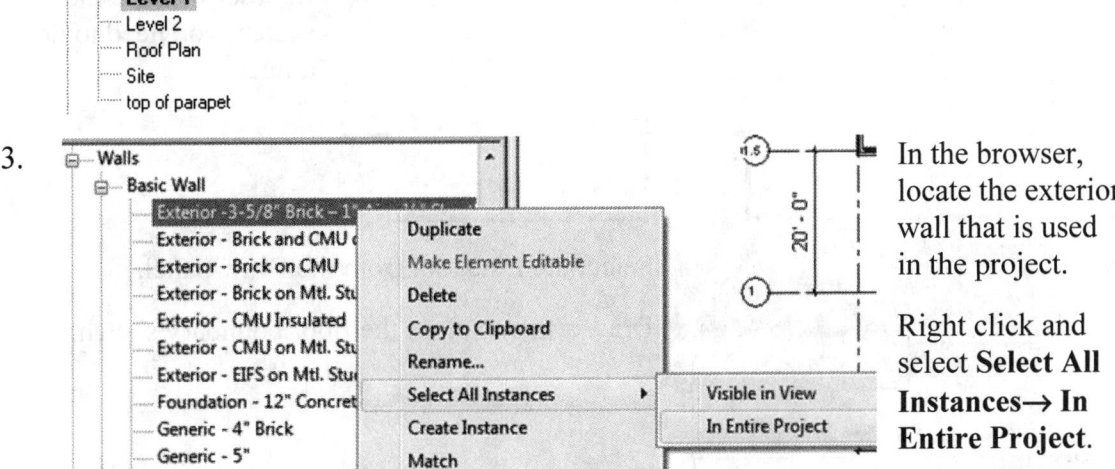

In the browser, locate the exterior wall that is used in the project.

Right click and select **Select All Instances→ In Entire Project**.

4.

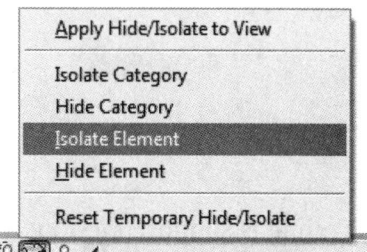

On the status bar:

Select **Isolate element**.

This will turn off the visibility of all elements except for the exterior walls.
This will make selecting the walls easier.

5.

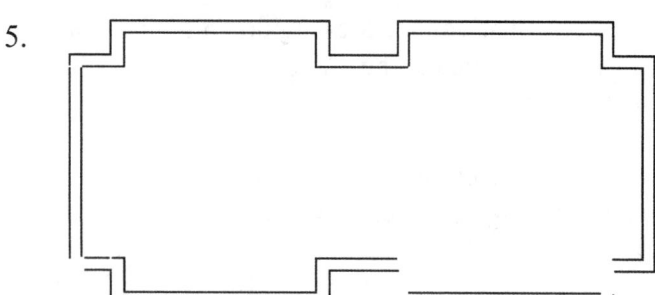

You should see the top view of your model with only the exterior walls visible.

6. 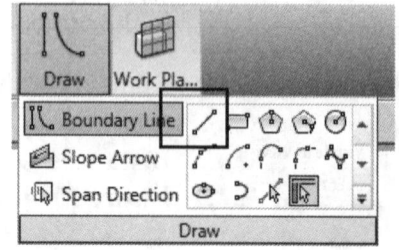 Activate the **Home** ribbon.

7.

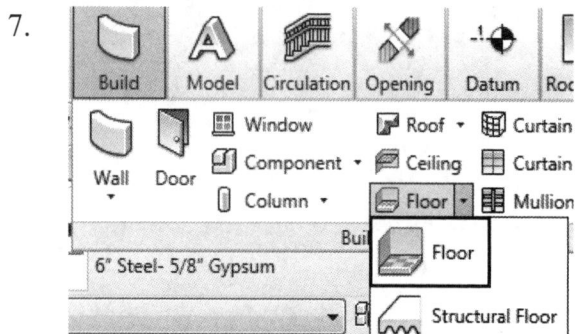

Activate the **Floor** tool under the Build panel.

8. Select all the exterior walls.

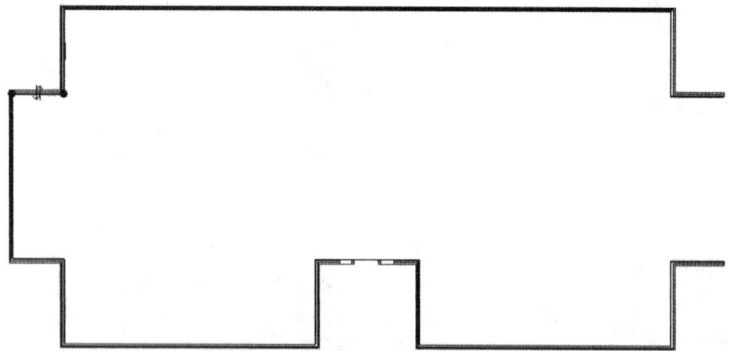

The curtain wall can not be selected.

In order to close the sketch, you need to draw a line.

9.

Select the Line tool from the Draw panel.

Draw a line to close the floor boundary sketch.

10. Verify that your floor boundary has no gaps or intersecting lines.

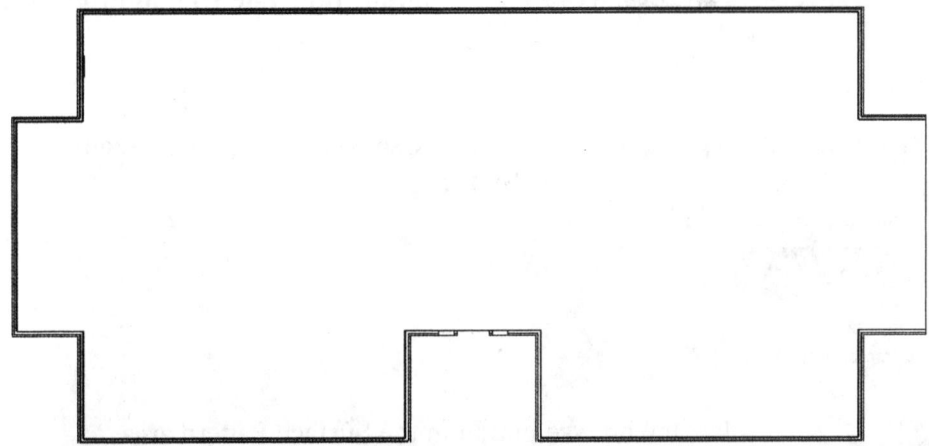

11.  Select **Edit Type** from the Properties pane.

12. Select **Wood Truss Joist 12″ - Carpet Finish** from the Type drop-down list.

13. Select **Duplicate**.

14. Change the Name to **Wood Truss Joist 12″ - Vinyl**.

Press **OK**.

15.  Select **Edit** under Structure.

16. For Layer 1: Finish 1 [4]:
Select the *browse* button in the Material column.

17. 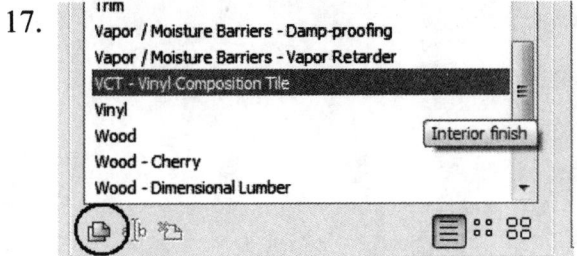 Highlight the **VCT – Vinyl Composition Tile** material.

Select **New Material**.

18. 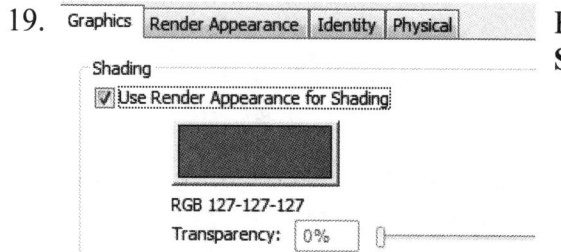 Name the new material **VCT- Vinyl Composition Tile Diamond Pattern**.

Press **OK**.

19. 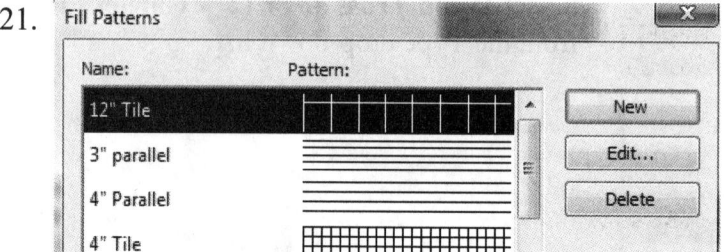 Enable **Use Render Appearance for Shading**.

20. 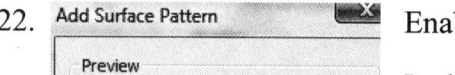 Select the browse button in the Surface Pattern area.

21. Select the **New** button.

22. 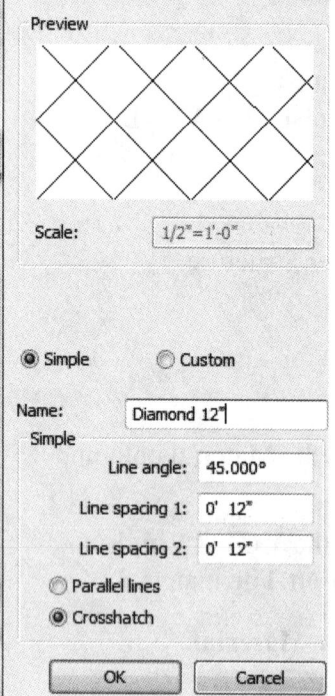 Enable **Simple**.

In the Name field, enter **Diamond 12″** [**Diamond 300**].

Set the Line Space 1: to **12″** [**300**].
Set the Line Space 2: to **12″** [**300**].
Enable **Crosshatch**.

Press **OK**.

23. 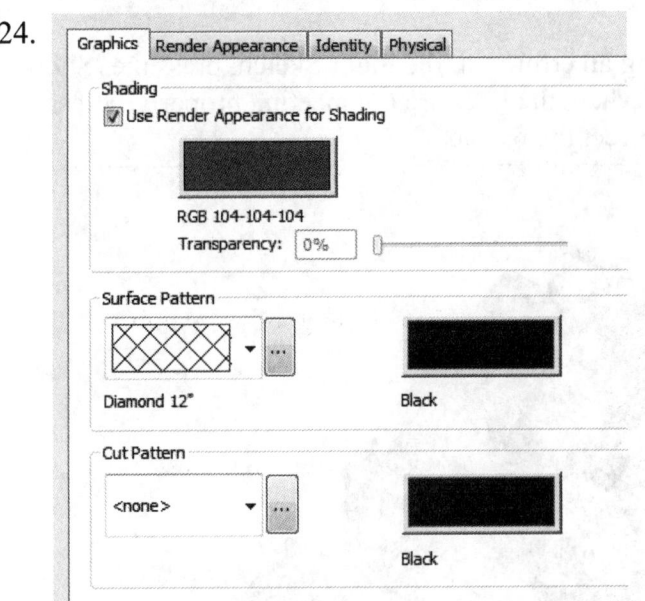 The new hatch pattern is listed.

Highlight to select and press **OK**.

24. The new hatch pattern is displayed on the Graphics tab.

25. Select the **Render Appearance** tab.

26.  Select **Replace**.

27. Select the **Vinyl Flooring Diamonds Pattern**.

Press **OK**.

28. Press **OK**.

29. 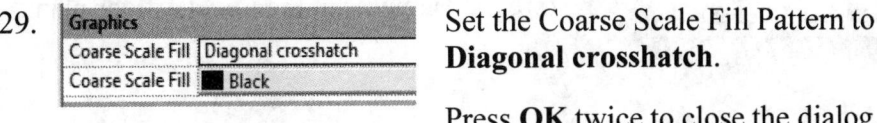 Set the Coarse Scale Fill Pattern to **Diagonal crosshatch**.

Press **OK** twice to close the dialog.

30. 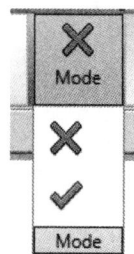 Select the **Green Check** under Mode to finish the floor.

 TIP: If you get a dialog box indicating an error with the Floor Sketch, press the 'Show' button. Revit will zoom into the area where the lines are not meeting properly. Press 'Continue' and use Trim/Extend to correct the problem.

31. Switch to a 3D View.

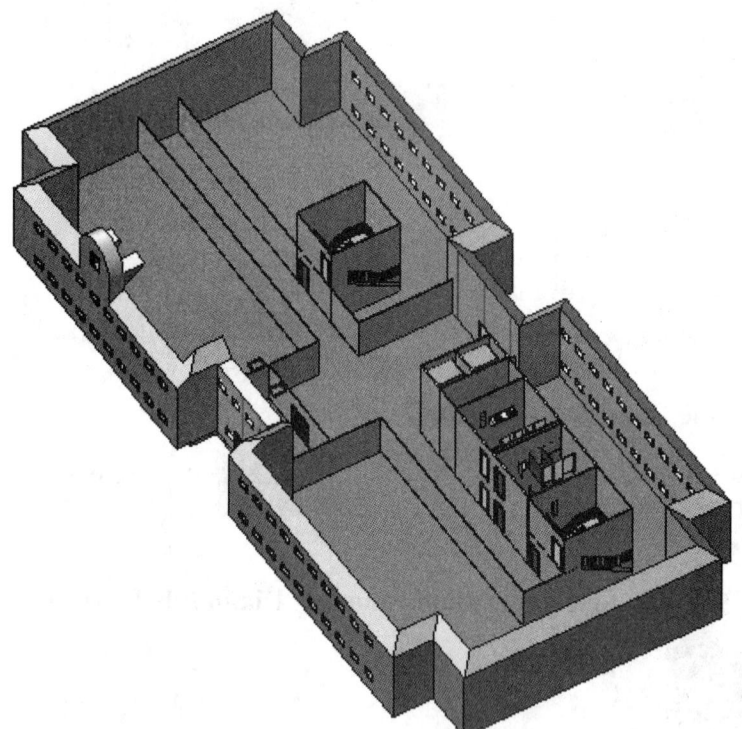

32. Activate **Level 1**.

33. Select **Reset Temporary Hide/Isolate** to restore the elements in the Level 1 floor plan.

34. Save as *ex4-1.rvt*.

Exercise 4-2
Copying Floors

Drawing Name: ex4-1.rvt
Estimated Time: 15 minutes

This exercise reinforces the following skills:

- ❑ Copy
- ❑ Paste Aligned
- ❑ Opening
- ❑ Shaft Opening
- ❑ Opening Properties

1. Open *ex4-1.rvt*

2.  Activate **Level 2**.

3. 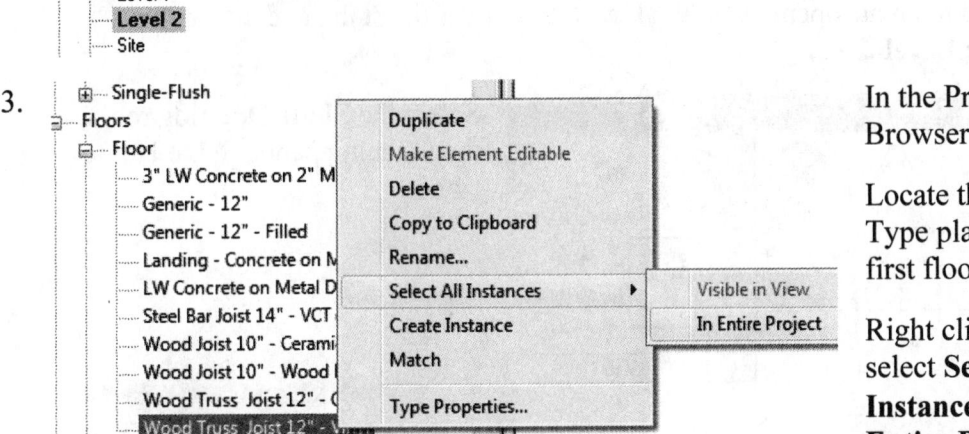 In the Project Browser:

   Locate the Floor Type placed on the first floor.

   Right click and select **Select All Instances→In Entire Project**.

4. 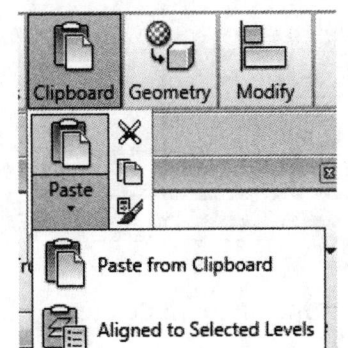 Select **Copy** from the Clipboard panel.

5. Select **Paste→Aligned to Selected Levels**.

6. 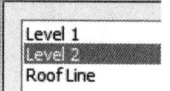 Select **Level 2**.

   Press **OK**.

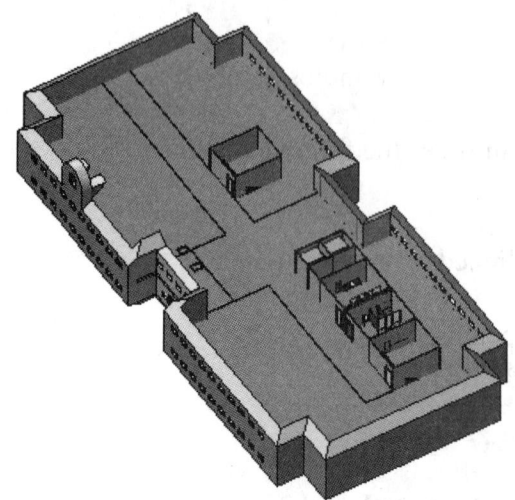

7. We need to create openings in the Level 2 floor for the stairs and elevators. Activate **Level 2**.

8. 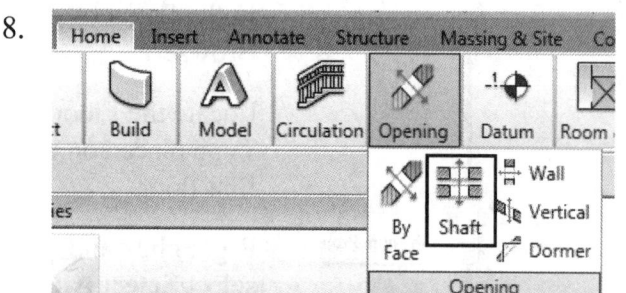 Select the **Shaft Opening** tool under the Opening panel on the Home ribbon.

9. Select the **Rectangle** tool from the Draw panel.

10. Draw three rectangles: one for each stairwell and one for the elevator shaft.

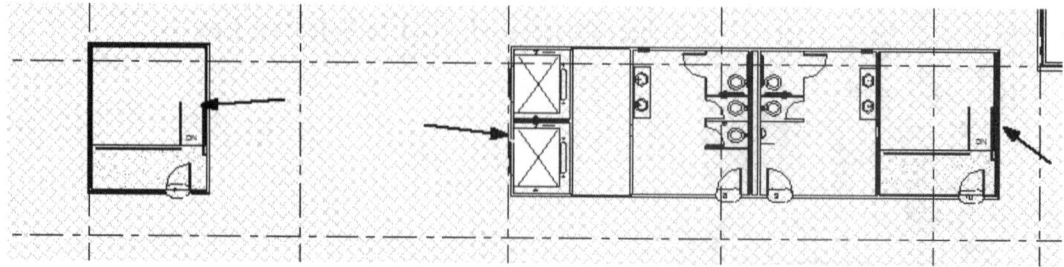

   Do not draw over the landings created earlier. The Shaft Opening will delete landings.

11. On the Properties pane:

Shaft Openings	▼	Edit
Constraints		
Top Offset	0' 0"	
Base Offset	-1' 0"	
Unconnected Height	11' 0"	
Base Constraint	Level 1	
Top Constraint	Up to level: Level 2	

Set the Base Offset at **1′ 0″ [600 mm]**.
Set the Base Constraint at **Level 1**.
Set the Top Constraint at **Level 2**.

12. Select the **Green Check** under the Mode panel.

13. Switch to a 3D view.
Orbit around to inspect the model.

14. Save as *ex4-2.rvt*.

Exercise 4-3
Creating Ceilings

Drawing Name: ex4-2.rvt
Estimated Time: 5 minutes

This exercise reinforces the following skills:

- Ceilings
- Visibility of Annotation Elements

1. Open *ex4-2.rvt*.

2. Activate **Level 1** under Ceiling Plans.

   Ceiling Plans
      Level 1
      Level 2
      Roof Line

3. Type **VG**.

4. 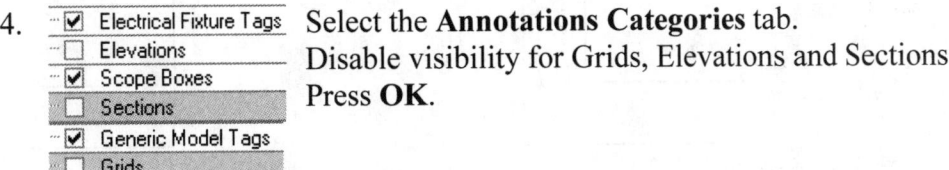 Select the **Annotations Categories** tab.

   Disable visibility for Grids, Elevations and Sections.

   Press **OK**.

5. The view display should update.

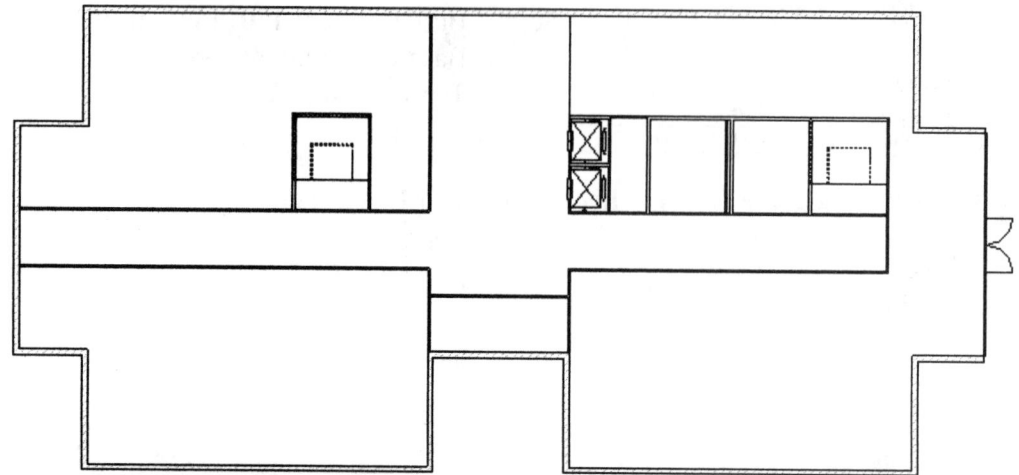

6. 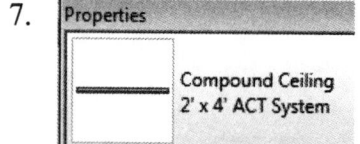   Select the **Ceiling** tool from Build panel on the Home ribbon.

7. 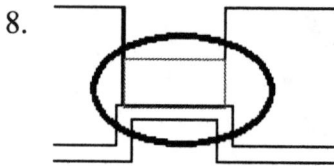   Select the **Ceiling: 2′ × 4′ ACT System [Compound Ceiling: 600 x 1200 mm Grid]** from the Properties pane.

8.   Left click in the building entry to place a ceiling.

The ceiling is placed.

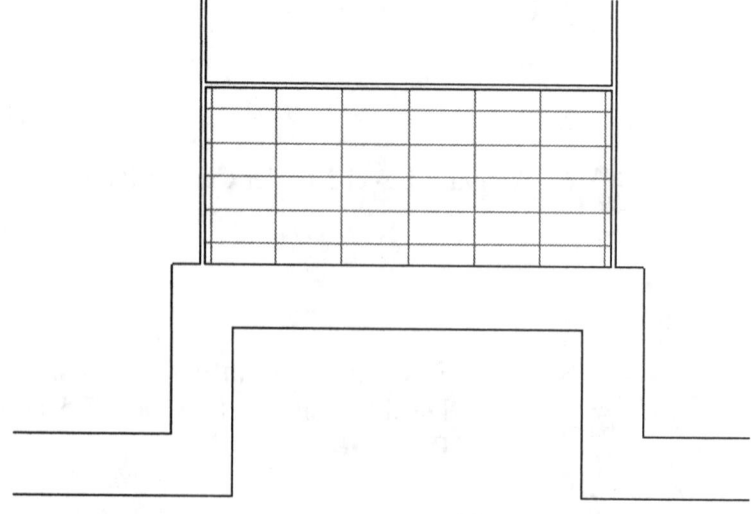

9. Save as *ex4-3.rvt*.

Exercise 4-4
Adding Lighting Fixtures

Drawing Name: ex4-3.rvt
Estimated Time: 10 minutes

This exercise reinforces the following skills:

- Add Component
- Load From Library

1.   Open or continue working in *ex4-3.rvt.*

2.   Ceiling Plans   Activate **Level 1 Ceiling Plan**.
         Level 1
         Level 2
         Roof Line

3.   Home   Activate the **Home** ribbon.

4.   Select the **Component→Place a Component** tool from the Build panel.

5.   Select **Load Family** from the Mode panel.

6.   Browse to the *Lighting Fixtures* folder.

OS (C:)
  ProgramData
    Autodesk
      RAC 2011
        Imperial Library
          Lighting Fixtures

OS (C:)
  ProgramData
    Autodesk
      RAC 2011
        Metric Library
          Lighting Fixtures

7.   File name: Ceiling Light - Linear Box.rfa   Locate the *Ceiling-Linear Box.rfa [M_ Ceiling-Linear Box.rfa]*.

File name: M_Ceiling Light - Linear Box.rfa   Press **Open**.

8. 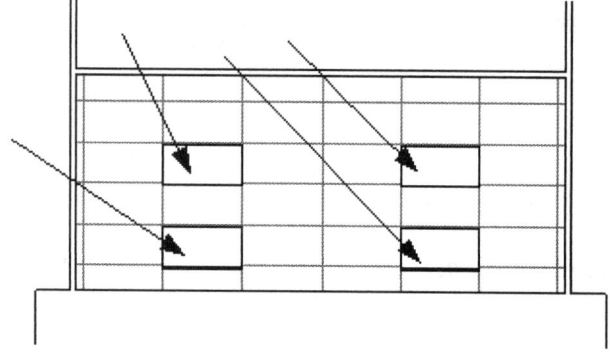 Ceiling Light - Linear Box 2'x4'(2 Lamp) - 120V

Select the **2′x 4′ (Lamp) [0600x 1200mm (2 Lamp) – 277V]** for the element type.

M_Ceiling Light - Linear Box
0600x1200mm(2 Lamp) - 277V

9.

Place fixtures on the grid.

Use the ALIGN tool to position the fixtures in the ceiling grid.

10. Save the file as *ex4-4.rvt*.

Exercise 4-5
Defining Paint Colors and Wallpaper

Drawing Name: ex4-4.rvt
Estimated Time: 10 minutes

This exercise reinforces the following skills:

- ❑ Materials
- ❑ Render Appearance Library

1. Open or continue working in *ex4-4.rvt*.

2. Go to **Manage→ Settings→Materials**.

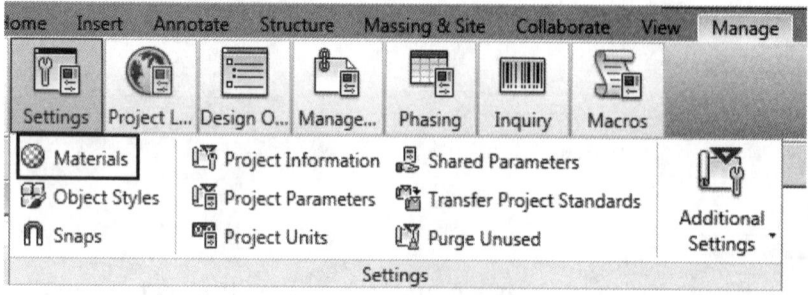

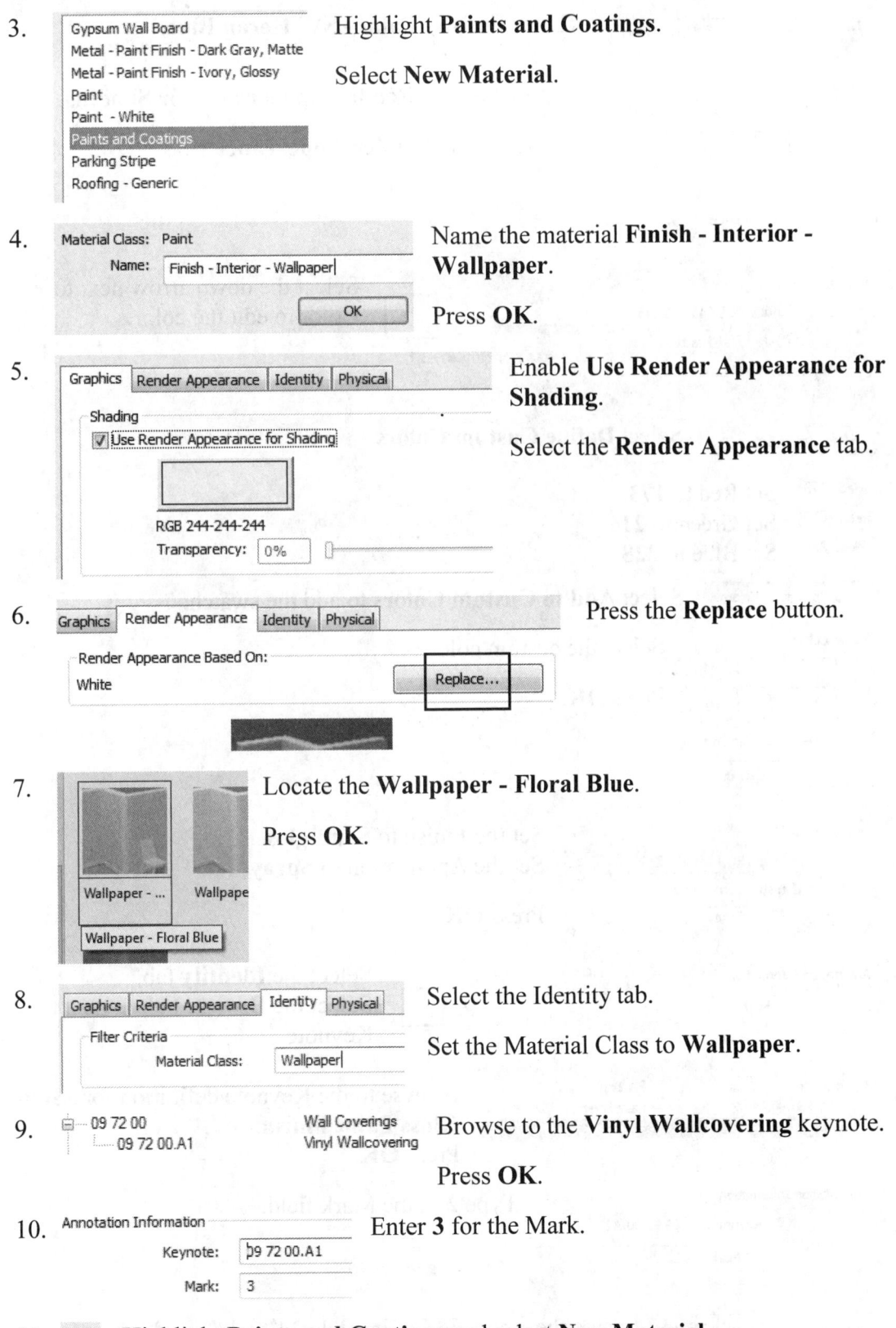

3. Highlight **Paints and Coatings**.

    Select **New Material**.

4. Name the material **Finish - Interior - Wallpaper**.

    Press **OK**.

5. Enable **Use Render Appearance for Shading**.

    Select the **Render Appearance** tab.

6. Press the **Replace** button.

7. Locate the **Wallpaper - Floral Blue**.

    Press **OK**.

8. Select the Identity tab.

    Set the Material Class to **Wallpaper**.

9. Browse to the **Vinyl Wallcovering** keynote.

    Press **OK**.

10. Enter **3** for the Mark.

11. Highlight **Paints and Coatings** and select **New Material**.

12. **Name:** Finish - Paint - SW Heron Blue|

Enter **Finish - Paint - SW Heron Blue**.

13. Shading
☑ Use Render Appearance for Shading

RGB 244-244-244
Transparency: 0%

Enable **Use Render Appearance for Shading**.

Select the **Render Appearance** tab.

14. **▼ Wall Paint**
Color RGB 245 245 245
Finish Flat/Matte
Application Brush

Select the down arrow next to Color to edit the color.

15. Define Custom Colors >>

Select **Define Custom Colors**.

16. Red: 173
Green: 216
Blue: 228

Set Red to **173**.
Set Green to **216**.
Set Blue to **228**.

17. Add to Custom Colors

Select **Add to Custom Colors** to add the swatch.

18. Custom colors:

Define Custom Colors >
OK   Cancel

Select the custom color.

Press **OK**.

19. **▼ Wall Paint**
Color RGB 173 216 228
Finish Semi-gloss
Application Spray

Set the Finish to **Semi-gloss**.
Set the Application to **Spray**.

Press **OK**.

20. Annotation Information
Keynote: [...]
Mark:

Select the **Identity** tab.
Select the **Browse** button next to Keynote.

21. 09 91 00   Painting
    09 91 00.A1   Paint Finish
    09 91 00.A2   Semi-Gloss Paint Finish

Browse to the Keynote definition for **Semi-Gloss Paint Finish**.
Press **OK**.

22. Annotation Information
Keynote: 09 91 00.A2
Mark: 2|

Type **2** in the Mark field.

23. Acoustic Ceiling Tile 24" x 24"
Acoustic Ceiling Tile 24" x 48"

Locate the Acoustic Ceiling Tile 24" x 48" used for the ceiling.

24. Enable **Use Render Appearance for Shading**.

Shading
☑ Use Render Appearance for Shading

RGB 145-144-143
Transparency: 0%

25. Select the **Identity** tab.
Select the **Browse** button next to Keynote.

Annotation Information
Keynote:
Mark:

26. Browse to the Keynote definition for **Acoustical Ceilings and locate the Square Edge (3/4 x 24 x 48)**.

Press **OK**.

09 51 00 — Acoustical Ceilings
09 51 00.A1 — Square Edge (3/4 x 12 x 12)
09 51 00.A2 — Square Edge (3/4 x 12 x 18)
09 51 00.A3 — Square Edge (3/4 x 18 x 18)
09 51 00.A4 — Square Edge (3/4 x 24 x 12)
09 51 00.A5 — Square Edge (3/4 x 24 x 24)
09 51 00.A6 — Square Edge (3/4 x 24 x 48)
09 51 00.A7 — Tegular Edge (3/4 x 12 x 12)
09 51 00.A8 — Tegular Edge (3/4 x 12 x 18)

27. Type **4** in the Mark field.

Annotation Information
Keynote: 09 51 00.A6
Mark: 4

28. Locate the VCT - Vinyl Composition Tile Diamond Pattern used for the floor.

VCT - Vinyl Composition Tile Diamond Pattern
Vinyl

29. Select the **Identity** tab.
Select the **Browse** button next to Keynote.

Annotation Information
Keynote:
Mark:

30. Browse to the Keynote definition for **Vinyl Composition Tile**.

Press **OK**.

09 65 00 — Resilient Flooring
09 65 00.A1 — Resilient Flooring
09 65 00.A2 — Vinyl Composition Tile
09 65 00.A3 — Rubber Flooring

31. Type **5** in the Mark field.

Annotation Information
Keynote: 09 65 00.A2
Mark: 5

32. Save as *ex4-5.rvt*.

Applying Paints and Wallpaper to Walls

Drawing Name: ex4-5.rvt
Estimated Time: 10 minutes

This exercise reinforces the following skills:

- ❑ Materials
- ❑ Load From Library
- ❑ Render Appearance Library

1. Open or continue working in *ex4-5.rvt*.

2. Switch to a 3D View.

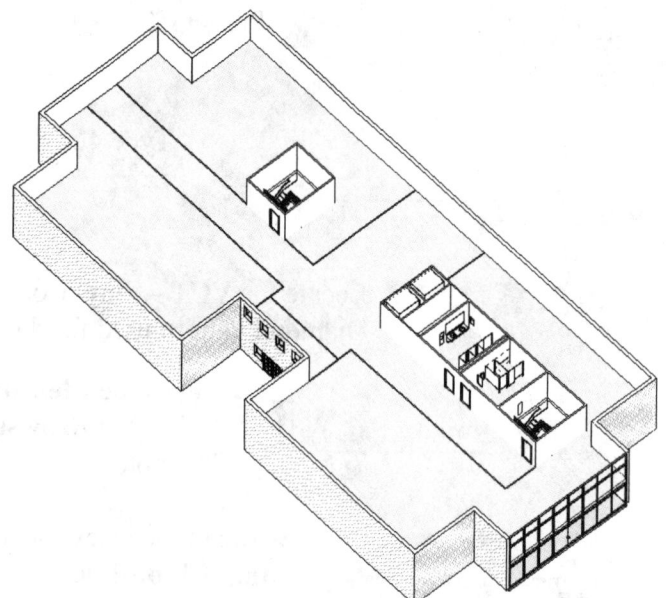

3.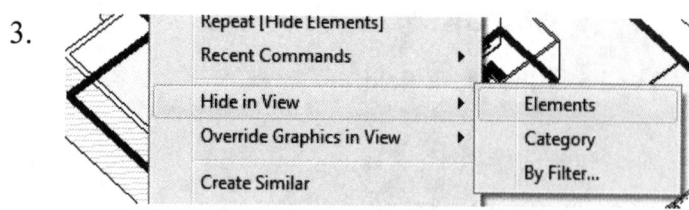
   Select the floor on Level 2. Right click and select **Hide in View→Elements**.

   This will hide only the selected element.

4. Repeat to hide the ceiling.

5.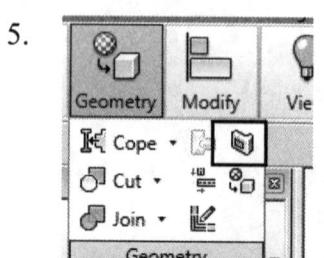
   Activate the Modify ribbon.

   Select the **Split Face** tool on the Geometry panel.

6.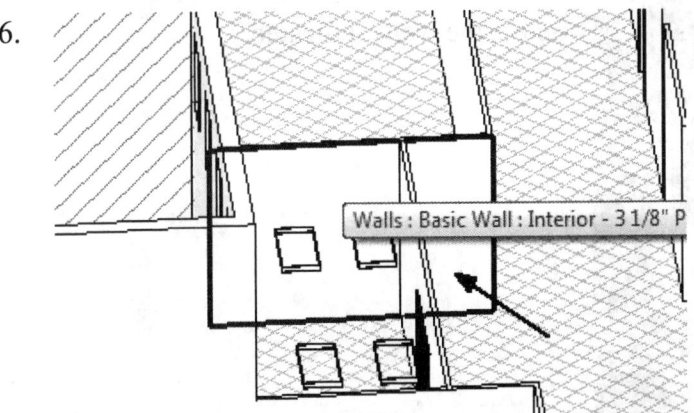

Select the wall indicated.

7.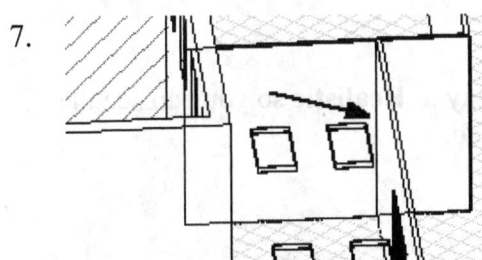

Draw a line to indicate where the wall should be split.

8.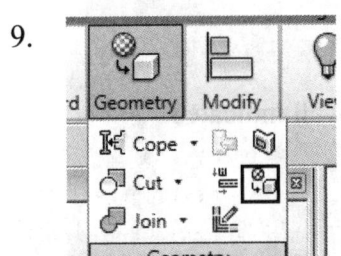

Select the **Green Check** on the Mode panel.

9.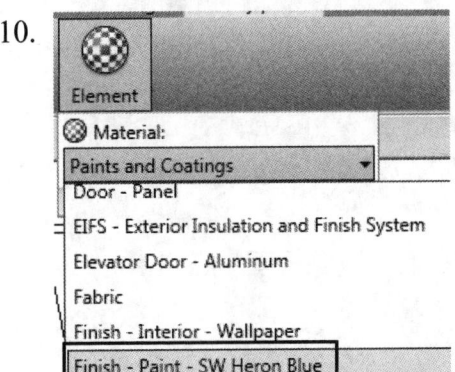

Select the **Paint** tool on the Geometry panel.

10.

Locate the **Finish – Paint - SW Heron Blue** from the Material drop-down list.

11.

Select the walls indicated.

12.

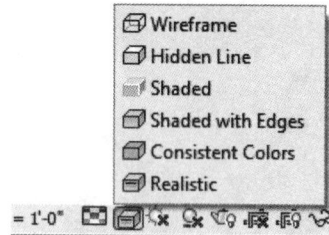

Change the display to **Realistic** so you can see the paint color applied.

13.

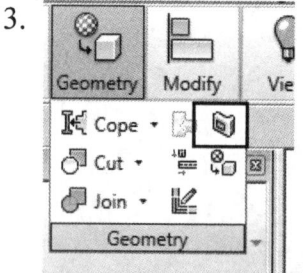

Activate the Modify ribbon.

Select the **Split Face** tool on the Geometry panel.

14.

Select the wall indicated.

15.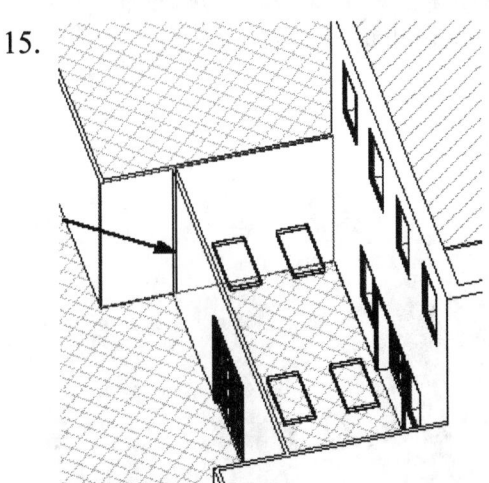

Draw a line to indicate where the wall should be split.

Switch to Hidden Line display if it will make it easier to draw the line.

16.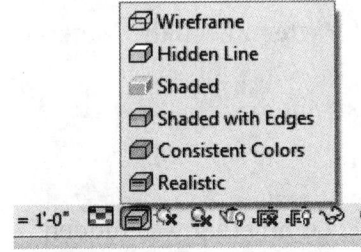

Select the **Green Check** on the Mode panel.

17.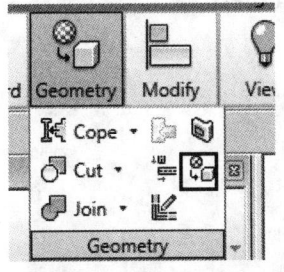

Change the display to **Realistic** so you can see the paint color applied.

18.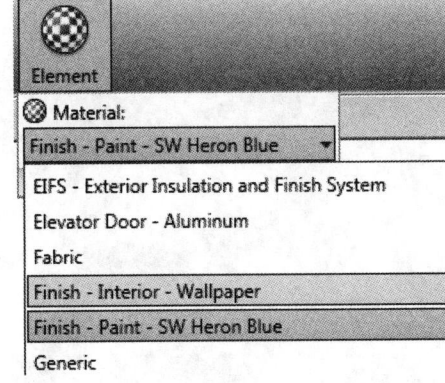

Select the **Paint** tool on the Geometry panel.

19.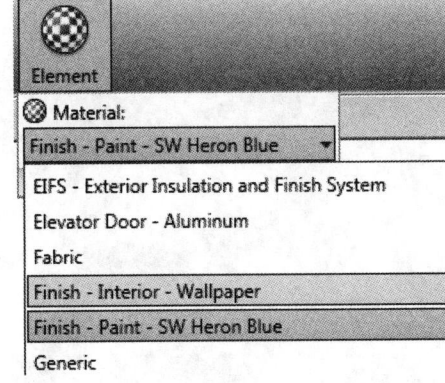

Locate the **Finish-Interior- Wallpaper** from the Material drop-down list.

20. 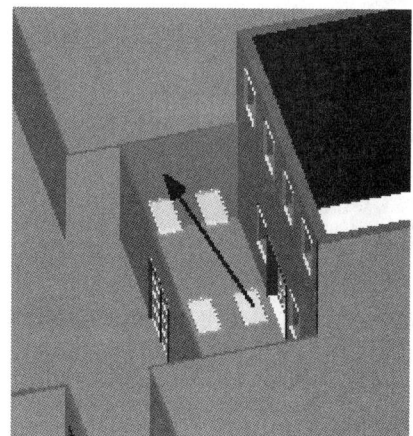   Select the walls indicated.

21. 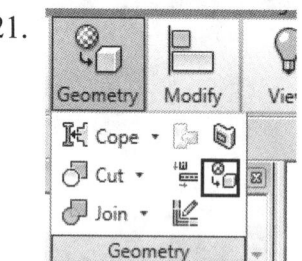   Select the **Paint** tool on the Geometry panel.

22. VCT - Vinyl Composition Tile Diamond Pattern

Locate the **VCT - Vinyl Composition Tile Diamond Pattern** from the Material drop-down list.

23. Select the floor.

24. Select the Unhide tool.
    Select the floor that was hidden and the ceiling that was hidden.
    Right click and select **Unhide in View→Elements**.

25. Save as *ex4-6.rvt*.

Additional Projects

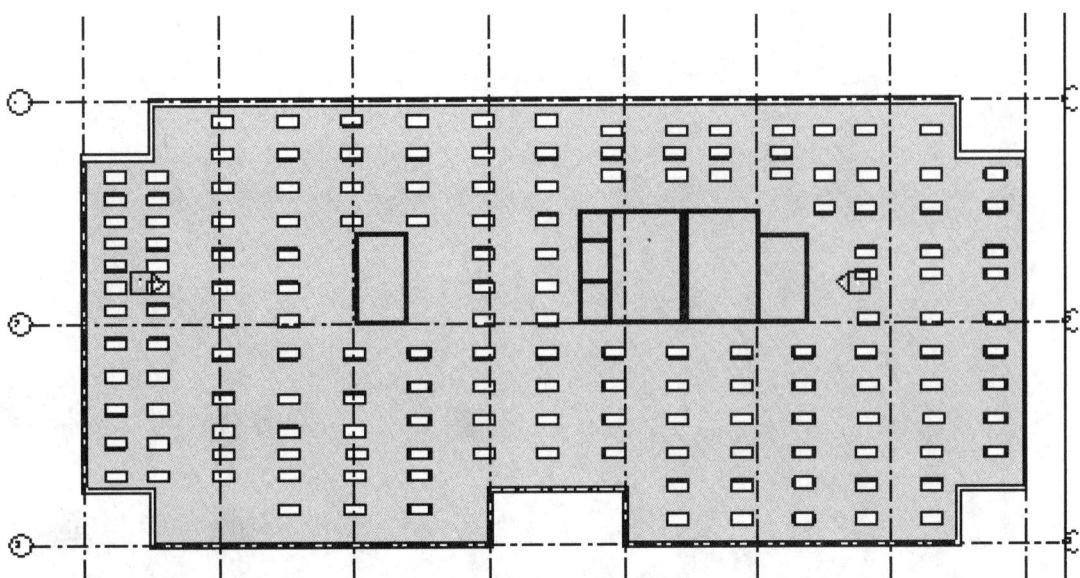

1)　　Add light fixtures and square registers to the Second Level Ceiling Plan.
Create a Ceiling Plan layout/sheet.

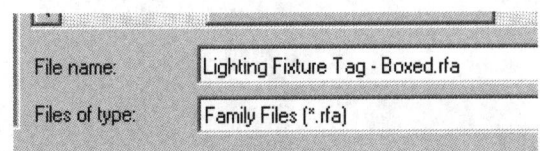

2)　　Load the Lighting Fixture Tag – Boxed using File →Load Family.
Use Tag All Not Tagged to tag all the lighting fixtures.
Create a schedule of lighting fixtures.
Add to your reflected ceiling plan sheet.

Notes:

Lesson 4 Quiz

True or False

1. Ceilings are not visible on the Floor Plan view.
2. Ceilings are visible on the Ceiling Plan view.
3. In order to place a ceiling-based light fixture, the model must have a ceiling.
4. To create an opening in a floor, use EDIT BOUNDARY.
5. Floors and ceilings are level-based.
6. Floors and ceilings can be offset from a level.
7. The boundaries for a floor or ceiling must be closed, non-intersecting loops.

Multiple Choice

8. When a floor is placed:

    A. The top of the floor is aligned to the level on which it is placed with the thickness projecting downward.
    B. The bottom of the floor is aligned to the level on which it is placed with the thickness projecting upwards.
    C. The direction of the thickness can be flipped going up or down.
    D. The floor offset can be above or below the level.

9. The structure of a floor is determined by its:

    A. Family type
    B. Placement
    C. Instance
    D. Geometry

10. Floors can be created by these two methods:
    Pick two answers.

    A. Sketching a closed polygon
    B. Picking Walls
    C. Place Component
    D. Drawing boundary lines

11. Ceilings are:
    Pick one answer.

    A. Level-based
    B. Floor-based
    C. Floating
    D. Non-hosted

12. Paint can be applied using the Paint tool which is located on this ribbon:

    A. Home
    B. Modify
    C. Rendering
    D. View

13. New materials are created using:

    A. Manage→Settings→Materials.
    B. View→Materials
    C. Home→Create→Materials
    D. Home→Render→Materials

14. This icon:

    A. Adjusts the brightness of a view.
    B. Temporarily isolates selected elements or categories
    C. Turns off visibility of elements
    D. Zooms into an element

15. To place a Shaft Opening, activate the _____ ribbon.

    A. Modify
    B. View
    C. Manage
    D. Home

ANSWERS:

    1) T; 2) T; 3) T; 4) T; 5) T; 6) T; 7) T; 8) A; 9) A; 10) A & B; 11) A; 12) B; 13) A; 14) B 15) D

Lesson 5
Schedules

Revit proves it's most powerful in the way it manages schedules. Schedules are automatically updated whenever the model changes. In this lesson, users learn how to add custom parameters to elements to be used in schedules, how to create and apply keynotes, and how to place schedules on sheets.

Exercise 5-1
Creating Shared Parameters

Drawing Name: ex3-21.rvt
Estimated Time: 30 minutes

This exercise reinforces the following skills:

❑ Shared Parameters
❑ Schedules
❑ Family Properties

Door Schedule

DOOR NO.	DOOR TYPE	SIZE			DETAILS			ASSEMBLY RATING	GLAZING TYPE	HARDWARE GROUP	NAMEPLATE	REMARKS
		W	H	THK	HEAD DETAIL	JAMB DETAIL	THRESHOLD DETAIL					
001	A	PR 1'-6"	5'-0"	1 3/4"	--	—	—	—	--	—	--	—
DD2	A	PR 1'-9"	6'-0"	1 3/4"	--	—	—	—	--	—	--	—
DD3	A	PR 1'-6"	6'-0"	1 3/4"	--	—	—	—	--	—	--	—
OD4	A	PR 1'-6"	6'-0"	1 3/4"	--	—	—	—	--	—	--	—

Many architectural firms have a specific format for schedules. The parameters for these schedules may not be included in the pre-defined instance and type parameters in Revit.

Door Schedule						
Mark	Type	Width	Height	Thickness	Head Height	Assembly Co
1	36" x 84"	3' - 0"	7' - 0"	0' - 2"	7' - 0"	C1020
2	36" x 84"	3' - 0"	7' - 0"	0' - 2"	7' - 0"	C1020
3	36" x 84"	3' - 0"	7' - 0"	0' - 2"	7' - 0"	C1020
4	36" x 84"	3' - 0"	7' - 0"	0' - 2"	7' - 0"	C1020
5	36" x 84"	3' - 0"	7' - 0"	0' - 2"	7' - 0"	C1020
7	72" x 78"	6' - 0"	6' - 6"	0' - 2"	6' - 6"	C1020
8	72" x 78"	6' - 0"	6' - 6"	0' - 2"	6' - 6"	C1020
9	36" x 84"	3' - 0"	7' - 0"	0' - 2"	7' - 0"	C1020
11	36" x 84"	3' - 0"	7' - 0"	0' - 2"	7' - 0"	C1020
12	36" x 84"	3' - 0"	7' - 0"	0' - 2"	7' - 0"	C1020
13	36" x 84"	3' - 0"	7' - 0"	0' - 2"	7' - 0"	C1020
14	36" x 84"	3' - 0"	7' - 0"	0' - 2"	7' - 0"	C1020

The Door Schedule in Revit doesn't have Glazing Type, Hardware Group, Nameplate, or Remarks as parameters available.

1. 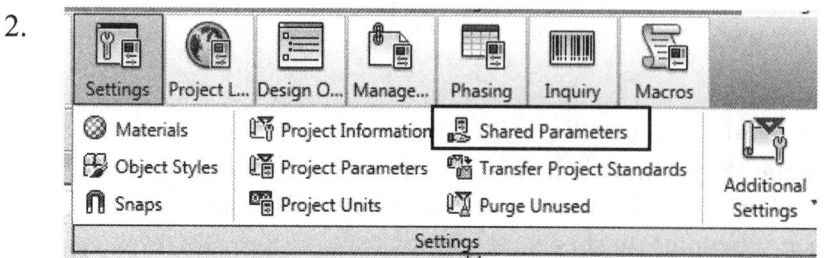 Activate the **Manage** ribbon.

2. Select the **Shared Parameters** tool from the Settings panel.

3. Press **Create** to create a file where you will store your parameters.

4. Locate the folder where you want to store your file.
   Set the file name to *custom parameters.txt*.
   Press '**Save**'.
   Note that this is a txt file.

5. 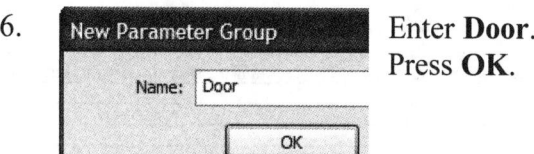 Under Groups, select **New**.

6. Enter **Door**.
   Press **OK**.

7. Under Parameters, select **New**.

8. 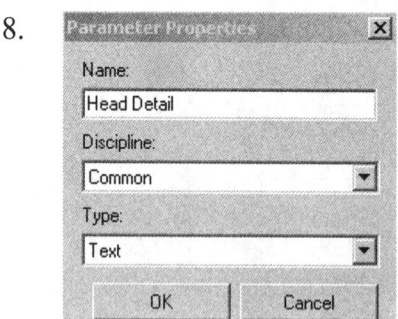 Enter **Head Detail** for Name.

   In the Type field, we have a drop-down list.
   Select '**Text**'.

   Press '**OK**'.

9.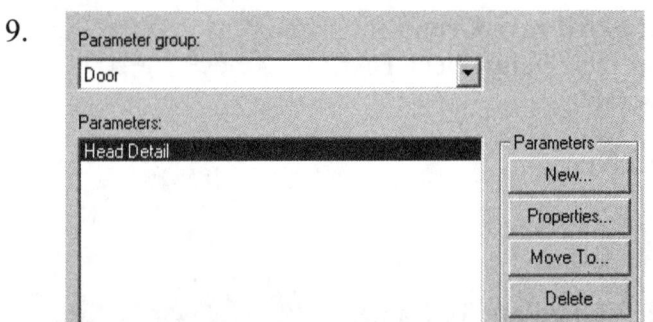

Notice that we have a Parameter Group called **Door** now.

Select **New**.

10.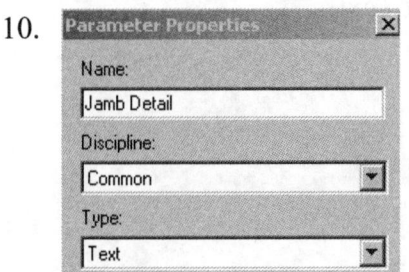

Enter **Jamb Detail** for Name.
In the Type field, select **Text**.
Press **OK**.

Select **New**.

11.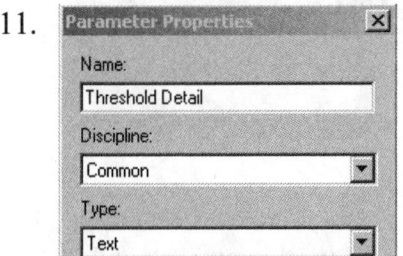

Enter **Threshold Detail** for Name.
In the Type field, select **Text**.
Press **OK**.

Select **New**.

12.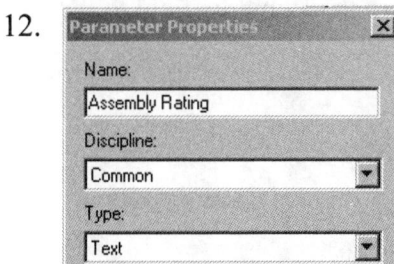

Enter **Assembly Rating** for Name.
In the Type field, select **Text**.
Press **OK**.

Select **New**.

13.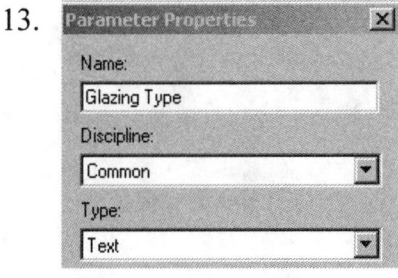

Enter **Glazing Type** for Name.
In the Type field, select **Text**.
Press **OK**.

Select **New**.

14. Enter **Hardware Group** for Name.
In the Type field, select **Text**.
Press **OK**.

Select **New**.

15. Enter **Nameplate** for Name.
In the Type field, select **Text**.
Press **OK**.

Select **New**.

16. Enter **Remarks** for Name.
In the Type field, select **Text**.
Press **OK**.

17. The Remarks field would be a good general column to be used in any schedule. Let's create a parameter group called General and move the Remarks field to the parameter group.

18. 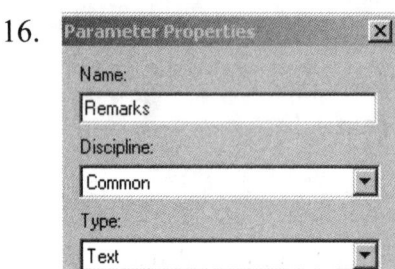 Select **New** under Groups.

19. Name the new group '**General**'.
Press '**OK**'.

20. 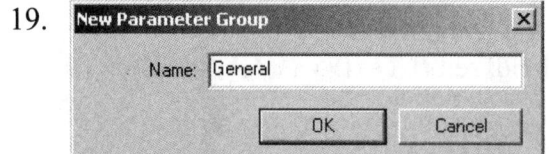 We now have two groups listed under Parameter group.

Select **Door**.

21.  Highlight the **Remarks** field.

Select **Move**.

22. Select **General** from the drop-down list.
Press **OK**.

23. **Remarks** is no longer listed in the Door parameter group.

Select **General** from the Parameter group list.

24.  We see **Remarks** listed.

Highlight **Remarks**.

Select **Properties**.

25. We see how **Remarks** is defined.
Press **OK**.

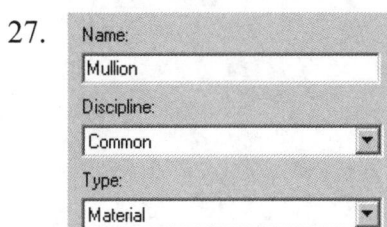

26. Select **New** under **Parameters**.

27. Enter **Mullion** for Name.

For Type, select **Material** from the drop-down.
Press **OK**.

Press **OK** to exit the dialog.

28. custom parameters.txt   Locate the *custom parameters.txt* file using Windows Explorer.
    Dispenser - Towel.rfa

29. custom parameters...   Right click and select **Open**.
    Dispenser - Towel.r   **Open**
    Elevator_Cab-Tract   Print

This should open the file using Notepad and assumes that you have associated txt files with Notepad.

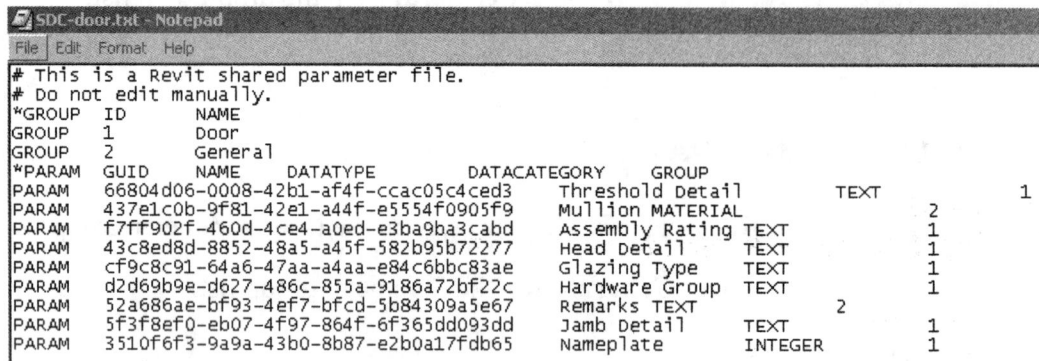

We see the format of the parameter file.
Note that we are advised not to edit manually.
However, currently this is the only place you can modify the parameter type from Text to Integer, etc.

30. 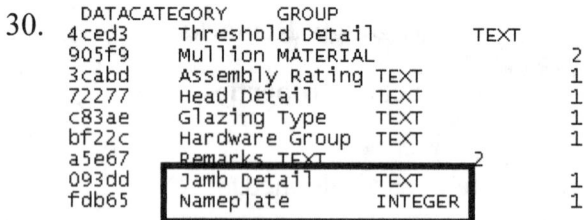   Change the data type to **INTEGER** for Nameplate.

    Do not delete any of the spaces!

31. Save the text file and close.

32. Shared Parameters   Select the **Shared Parameters** tool.

If you get an error message when you attempt to open the file, it means that you made an error when you edited the file. Re-open the file and check it.

33.    Highlight **Nameplate**.
    Select **Properties**.

34. **Name:** | Nameplate
    Discipline: | Common
    Type: | Integer

Note that Nameplate is now defined as an Integer.

Press **OK** twice to exit the Shared Parameters dialog.

35. Save as *ex5-1.rvt*.

Exercise 5-2
Adding Shared Parameters to Families

Drawing Name: ex5-1.rvt
Estimated Time: 45 minutes

This exercise reinforces the following skills:

- Shared Parameters
- Rfa files
- Family Properties
- Purge Unused

1. Open *ex5-1.rvt*.

2. Browse in the Project Navigator and locate the Door families. Note that there are three door families currently used in the project.

3. 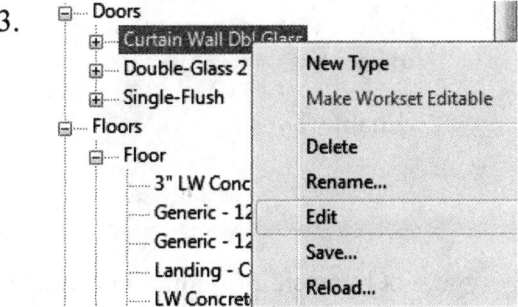 Highlight the **Curtain Wall Dbl Glass** door in the Project Browser.
Right click and select **Edit**.

4.  Select **Family Types** from the Properties panel on the ribbon.

5. 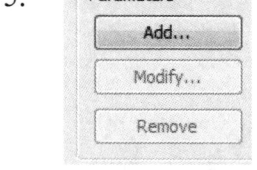 Select **Add** under Parameters.

6. Enable **Shared Parameter**. Press **Select**.

7. Select '**Door**' from the drop-down list.

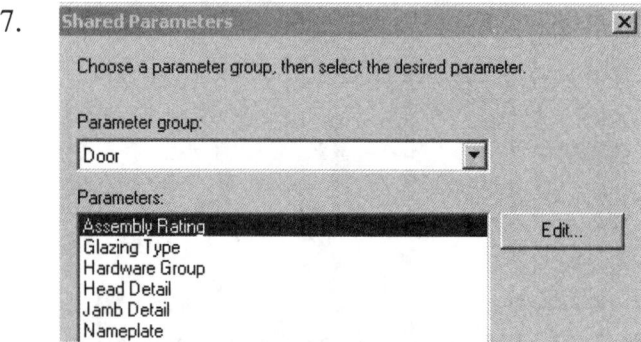

Highlight **Assembly Rating**. Press '**OK**'.

[If you select '**Edit**', you will bring up the Shared Parameters dialog we used in the previous lesson to define parameters.]

8. We see Assembly Rating in the list.

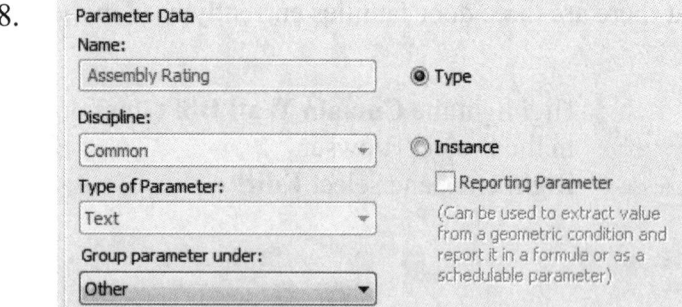

Select **Other** from the drop-down list.

Enable **Type**.

This sets the parameter defined by the family type, not by each individual instance. Press **OK**.

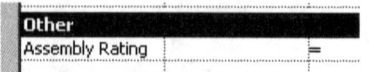 We see Assembly Rating added as a field in our parameter list.

9. 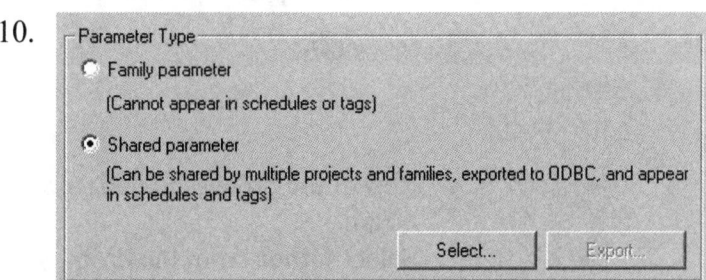 Select **Add** under Parameters.

10. 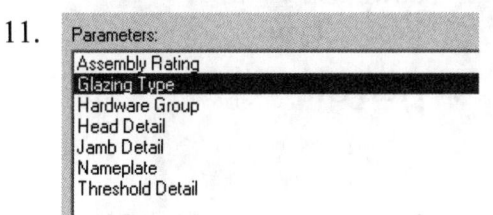 Enable **Shared Parameter**. Press **Select**.

11.

Parameters:

Assembly Rating
Glazing Type
Hardware Group
Head Detail
Jamb Detail
Nameplate
Threshold Detail

Select **Door** from the drop-down list. Highlight **Glazing Type**. Press **OK**.

12.

Parameter Data

Name:
Glazing Type

Discipline:
Common

Type of Parameter:
Text

Group parameter under:
Materials and Finishes

◉ Type

○ Instance
☐ Reporting Parameter
(Can be used to extract value from a geometric condition and report it in a formula or as a schedulable parameter)

Repeat to add the Glazing Type.

Select **Materials and Finishes** from the drop-down list.

Enable **Type**.

Press **OK**.

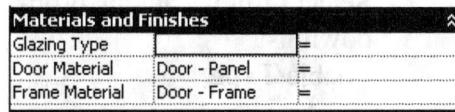

You see that the Glazing Type has been added under Materials and Finishes.

13.

Parameter Data

Name:
Hardware Group

Discipline:
Common

Type of Parameter:
Text

Group parameter under:
Other

○ Type

◉ Instance
☐ Reporting Parameter
(Can be used to extract value from a geometric condition and report it in a formula or as a schedulable parameter)

Repeat the process for Hardware Group.

Select **Other** from the drop-down list.

Enable **Instance**.

Press **OK**.

14. 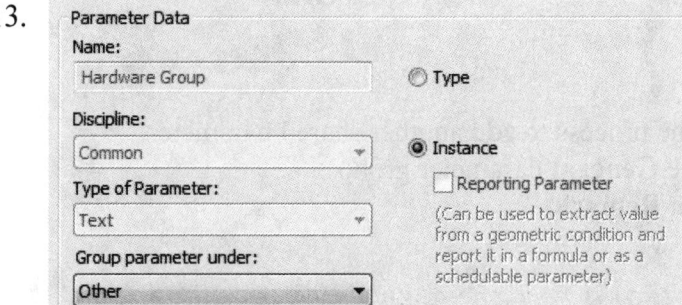 We see the Hardware Group listed under Other.

15.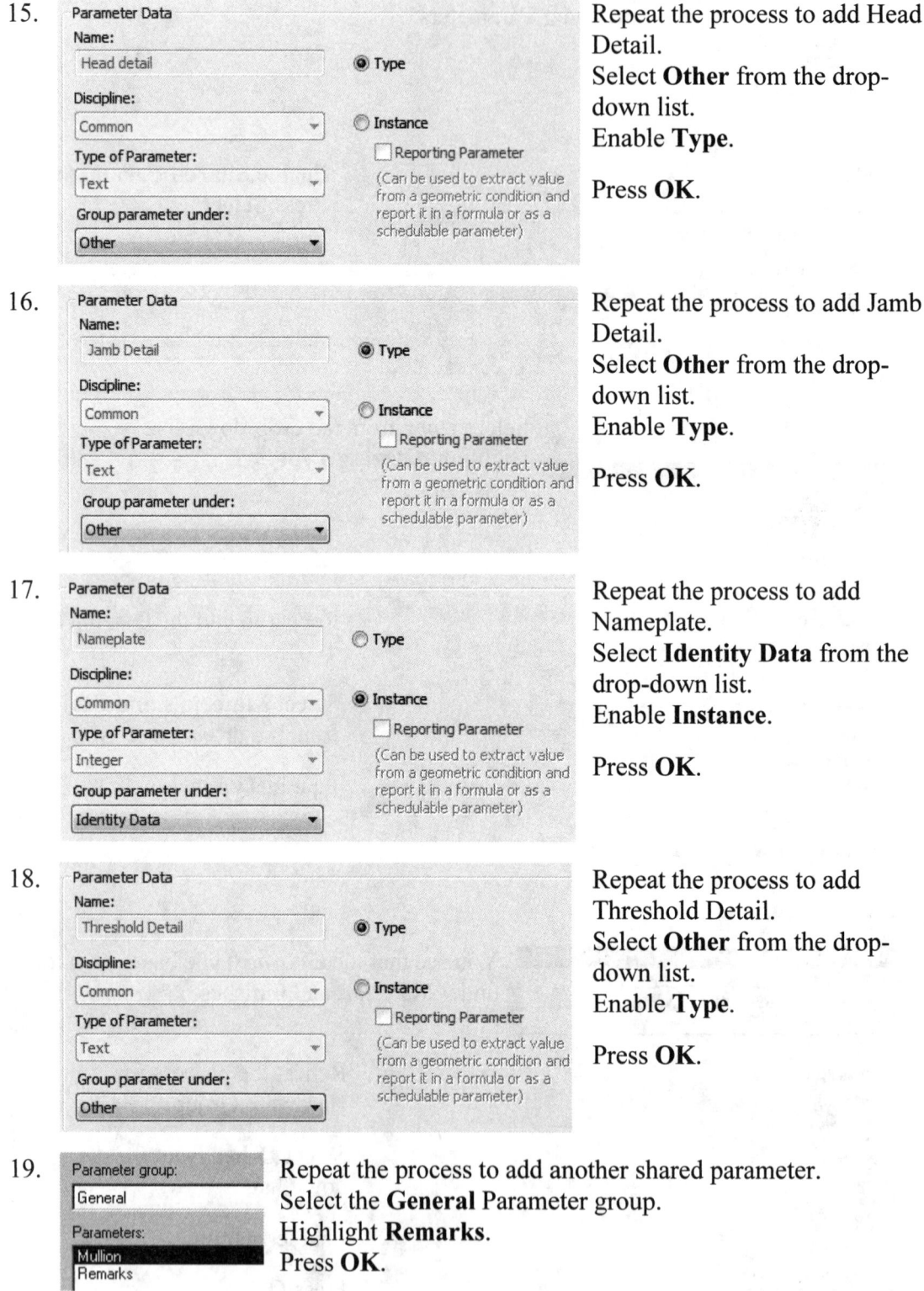

Repeat the process to add Head Detail.
Select **Other** from the drop-down list.
Enable **Type**.

Press **OK**.

16.

Repeat the process to add Jamb Detail.
Select **Other** from the drop-down list.
Enable **Type**.

Press **OK**.

17.

Repeat the process to add Nameplate.
Select **Identity Data** from the drop-down list.
Enable **Instance**.

Press **OK**.

18.

Repeat the process to add Threshold Detail.
Select **Other** from the drop-down list.
Enable **Type**.

Press **OK**.

19.

Repeat the process to add another shared parameter.
Select the **General** Parameter group.
Highlight **Remarks**.
Press **OK**.

20.

Select **Text** from the drop-down list.
Enable **Instance**.
Group under **Text**.

Press **OK**.

21.

You can reset a parameter from Instance to Type by highlighting in the parameter list and selecting '**Modify**'.
When you have added all the shared parameters, press '**OK**'.

22.

In the shared parameter fields, enter '--' for each family type.

23.

For Glazing Type, enter **None**.

24.

Go to the File Application Menu.

Select **Save As→Family**.

25.

Browse to your work folder.
Rename the family **Curtain Wall Dbl Glass Custom**.rfa

Press **Save**.

26.

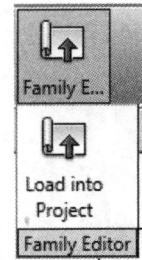

Select **Load into Projects** from the Family Editor panel.

27.

Select the project to load the family file.
Press **OK**.

28. 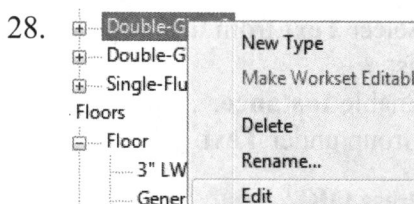 Go to the Doors category in the Families folder of the browser.

Highlight the **Double Glass 2** door.
Right click and select **Edit**.

29. Add the shared parameters using the instructions.

30. When you have added all the shared parameters, press **OK**.

31.

Materials and Finishes	
Glazing Type	Glass
Door Material	Door - Panel
Frame Material	Door - Frame

In the shared parameter fields, enter '--' for each family type.

For the Glazing Type, enter **Glass**.

32. Go to the File Application Menu.

Select **Save As→Family**.

33.

File name:	Double-Glass custom.rfa
Files of type:	Family Files (*.rfa)

Browse to your work folder.
Rename the family **Double-Glass custom**.

Press **Save**.

34. Select **Load into Projects**.

Load into Project

Family Editor

35.

Load into Projects

Check the open Projects/Families you want to load the edited Family into

☐ double glass custom.rfa
☑ ex4-21.rvt

Select the project to load the family file.

Press **OK**.

36.

Doors
  double glass custom
  Double-Glass 2
  Single-Fl...
Floors
Furniture
Parking
Planting
Plumbing F
  Sink - V

New Type
Make Workset Editable
Delete
Rename...
Edit

Go to the Doors category in the Families folder of the browser.

Highlight the Single Flush door.
Right click and select **Edit**.

37. Add the shared parameters using the instructions.

38. When you have added all the shared parameters, press **OK**.

39.

Materials and Finishes	
Glazing Type	Glass
Door Material	Door - Panel
Frame Material	Door - Frame

In the shared parameter fields, enter '--' for each family type.

For the Glazing Type, enter **Glass**.

40. Go to the File Application Menu.

Select **Save As→Family**.

41.

File name: Single-Flush custom.rfa

Files of type: Family Files (*.rfa)

Browse to your work folder.
Rename the family **single flush custom**.

Press **Save**.

42. Load into Project

Family Editor

Select **Load into Projects**.

43. Load into Projects

Check the open Projects/Families you want to load the edited Family into

Double glass custom.rfa
☑ ex4-21.rvt

Select the project to load the family file.

Press **OK**.

44.
- Doors
  - Curtain Wall Dbl Glass
  - Curtain Wall Dbl Glass Custom
  - Double-Glass 2
  - Double-Glass custom
  - Single-Flush
  - Single-Flush custom

Verify that you have loaded the custom version of each door.

The custom versions should have the shared parameters added.

45.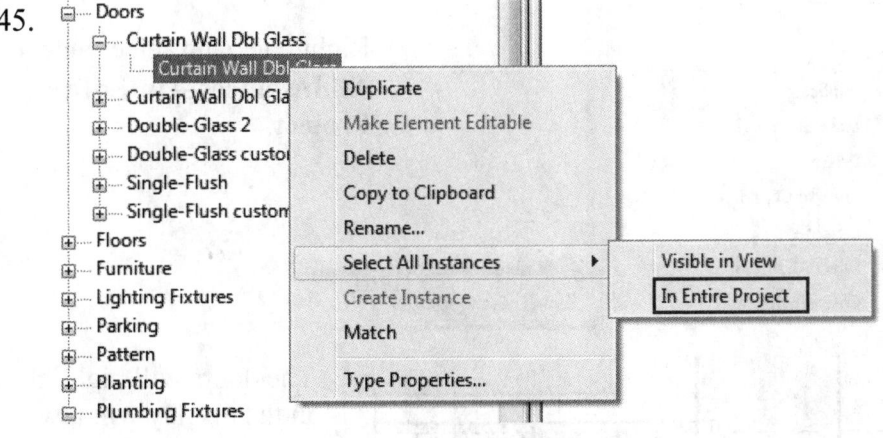

Highlight the **Curtain Wall Dbl Glass** door (this is the door that is currently in use in the project.

Right click and select **Select All Instances→In Entire Project**.

46. The door will highlight in the display window.

47. 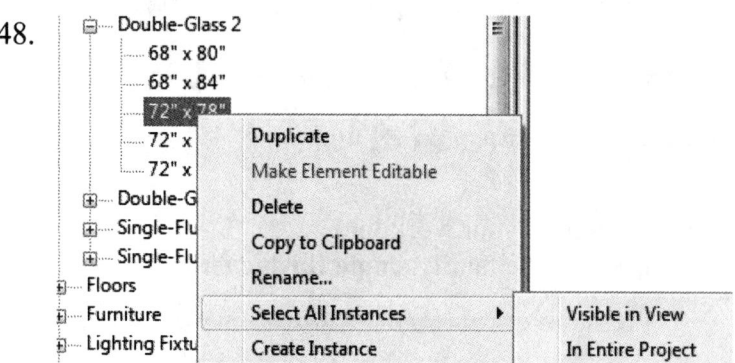 Change the Element Type to the **Curtain Wall Dbl Glass** custom door.

48. Highlight the **Double-Glass 2 72″ x 78″** door (this is the door that is currently in use in the project.

Right click and select **Select All Instances→In Entire Project**.

49. 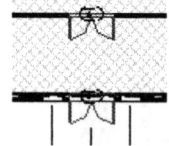 The doors will highlight in the display window.

50. Change the Element Type to the **Double_Glass custom** door that is the same size.

51. Highlight the **Single Flush 36″ x 84″** door (this is the door that is currently in use in the project.

Right click and select **Select All Instances→In Entire Project**.

52. 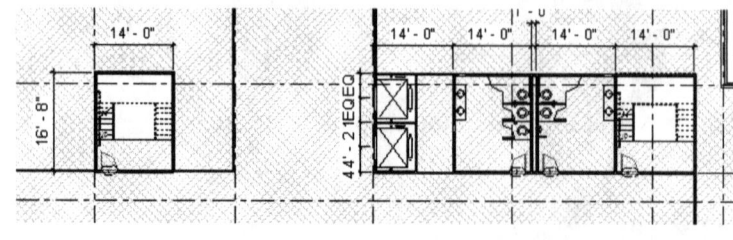 The doors will highlight in the display window.

53. Single-Flush custom
30" x 80"
30" x 84"
32" x 84"
34" x 80"
34" x 84"
36" x 80"
36" x 84"

Change the Element Type to the **Single-Flush custom** door that is the same size: **36" x 84"**.

54.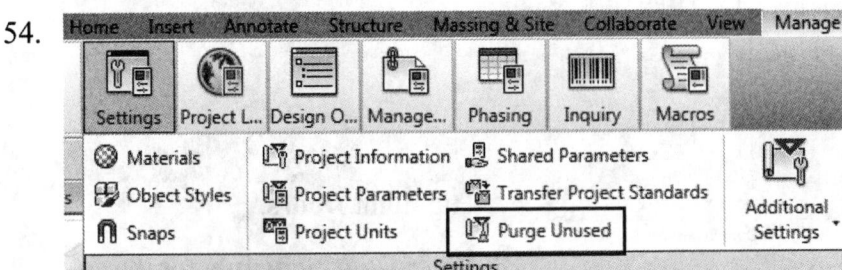

Select **Settings→ Purge Unused** from the Manage ribbon.

55. Check None

Press **Check None**.

56. Doors
☑ Curtain Wall Dbl Glass
☑ Double-Glass 2
☐ Double-Glass custom
☑ Single-Flush
☐ Single-Flush custom

Expand the Doors category.
Place a checkmark on the three door families that are no longer used.

Press **OK**.

57. Doors
Curtain Wall Dbl Glass Custom
Double-Glass custom
Single-Flush custom

The browser now only lists the doors which are used.

58. Save as *ex5-2.rvt*.

Exercise 5-3
Creating a Custom Door Schedule

Drawing Name: ex5-2.rvt
Estimated Time: 30 minutes

This exercise reinforces the following skills:

❑ Shared Parameters
❑ Schedule/Quantities

1. Open *ex5-2.rvt*.

2. View Activate the **View** ribbon.

3.

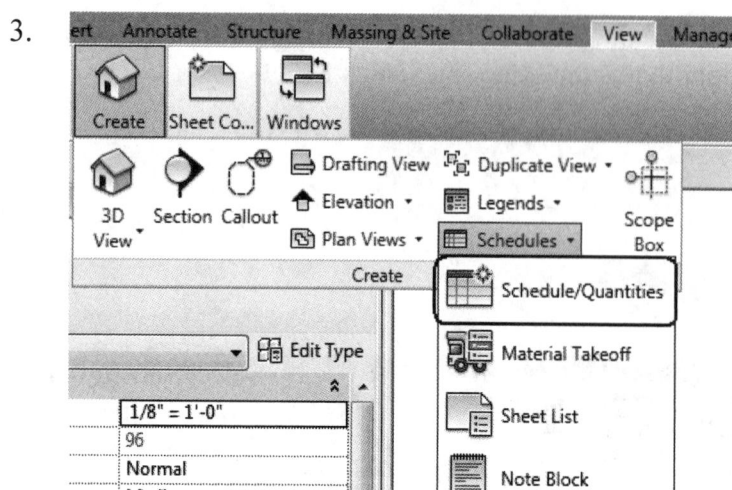

Select **Create→Schedule/ Quantities**.

4.

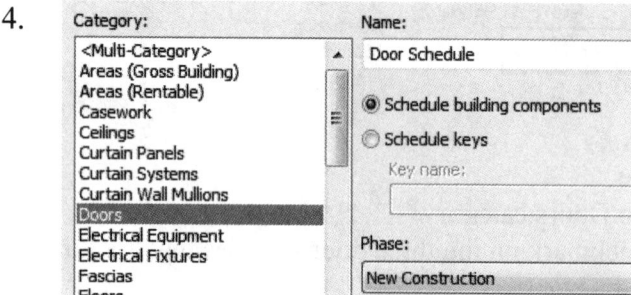

Highlight **Doors**.

Enter **Door Schedule** for the schedule name.

Press **OK**.

Note that you can create a schedule for each phase of construction.

5.

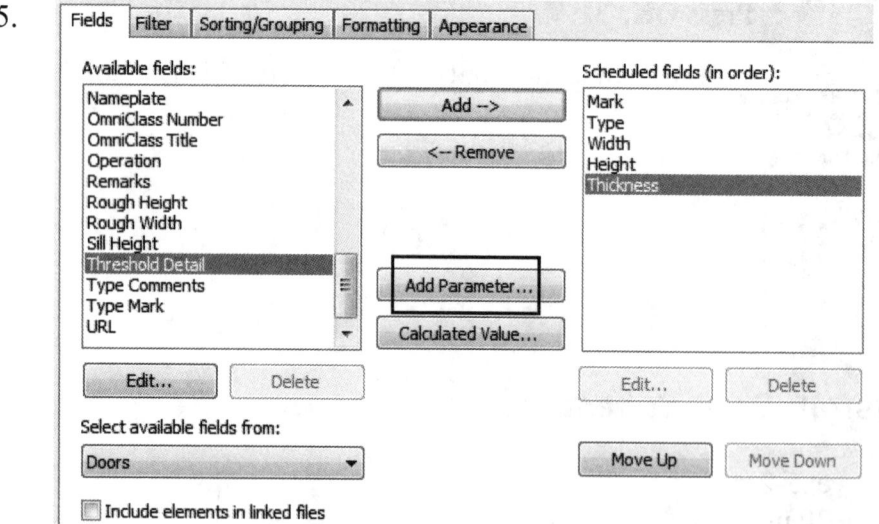

Add **Mark**, **Type**, **Width**, **Height**, and **Thickness**.

Select **Add Parameter**.

6.

○ Shared parameter
(Can be shared by multiple projects and families, exported to ODBC, and appear in schedules and tags)

Select...   Export...

Enable **Shared Parameter**.

Press **Select**.

7.

Add the shared parameters fields we defined to the scheduled fields list.

Scheduled fields (in order):
- Type
- Width
- Height
- Thickness
- Head detail
- Jamb Detail
- Threshold Detail
- Assembly Rating
- Glazing Type
- Hardware Group
- Nameplate
- Remarks

8.

Select the **Formatting** tab.

Highlight **Mark**.

Change the Heading to **Door No.**

Fields:
- Mark
- Type
- Width
- Height
- Thickness
- Head Detail
- Jamb detail
- Threshold Detail
- Assembly Rating
- Glazing Type
- Hardware Group
- Nameplate
- Remarks

Heading: Door No.

Heading orientation: Horizontal

Alignment: Left

Field formatting:

9.

Change the Heading for Type to **Door Type**.

Fields:
- Mark
- Type
- Width
- Height
- Thickness
- Head detail
- Jamb Detail
- Threshold Detail
- Assembly Rating
- Glazing Type
- Hardware Group

Heading: Door Type

Heading orientation: Horizontal

Alignment: Left

10.

Change the Heading for Width to **W**.

Fields:
- Mark
- Type
- Width
- Height
- Thickness
- Head detail
- Jamb Detail
- Threshold Detail
- Assembly Rating
- Glazing Type
- Hardware Group

Heading: W

Heading orientation: Horizontal

Alignment: Left

11.

Change the Heading for Height to **H**.

Fields:
- Mark
- Type
- Width
- Height
- Thickness
- Head detail
- Jamb Detail
- Threshold Detail
- Assembly Rating
- Glazing Type
- Hardware Group

Heading: H

Heading orientation: Horizontal

Alignment: Left

12. 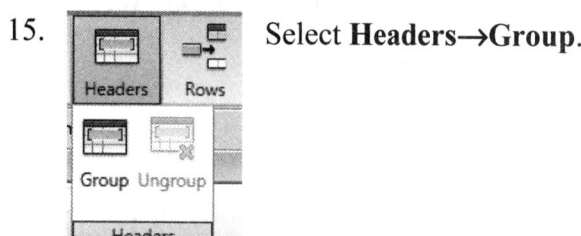 Change the Heading for Thickness to **THK**.
Press **OK**.

13. A window will appear with your new schedule.

14. 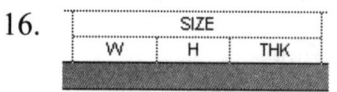 Select the W column, then drag your mouse to the right to highlight the H and THK columns.

15. Select **Headers→Group**.

16. Type '**SIZE**' as the header for the three columns.

17. Select the Head Detail column, then drag your mouse to the right to highlight the Jamb Detail and Threshold Detail columns.

18. Select **Headers→Group**.

19. 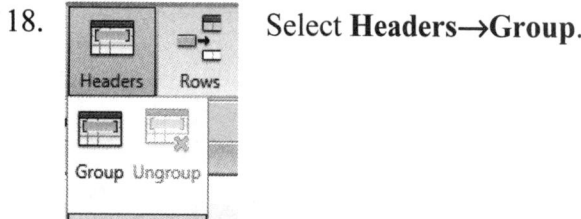 Type '**DETAILS**' as the header for the three columns.

20. Our schedule now appears in the desired format.

| | | Door Schedule | | | | | | | | | | |
| | | SIZE | | | DETAILS | | | Assembly Rating | Glazing Type | Hardware Group | Nameplate | Remarks |
Door No.	Door Type	W	H	THK	Head detail	Jamb Detail	Threshold Detail					
1	36" x 84"	3' - 0"	7' - 0"	0' - 2"							0	
2	36" x 84	3' - 0"	7' - 0"	0' - 2"							0	
3	36" x 84"	3' - 0"	7' - 0"	0' - 2"							0	
4	36" x 84"	3' - 0"	7' - 0"	0' - 2"							0	
5	72" x 78"	6' - 0"	6' - 6"	0' - 2"							0	
6	72" x 78"	6' - 0"	6' - 6"	0' - 2"							0	
7	36" x 84"	3' - 0"	7' - 0"	0' - 2"							0	
8	36" x 84"	3' - 0"	7' - 0"	0' - 2"							0	
9	36" x 84"	3' - 0"	7' - 0"	0' - 2"							0	
10	36" x 84"	3' - 0"	7' - 0"	0' - 2"							0	
	Curtain Wall Dbl	9' - 6 1/2"	7' - 8 1/2"						Tempered		0	

21. Save as *ex5-3.rvt*.

Exercise 5-4
Creating a Custom Window Schedule

Drawing Name: ex5-4.rvt
Estimated Time: 25 minutes

This exercise reinforces the following skills:

- Shared Parameters
- Schedule/Quantities

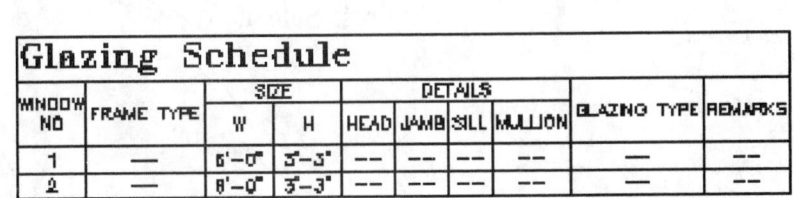

Glazing Schedule									
WINDOW NO	FRAME TYPE	SIZE		DETAILS				GLAZING TYPE	REMARKS
		W	H	HEAD	JAMB	SILL	MULLION		
1	—	6'-0"	3'-3"	--	--	--	--	—	--
2	—	8'-0"	3'-3"	--	--	--	--	—	--

We want our window schedule to appear as shown.

1. Open *ex5-3.rvt*.

2.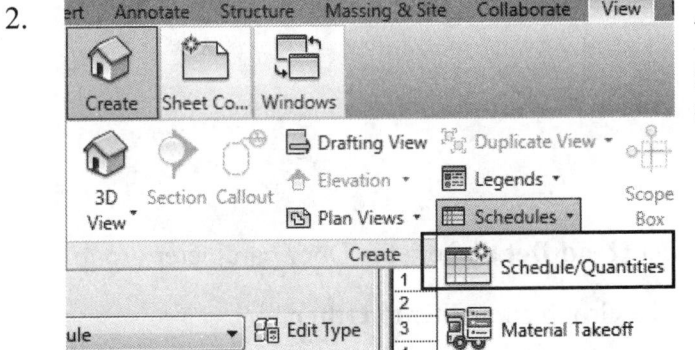

   Activate the **View** ribbon.

   Select **Create→Schedule/ Quantities**.

3.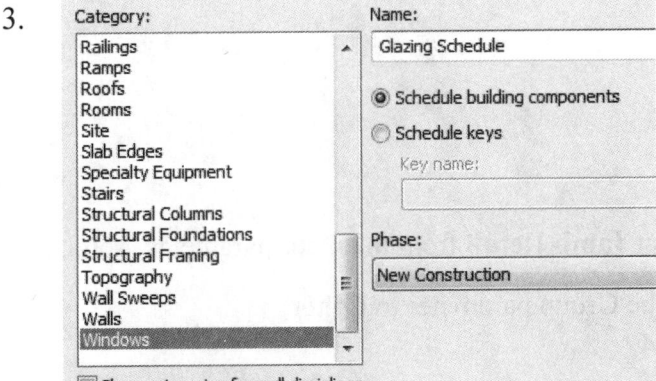

   Highlight **Windows**.

   Change the Schedule name to **Glazing Schedule**.

   Press **OK**.

4.

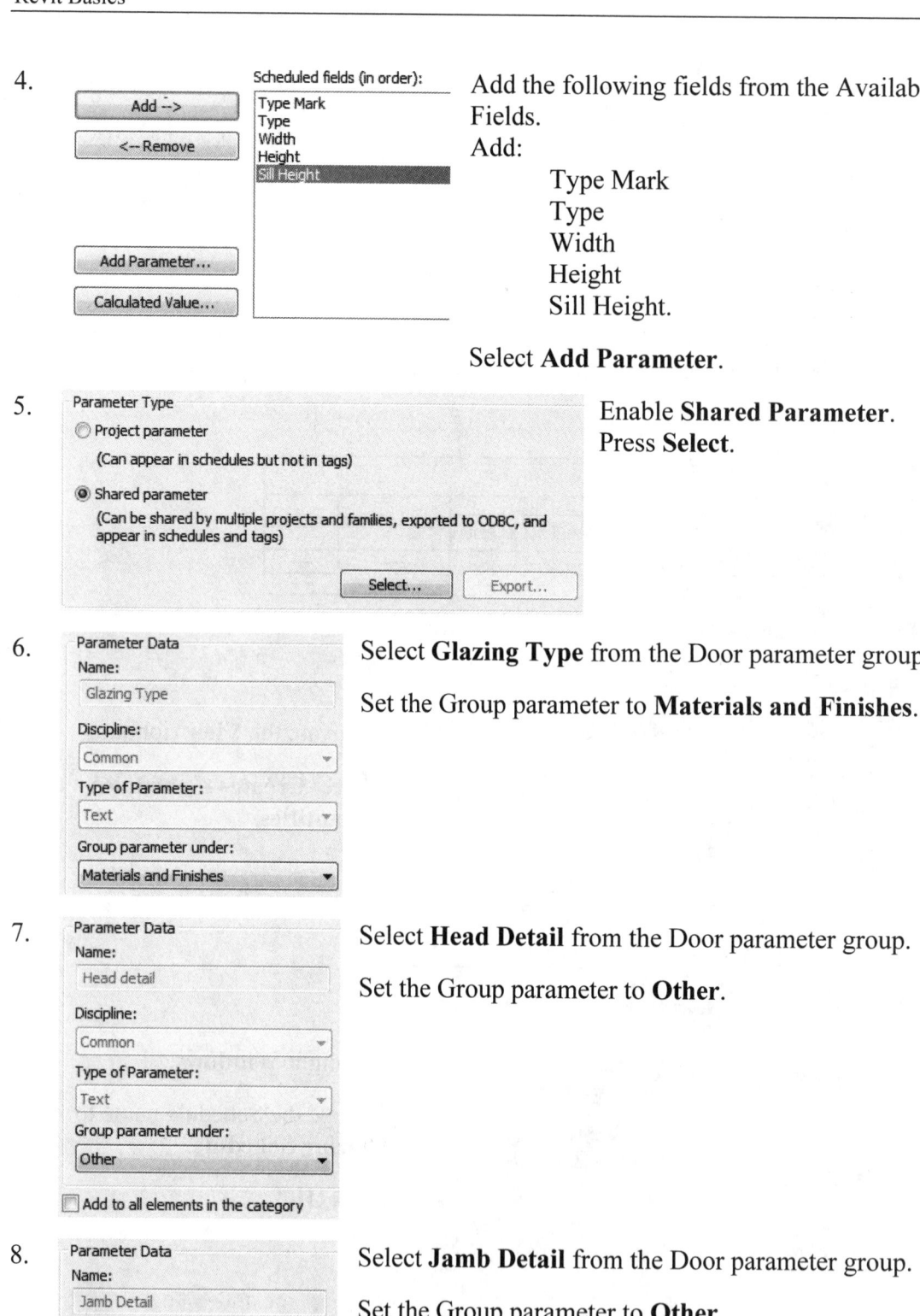

Add the following fields from the Available Fields.

Add:

    Type Mark
    Type
    Width
    Height
    Sill Height.

Select **Add Parameter**.

5.

Enable **Shared Parameter**.
Press **Select**.

6.

Select **Glazing Type** from the Door parameter group.

Set the Group parameter to **Materials and Finishes**.

7.

Select **Head Detail** from the Door parameter group.

Set the Group parameter to **Other**.

8.

Select **Jamb Detail** from the Door parameter group.

Set the Group parameter to **Other**.

9.

Parameter Data
Name:
Mullion

Discipline:
Common

Type of Parameter:
Material

Group parameter under:
Materials and Finishes

Select **Mullion** from the General parameter group.

Set the Group parameter to **Materials and Finishes**.

10.

Parameter Data
Name:
Remarks

Discipline:
Common

Type of Parameter:
Text

Group parameter under:
Text

Select **Remarks** from the General parameter group.

Set the Group parameter to **Text**.

11.

Scheduled fields (in order):
Type Mark
Type
Width
Height
Head detail
Jamb Detail
Sill Height
Mullion
Glazing Type
Remarks

Edit...   Delete

Move Up   Move Down

Use the Move Up and Move Down buttons to reorder the fields as shown.

12.

Fields:
Type Mark
Type
Width
Height
Head detail
Jamb Detail
Sill Height
Mullion
Glazing Type
Remarks

Heading:
WINDOW NO

Heading orientation:
Horizontal

Alignment:
Left

Select the Formatting tab.

Highlight Type Mark and change the Heading to **WINDOW NO**.

13.

Fields:
Type Mark
Type
Width
Height
Head detail
Jamb Detail
Sill Height
Mullion
Glazing Type
Remarks

Heading:
FRAME TYPE

Heading orientation:
Horizontal

Alignment:
Left

Highlight Type and change the Heading to **FRAME TYPE**.

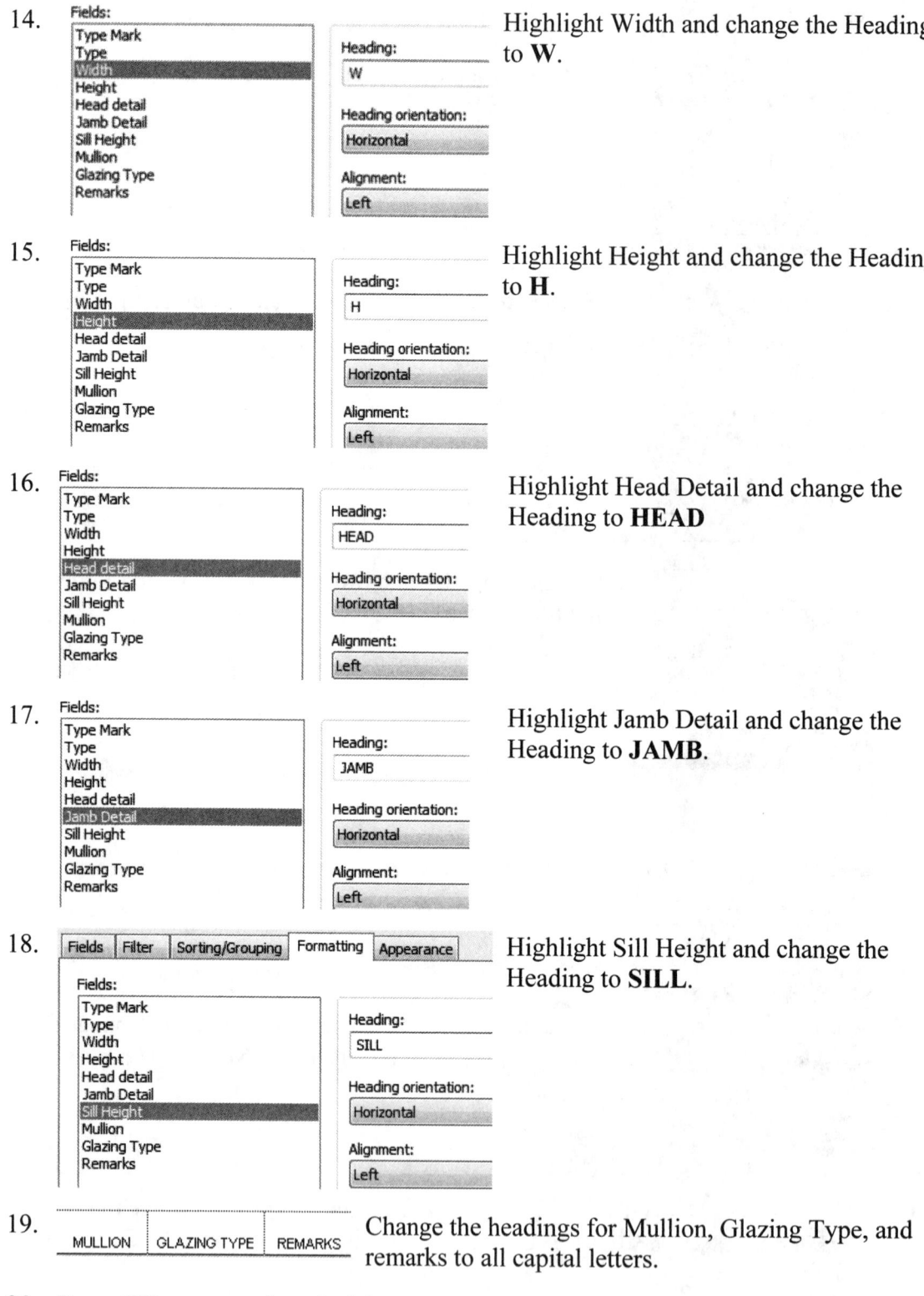

14. Highlight Width and change the Heading to **W**.

15. Highlight Height and change the Heading to **H**.

16. Highlight Head Detail and change the Heading to **HEAD**

17. Highlight Jamb Detail and change the Heading to **JAMB**.

18. Highlight Sill Height and change the Heading to **SILL**.

19. Change the headings for Mullion, Glazing Type, and remarks to all capital letters.

20. Press **OK** to create the schedule.

21. Select the W and H columns to group.

22. 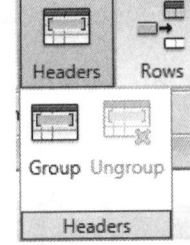 Select **Headers→Group**.

23. | SIZE | |
    |------|---|
    | W | H |

    Add a header called **SIZE** above the W and H columns.

24. Glazing Schedule

    | HEAD | JAMB | SILL | MULLION |

    Group the Head, Jamb, Sill, and Mullion columns.

25.

		Glazing Schedule							
WINDOW NO	FRAME TYPE	SIZE		DETAILS				GLAZING TYPE	REMARKS
		W	H	HEAD	JAMB	SILL	MULLION		
1	36" x 48"	3' - 0"	4' - 0"			2' - 9"			
1	36" x 48"	3' - 0"	4' - 0"			2' - 9"			
1	36" x 48"	3' - 0"	4' - 0"			4' - 0"			
1	36" x 48"	3' - 0"	4' - 0"			4' - 0"			
1	36" x 48"	3' - 0"	4' - 0"			4' - 0"			
1	36" x 48"	3' - 0"	4' - 0"			4' - 0"			

Add the header DETAILS over the head/jamb/sill/mullion group.

26. Save as *ex5-4.rvt.*

Exercise 5-5
Adding Schedule Keys

Drawing Name: ex5-4.rvt
Estimated Time: 15 minutes

This exercise reinforces the following skills:

- Schedule Keys
- Schedule/Quantities
- Rooms
- Materials

1. Open *ex5-4.rvt.*

2. 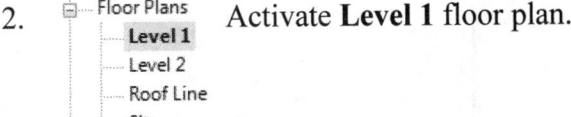 Activate **Level 1** floor plan.

3. Activate the Home ribbon.

Select **Build→Room & Area→Room→Room**.

4. Place a room in the Lobby Area.

Materials were applied in Lesson 4. If you skipped those exercises, you should do Lesson 4 before you do this exercise or use the exercise file available on the CD.

5. Select the Room using the FILTER tool or TAB SELECT.

6.

Identity Data	☆
Number	1
Name	Lobby
Comments	
Occupancy	
Department	
Base Finish	
Ceiling Finish	
Wall Finish	
Floor Finish	
Occupant	
Phasing	☆
Phase	New Construction

Change the name of the room to **Lobby**.

Note there are parameters for finish in the Properties list.

7.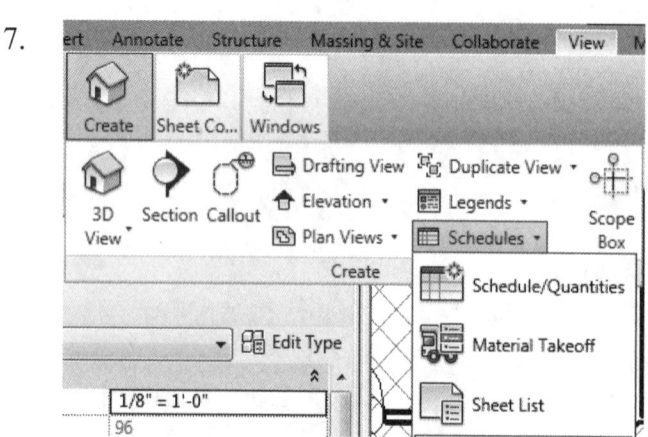

Activate the View ribbon.

Select **Create→Schedules\ Quanitities**.

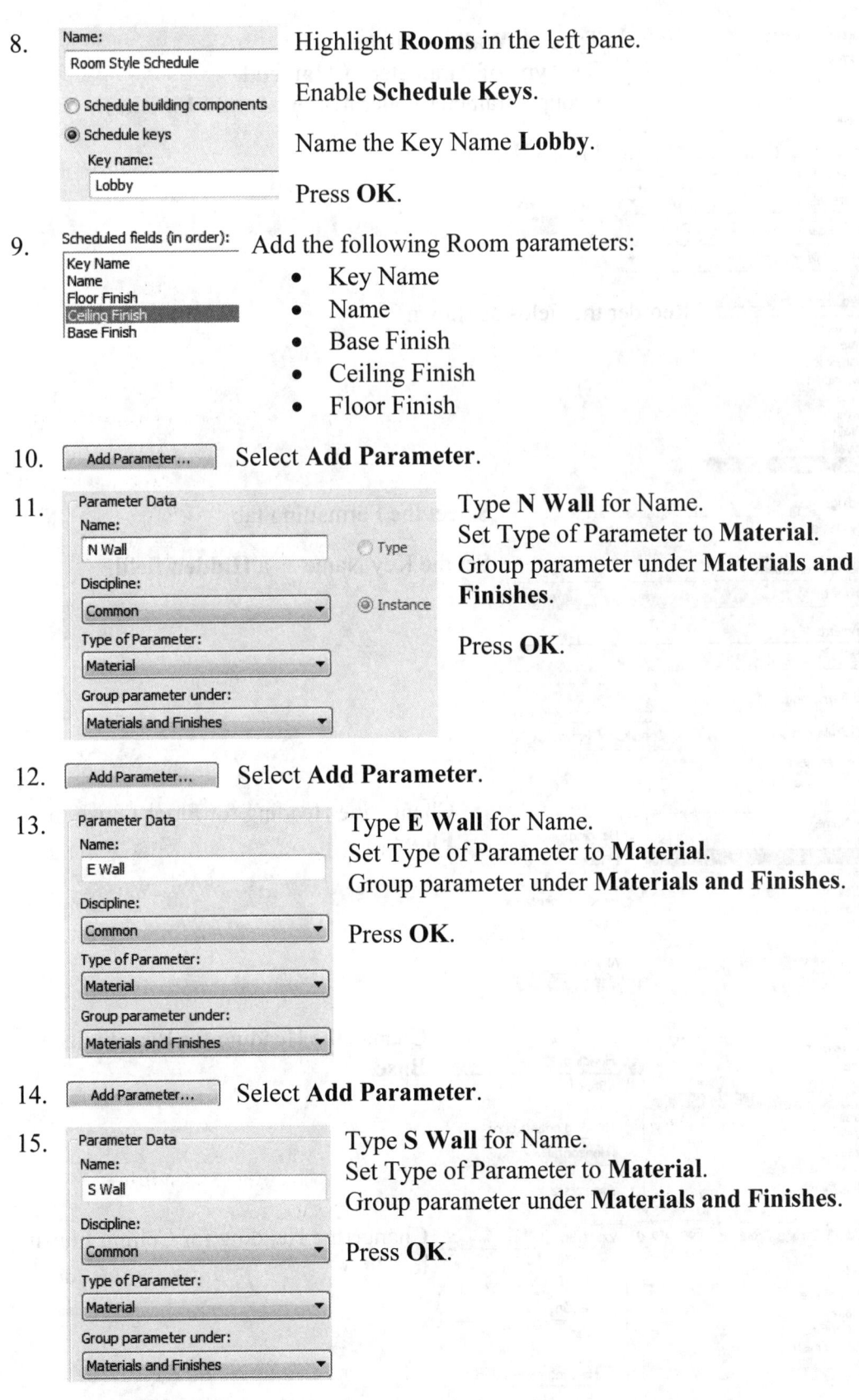

8. **Name:**
Room Style Schedule

○ Schedule building components
◉ Schedule keys
Key name:
Lobby

Highlight **Rooms** in the left pane.

Enable **Schedule Keys**.

Name the Key Name **Lobby**.

Press **OK**.

9. Scheduled fields (in order):
Key Name
Name
Floor Finish
Ceiling Finish
Base Finish

Add the following Room parameters:
- Key Name
- Name
- Base Finish
- Ceiling Finish
- Floor Finish

10. Add Parameter...   Select **Add Parameter**.

11. Parameter Data
Name:
N Wall
Discipline:
Common
Type of Parameter:
Material
Group parameter under:
Materials and Finishes

○ Type
◉ Instance

Type **N Wall** for Name.
Set Type of Parameter to **Material**.
Group parameter under **Materials and Finishes**.

Press **OK**.

12. Add Parameter...   Select **Add Parameter**.

13. Parameter Data
Name:
E Wall
Discipline:
Common
Type of Parameter:
Material
Group parameter under:
Materials and Finishes

Type **E Wall** for Name.
Set Type of Parameter to **Material**.
Group parameter under **Materials and Finishes**.

Press **OK**.

14. Add Parameter...   Select **Add Parameter**.

15. Parameter Data
Name:
S Wall
Discipline:
Common
Type of Parameter:
Material
Group parameter under:
Materials and Finishes

Type **S Wall** for Name.
Set Type of Parameter to **Material**.
Group parameter under **Materials and Finishes**.

Press **OK**.

16. Add Parameter...   Select **Add Parameter**.

17.

Parameter Data

Name:

W Wall

Discipline:

Common

Type of Parameter:

Material

Group parameter under:

Materials and Finishes

Type **W Wall** for Name.
Set Type of Parameter to **Material**.
Group parameter under **Materials and Finishes**.

Press **OK**.

18.

Scheduled fields (in order):

Key Name
Name
Floor Finish
Base Finish
N Wall
E Wall
S Wall
W Wall
Ceiling Finish

Reorder the fields as shown.

19.

Heading:

Key Name

Heading orientation:

Horizontal

Alignment:

Left

Field formatting: Field Format...

☐ Calculate totals   Conditional Format...

☑ Hidden field

Select the Formatting tab.

Set the Key Name as a **Hidden field**.

20.

Fields:

Key Name
Name
Floor Finish
Base Finish
N Wall
E Wall
S Wall
W Wall
Ceiling Finish

Heading:

Floor

Heading orientation:

Horizontal

Alignment:

Left

Change the Heading for Floor Finish to **Floor**.

21.

Fields:

Key Name
Name
Floor Finish
Base Finish
N Wall
E Wall
S Wall
W Wall
Ceiling Finish

Heading:

Base |

Heading orientation:

Horizontal

Alignment:

Change the Heading for Base Finish to **Base**.

22.

Fields | Sorting/Grouping | Formatting | Appearance

Fields:

Key Name
Name
Floor Finish
Base Finish
N Wall
E Wall
S Wall
W Wall
Ceiling Finish

Heading:

Clg|

Heading orientation:

Horizontal

Alignment:

Change the Heading for Ceiling Finish to **Clg**.

23.

Activate the Appearance tab.

Disable **Blank row before data**.

Press **OK**.

24.

Activate **Level 1**.

Select the Room using the FILTER tool or TAB SELECT.

25.

Note the parameters added now appear in the Properties panel.

26.

Select in the material column and assign the appropriate material for each wall.

Materials and Finishes	
N Wall	Finish - Paint - SW Heron Blue
E Wall	Finish - Interior - Wallpaper
S Wall	Finish - Paint - SW Heron Blue
W Wall	Finish - Paint - SW Heron Blue

27.

Under Identity Data:

Assign letters to each of the remaining finish elements.

Identity Data	
Number	1
Name	Lobby
Lobby	(none)
Comments	
Occupancy	
Department	
Base Finish	A
Ceiling Finish	B
Wall Finish	C
Floor Finish	D
Occupant	

28. 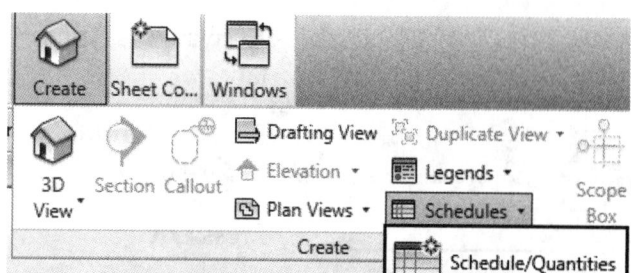 Activate the View ribbon.

Select **Create→ Schedule/ Quantities**.

29.

FINISH SCHEDULE								
NO	NAME	FLOOR	BASE	N WALL	E WALL	S WALL	W WALL	CLG
1	Lobby	D	A	Finish - Paint - SW Heron Blue	Finish - Interior - Wallpaper	Finish - Paint - SW Heron Blue	Finish - Paint - SW Heron Blue	B

Create a FINISH SCHEDULE as shown.

30. Save as *ex5-5.rvt*.

Exercise 5-6
Adding Schedules and Tables to Sheets

Drawing Name: ex5-5.rvt
Estimated Time: 15 minutes

This exercise reinforces the following skills:

- ❑ Shared Parameters
- ❑ Schedule/Quantities
- ❑ Sheets

1. Open *ex5-5.rvt*.

2. Right click on Sheets and select **New Sheet**.

> New Sheet...
> Type Properties...

3. Select a titleblock
E1 30 x 42 Horizontal : E1 30x42 Horizontal

Select a titleblock
A1 metric

Press **OK** to accept the default title block.

4. Drag and drop the door schedule from the browser onto the sheet.

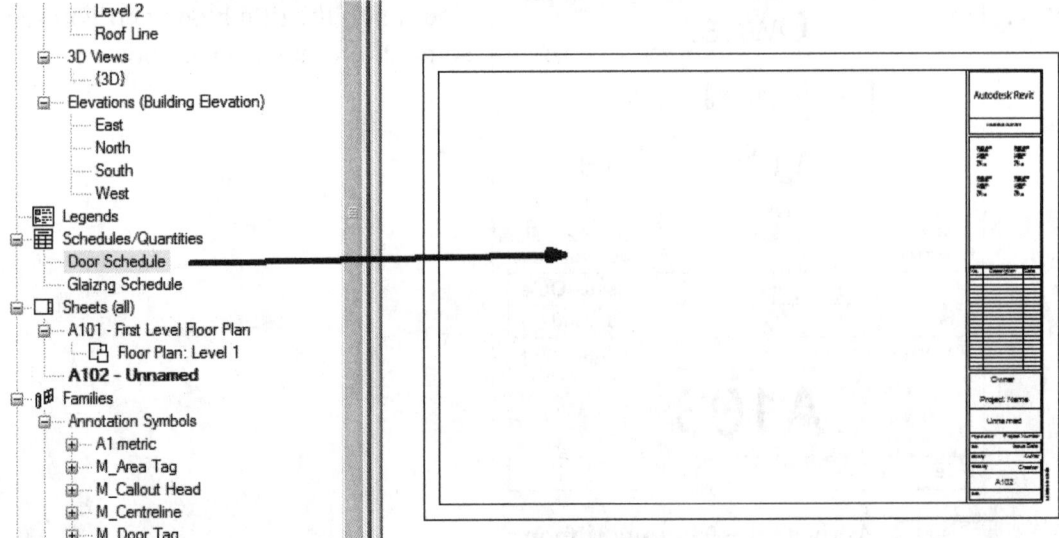

5.

Approved By	Approver
Designed By	Designer
Checked By	Checker
Sheet Number	A102
Sheet Name	Door Schedule
Sheet Issue Date	07/19/10
Appears In Sheet List	☑
Revisions on Sheet	Edit...

On the Properties pane:

Change the Sheet Name to **Door Schedule**.

6. 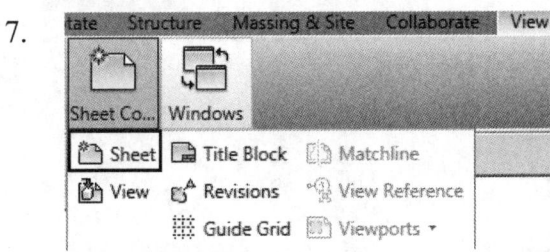 Activate the **View** ribbon.

7.

Select the **New Sheet** tool from the Sheet Composition panel.

Press **OK** to accept the default title block.

8.

Approved By	Approver
Designed By	Designer
Checked By	M. Instructor
Sheet Number	A103
Sheet Name	Glazing Schedule
Sheet Issue Date	07/19/10
Appears In Sheet List	☑
Revisions on Sheet	Edit...
Other	
File Path	
Drawn By	J. Student
Guide Grid	<None>

In the Properties pane:

Change the Sheet Name to **Glazing Schedule**.
Change the Drawn By to your name.
Change the Checked By to your instructor's name.

9.

Zoom into the title block and you see that some of the fields have updated.

10. | Manage | Activate the **Manage** ribbon.

11.

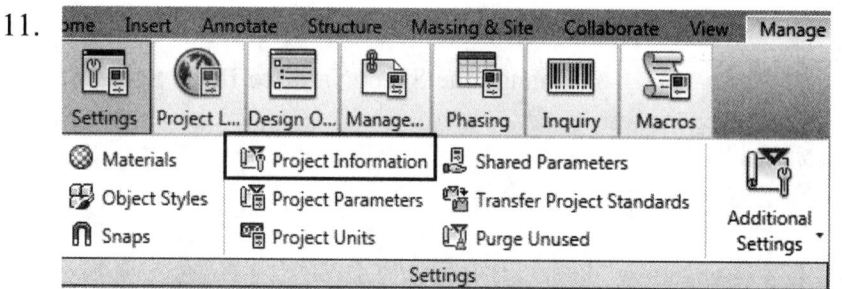

Select **Project Information** from the Settings panel.

12.

Parameter	Value
Energy Analysis	
Energy Settings	Edit...
Other	
Project Issue Date	Issue Date
Project Status	Project Status
Client Name	B. Brown
Project Address	Edit...
Project Name	Brown Office Building
Project Number	Project Number

Fill in the Project Data. Press **OK**.

13.

B. Brown	
Brown Office Building	
Glazing Schedule	

Project Number	Project Number
Date	04-09-2009
Drawn By	J. Student
Checked By	M. Teacher

A103

| Scale | |

Note that the title block updates.

- Sheets (all)
  - **A101 - First Level Floor Plan**
  - A102 - Unnamed
  - A103 - Glazing Schedule

Activate the other sheets and note that the project information has updated on all sheets in the project.

14.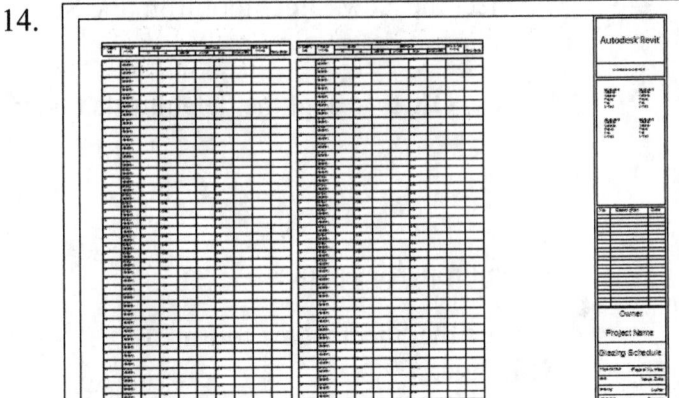

Drag and drop the **Glazing Schedule** onto the A103 sheet.

Break the schedule into two parts by dragging and dropping.

15.

Approved By	Approver
Designed By	Designer
Checked By	Checker
Sheet Number	A102
Sheet Name	Door Schedule
Sheet Issue Date	07/19/10
Appears In Sheet List	☑
Revisions on Sheet	Edit...

On the Properties pane:

Change the Sheet Name to **Door Schedule**.

16. Save the file as *ex5-6.rvt*.

Exercise 5-7
Creating a Finish Schedule

Drawing Name: ex5-6.rvt
Estimated Time: 60 minutes

This exercise reinforces the following skills:

- ❑ Schedules
- ❑ Keynotes
- ❑ Keynote Legends

1. Open *ex5-6.rvt*.

2. [View] Activate the **View** ribbon.

3. 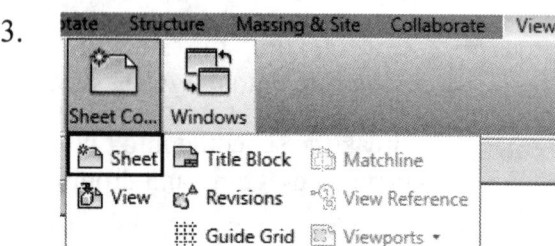 Select the **New Sheet** tool from the Sheet Composition panel.

    Press **OK** to accept the default title block.

4.

Approved By	M. Instructor
Designed By	Designer
Checked By	Checker
Sheet Number	A104
Sheet Name	Finish Schedule
Sheet Issue Date	07/19/10
Appears In Sheet List	☑
Revisions on Sheet	Edit...
Other	
File Path	
Drawn By	J. Student
Guide Grid	<None>

    In the Properties pane:

    Change the Sheet Name to **Finish Schedule**.
    Change the Drawn By to your name.
    Change the Checked By to your instructor's name.

5. Floor Plans
        Level 1
        Level 2
        Roof Line
        Site   Activate the **Level 1** floor plan.

6.

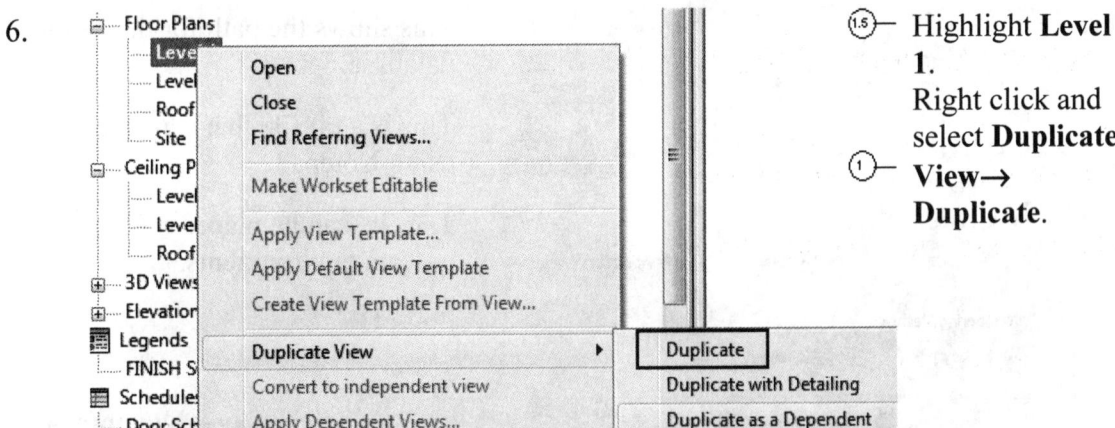

Highlight **Level 1**.
Right click and select **Duplicate View→ Duplicate**.

7.

Floor Plans
— Level 1
— Level 1 - Lobby Detail
— Level 2

Rename the duplicate **view Level 1 - Lobby Detail**.

8.

Extents	
Crop View	☑
Crop Region Visible	☑

In the Properties pane:
Enable **Crop View**.
Enable **Crop Region Visible**.

9.

Use the blue triangle grips to crop the view so that only the lobby area is displayed.

10.

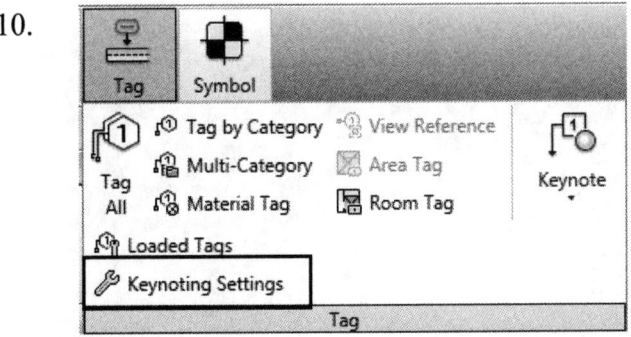

Activate the **Annotation** ribbon.

Select **Tag→Keynoting Settings**.

11.

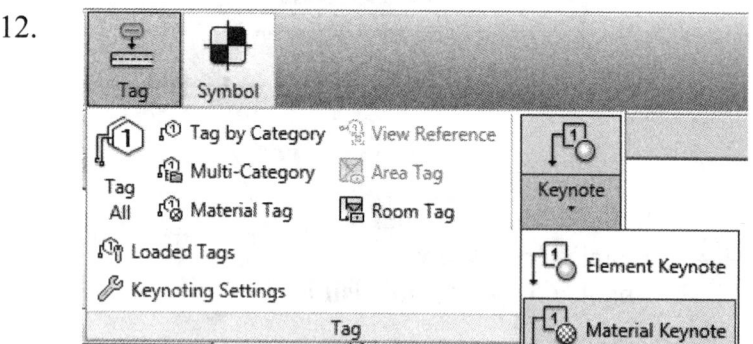

This shows the path for the keynote database.

This is a txt file that can be edited using Notepad.

The file can be placed on a server in team environments.

Press **OK**.

12.

Select **Tag→Keynote→ Material Keynote**.

13.

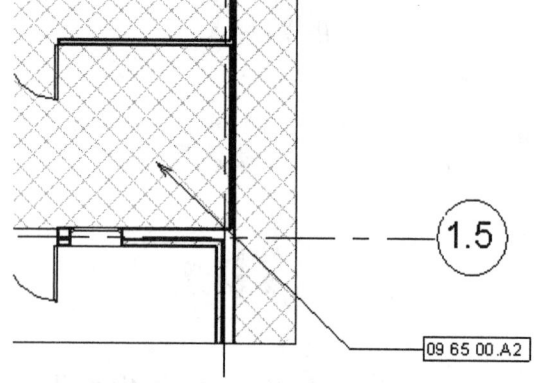

Select the floor.

14.

Place the keynote tag.

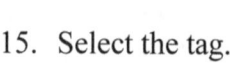

15. Select the tag.

Identity Data	
Key Source	Material
Keynote Text	Vinyl Composition Tile
Key Value	09 65 00.A2

In the Properties pane:
Verify that the material displayed is Vinyl Composition Tile.

16. 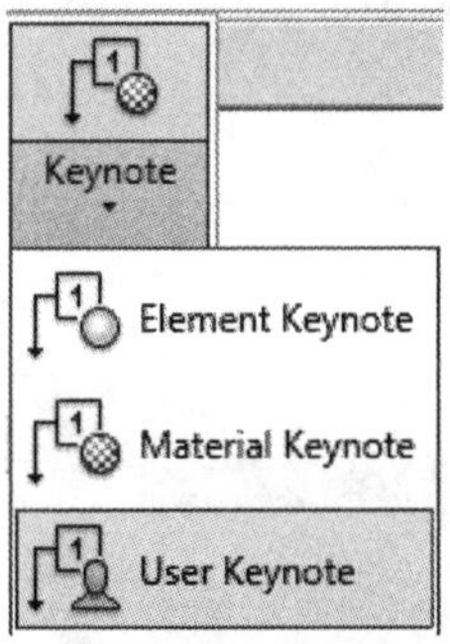

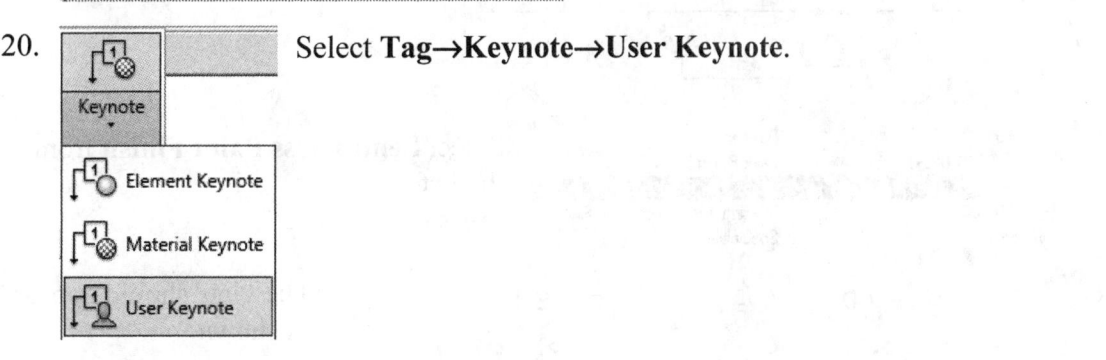

Select **Tag→Keynote→User Keynote**.

17. 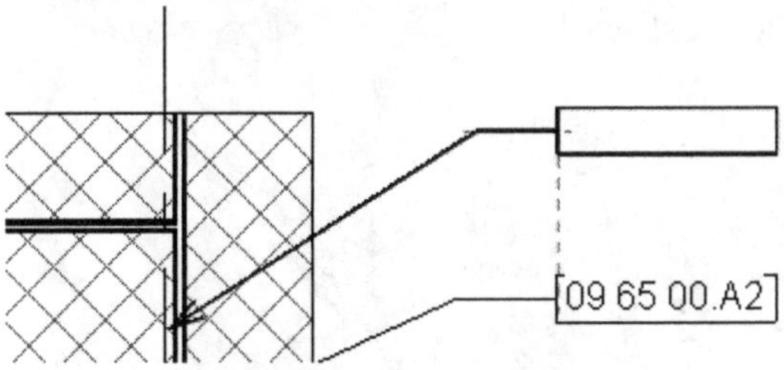

Select the east wall.

18. 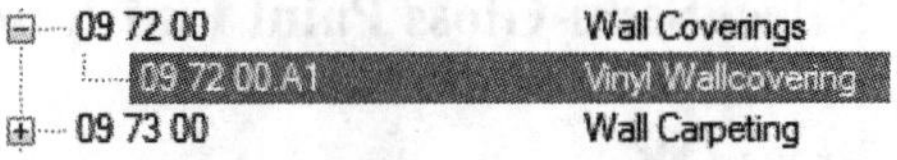

Select **Vinyl Wallcovering** from the list.
Press **OK**.

19. Select the tag.

Identity Data	
Key Source	User
Keynote Text	Vinyl Wallcovering
Key Value	09 72 00.A1

In the Properties pane:
Verify that the material displayed is **Vinyl Wallcovering**.

20.

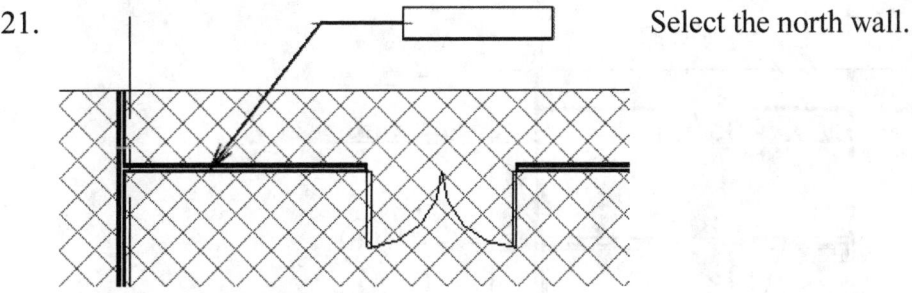

Select **Tag→Keynote→User Keynote**.

21.

Select the north wall.

22.

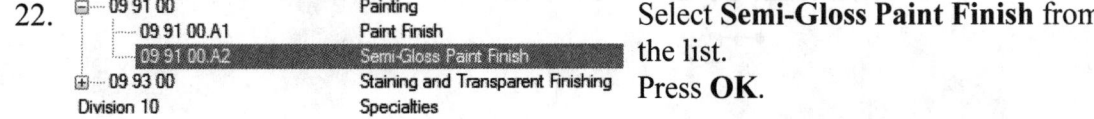

Select **Semi-Gloss Paint Finish** from the list.
Press **OK**.

23. 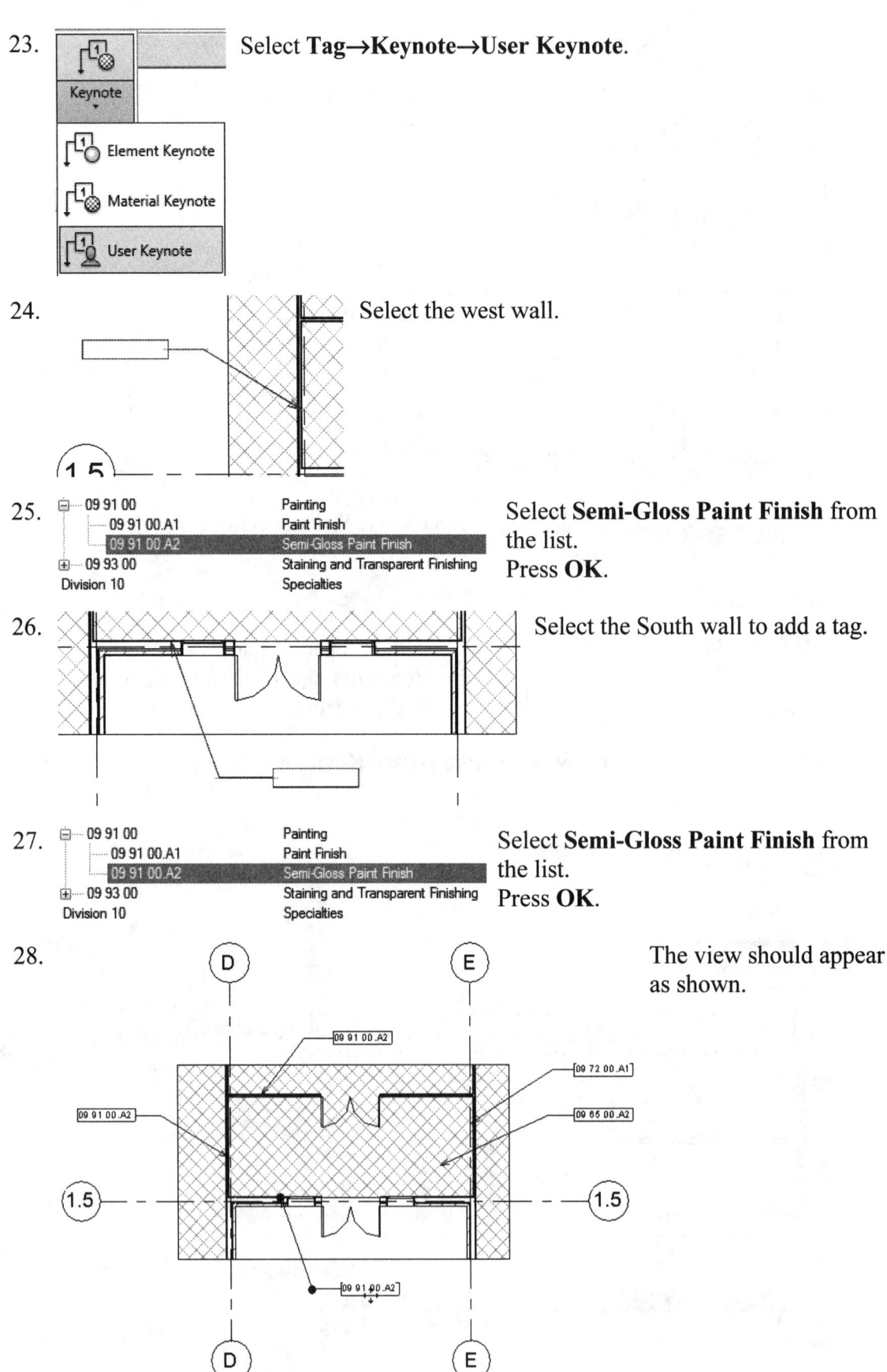 Select **Tag→Keynote→User Keynote**.

Keynote

Element Keynote

Material Keynote

User Keynote

24. Select the west wall.

1.5

25. 09 91 00   Painting
    09 91 00.A1   Paint Finish
    09 91 00.A2   Semi-Gloss Paint Finish
09 93 00   Staining and Transparent Finishing
Division 10   Specialties

Select **Semi-Gloss Paint Finish** from the list.
Press **OK**.

26. Select the South wall to add a tag.

27. 09 91 00   Painting
    09 91 00.A1   Paint Finish
    09 91 00.A2   Semi-Gloss Paint Finish
09 93 00   Staining and Transparent Finishing
Division 10   Specialties

Select **Semi-Gloss Paint Finish** from the list.
Press **OK**.

28. The view should appear as shown.

29.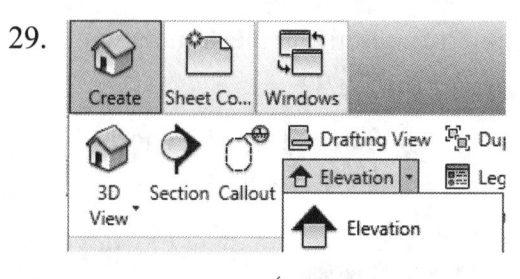

Activate the View ribbon.

Select **Create→Elevation→Building Elevation**.

30.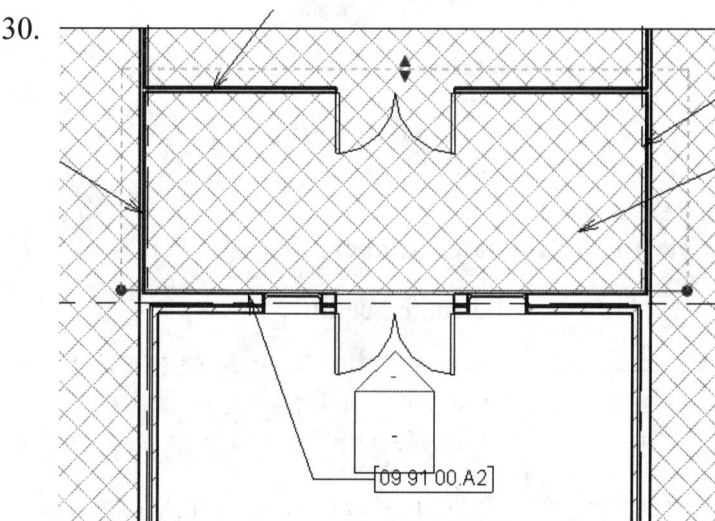

Place an elevation marker as shown.

Adjust the boundaries of the elevation view to contain the lobby room.

31.

Elevations (Building Elevation)
- East
- Elevation 1 - a
- North
- South
- West

Locate the elevation in the Project Browser.

Rename to **South - Lobby**.

32.

Elevations (Building Elevation)
- East
- North
- South
- **South - Lobby**
- West

Activate the **South-Lobby** view.

33.

Adjust the crop region to show the entire lobby including floor and ceiling.

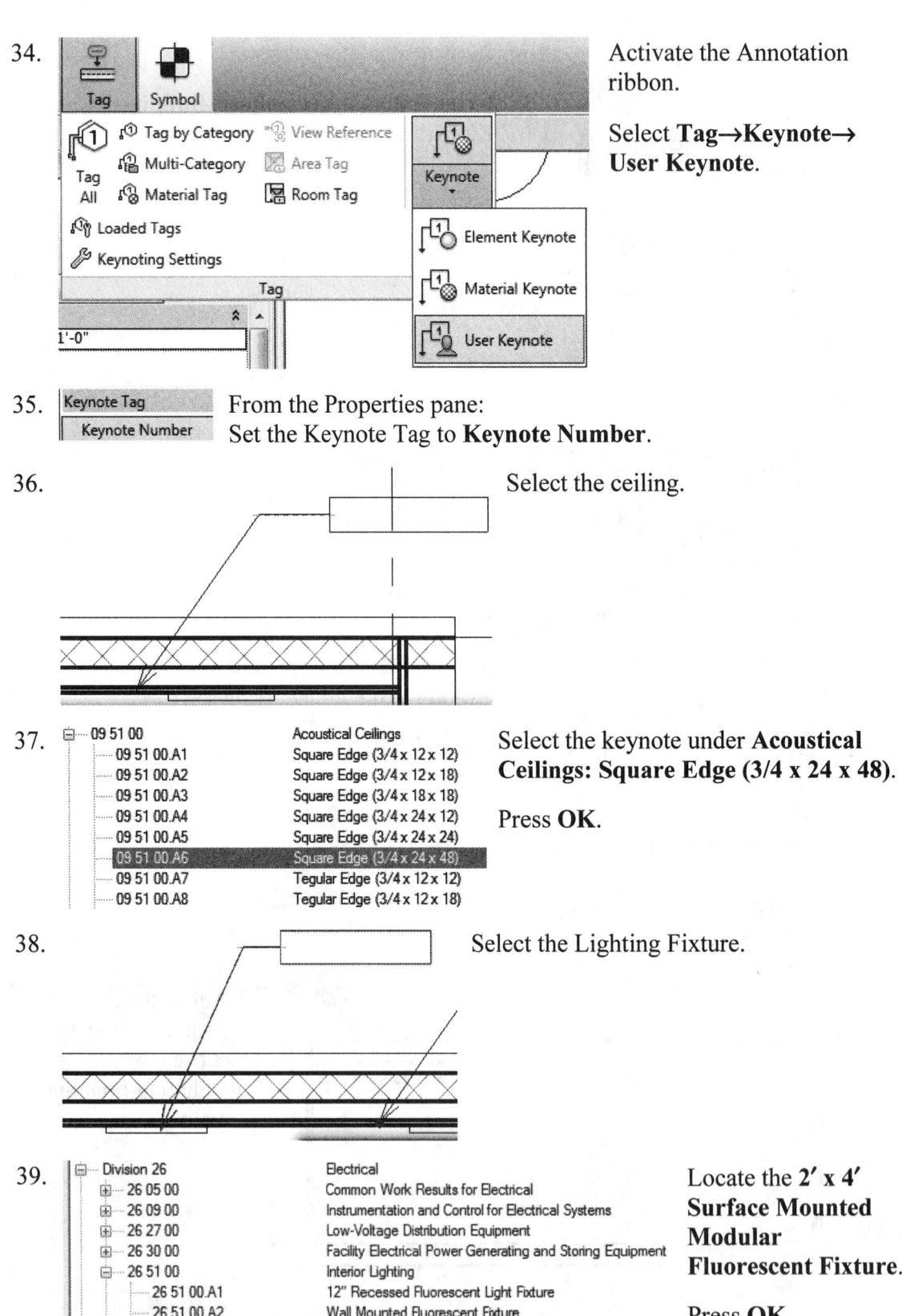

34. Activate the Annotation ribbon.

Select **Tag→Keynote→ User Keynote**.

35. From the Properties pane:
Set the Keynote Tag to **Keynote Number**.

36. Select the ceiling.

37. Select the keynote under **Acoustical Ceilings: Square Edge (3/4 x 24 x 48)**.

Press **OK**.

38. Select the Lighting Fixture.

39. Locate the **2' x 4' Surface Mounted Modular Fluorescent Fixture**.

Press **OK**.

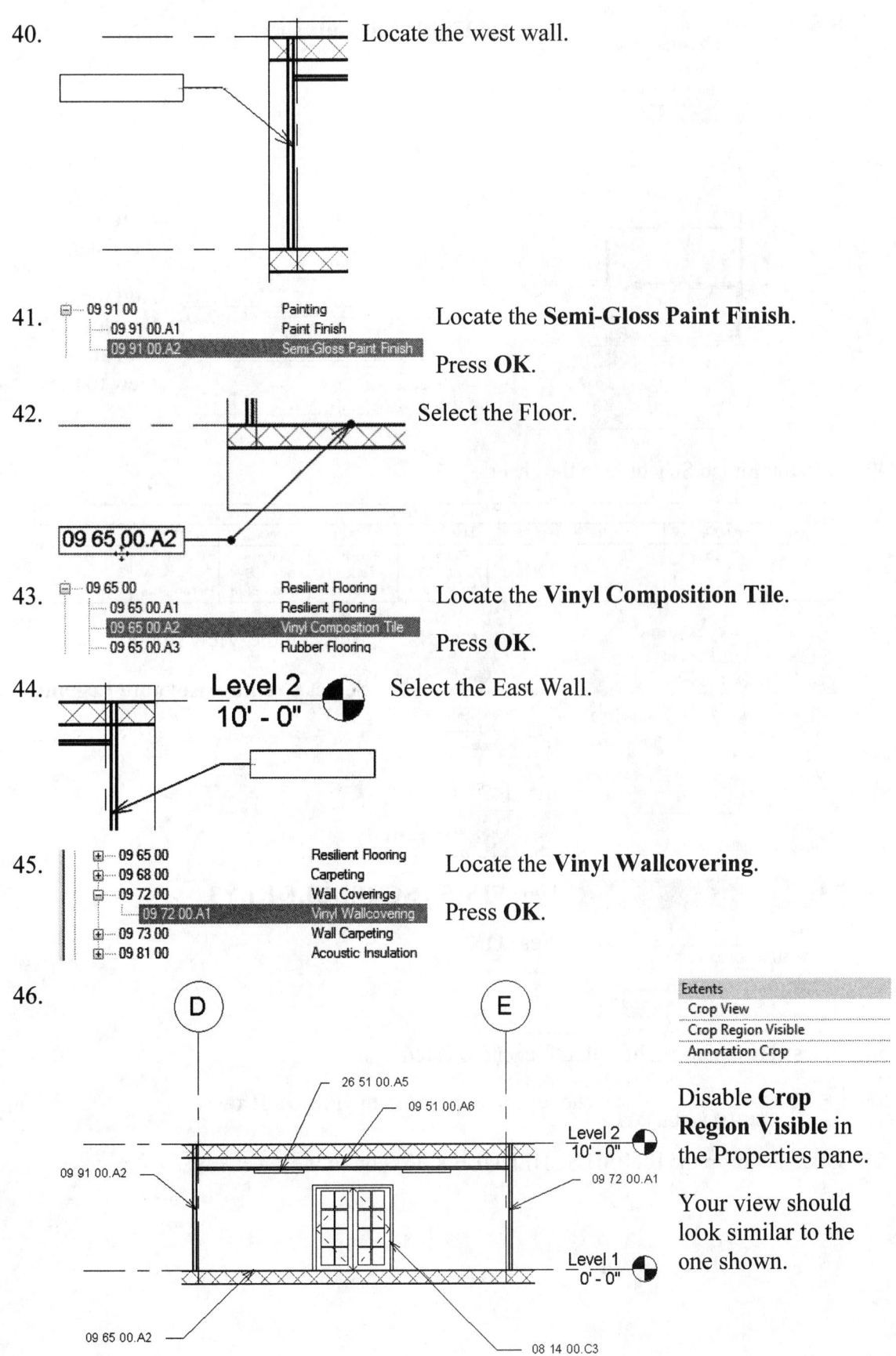

40. Locate the west wall.

41.
09 91 00	Painting	
09 91 00.A1	Paint Finish	
09 91 00.A2	Semi-Gloss Paint Finish	

Locate the **Semi-Gloss Paint Finish**.

Press **OK**.

42. Select the Floor.

09 65 00.A2

43.
09 65 00	Resilient Flooring	
09 65 00.A1	Resilient Flooring	
09 65 00.A2	Vinyl Composition Tile	
09 65 00.A3	Rubber Flooring	

Locate the **Vinyl Composition Tile**.

Press **OK**.

44.
Level 2
10' - 0"

Select the East Wall.

45.
09 65 00	Resilient Flooring	
09 68 00	Carpeting	
09 72 00	Wall Coverings	
09 72 00.A1	Vinyl Wallcovering	
09 73 00	Wall Carpeting	
09 81 00	Acoustic Insulation	

Locate the **Vinyl Wallcovering**.

Press **OK**.

46.

Extents
Crop View
Crop Region Visible
Annotation Crop

Disable **Crop Region Visible** in the Properties pane.

Your view should look similar to the one shown.

D   E

26 51 00.A5

09 51 00.A6

Level 2
10' - 0"

09 91 00.A2

09 72 00.A1

Level 1
0' - 0"

09 65 00.A2

08 14 00.C3

47. Activate the **Finish Schedule** sheet.

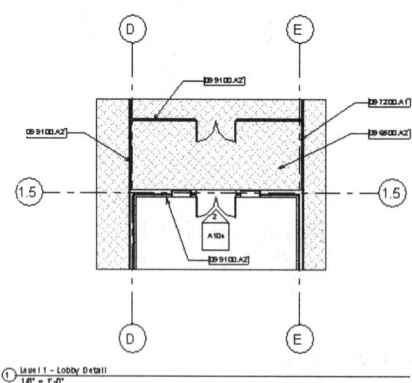

Sheets (all)
A101 - First Level Floor Plan
A102 - Door Schedule
A103 - Glazing Schedule
A104 - Finish Schedule

48. 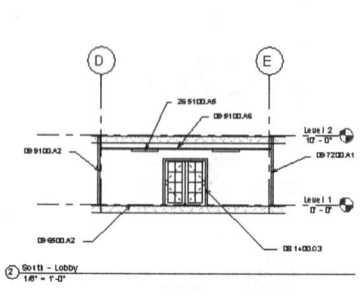 Add the **Level 1 - Lobby Detail** view to the sheet.

Add the **South Lobby Elevation** view to the sheet.

49. Add the Finish Schedule to the sheet.

				FINISH SCHEDULE				
NO	NAME	FLOOR	BASE	N WALL	E WALL	S WALL	W WALL	CLG
1	Lobby	D	A	Finish - Paint - SW Heron Blue	Finish - Interior - Wallpaper	Finish - Paint - SW Heron Blue	Finish - Paint - SW Heron Blue	B

50. Activate the View ribbon.

Select **Create→Keynote Legend**.

51. Type **FINISH SCHEDULE KEYS**.

Press **OK**.

New Keynote Legend
Name:
FINISH SCHEDULE KEYS
OK   Cancel

52. Press **OK** to accept the default legend created.

53. 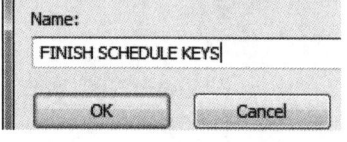 The legend appears in the Project Browser.

Legends
FINISH SCHEDULE KEYS

54. Drag and drop the FINISH SCHEDULE KEYS on to the sheet.

FINISH SCHEDULE								
NO	NAME	FLOOR	BASE	N WALL	E WALL	S WALL	W WALL	CLG
1	Lobby	D	A	Finish - Paint - S/W Heros Tile	Finish - Interior - Wallpaper	Finish - Paint - S/W Heros Tile	Finish - Paint - S/W Heros Tile	B

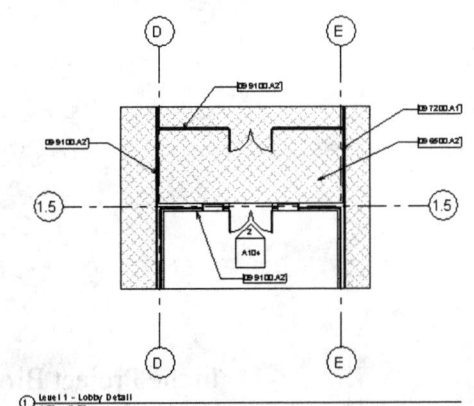

FINISH SCHEDULE KEYS	
Key Value	Keynote Text
08 14 00.C3	Wood Door Frame
09 51 00.A6	Square Edge (3/4 x 24 x 48)
09 65 00.A2	Vinyl Composition Tile
09 72 00.A1	Vinyl Wallcovering
09 91 00.A2	Semi-Gloss Paint Finish
26 51 00.A5	2 X 4' Surface Mounted Modular Fluorescent Fixture

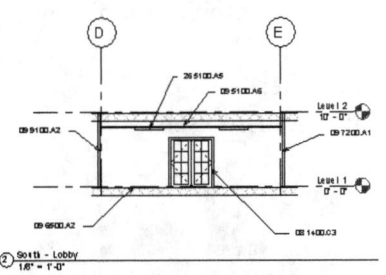

55. 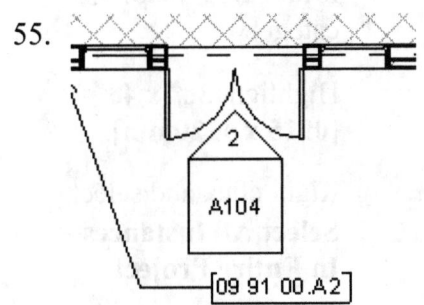 Zoom in and you will see the elevation marker now indicates the Sheet Number.

56. Save as *ex5-7.rvt*.

Exercise 5-8
Find and Replace Families

Drawing Name: ex5-7.rvt
Estimated Time: 5 minutes

This exercise reinforces the following skills:

❑   Families
❑   Project Browser

1.   Open *ex5-7.rvt*.

2.   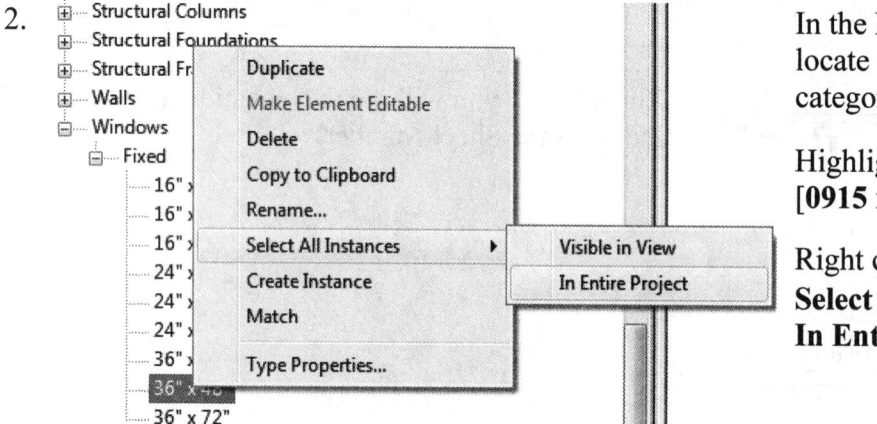   In the Project Browser, locate the *Windows* category.

Highlight **36″ x 48″ [0915 x 1220mm]**.

Right click and select **Select All Instances→ In Entire Project**.

3.   Select **Fixed: 36″ x 24″ [M_Fixed: 0915 x 0610mm]** from the Properties pane Type selector.

Fixed
16" x 24"
16" x 48"
16" x 72"
24" x 24"
24" x 48"
24" x 72"
36" x 24"
36" x 48"
36" x 72"

4.   All the selected windows have been replaced with the new type.

5.

8	36" x 24"	3' - 0"
8	36" x 24"	3' - 0"
8	36" x 24"	3' - 0"
8	36" x 24"	3' - 0"
8	36" x 24"	3' - 0"

Activate the Glazing Schedule sheet. Zoom into the window schedule and you will see that it has automatically updated.

6.   Save as *ex5-8.rvt*.

Exercise 5-9
Export a Schedule

Drawing Name: ex5-8.rvt
Estimated Time: 5 minutes

This exercise reinforces the following skills:

❑ Schedules

1. Open *ex5-8.rvt*.

2. FINISH SCHEDULE   Activate the **Glazing Schedule**.
    Glazing Schedule
    Room Style Schedule

3.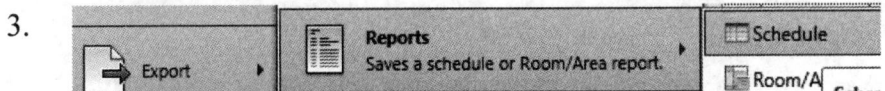

    Go to the Applications Menu.
    Select **File→Export→Reports→Schedule**.

4. File name: Glazing Schedule.txt   The schedule will be saved as a comma delimited text file.
    Files of type: Delimited text (*.txt)
    Browse to your exercise folder.
    Press **Save**.

5. 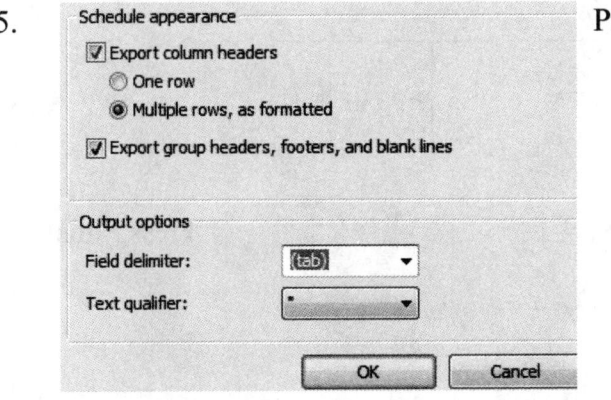   Press **OK**.

6. Launch **Excel**.

7. Open Select **Open**.

8. Text Files   Set the file types to Text **Files**.

9. Glazing Schedule   7/25/2010 4:04 PM   Text Document   10 KB

    Browse to where you saved the file and select it.

10. The Text Wizard has determined that your data is Delimited.

Press **Next**.

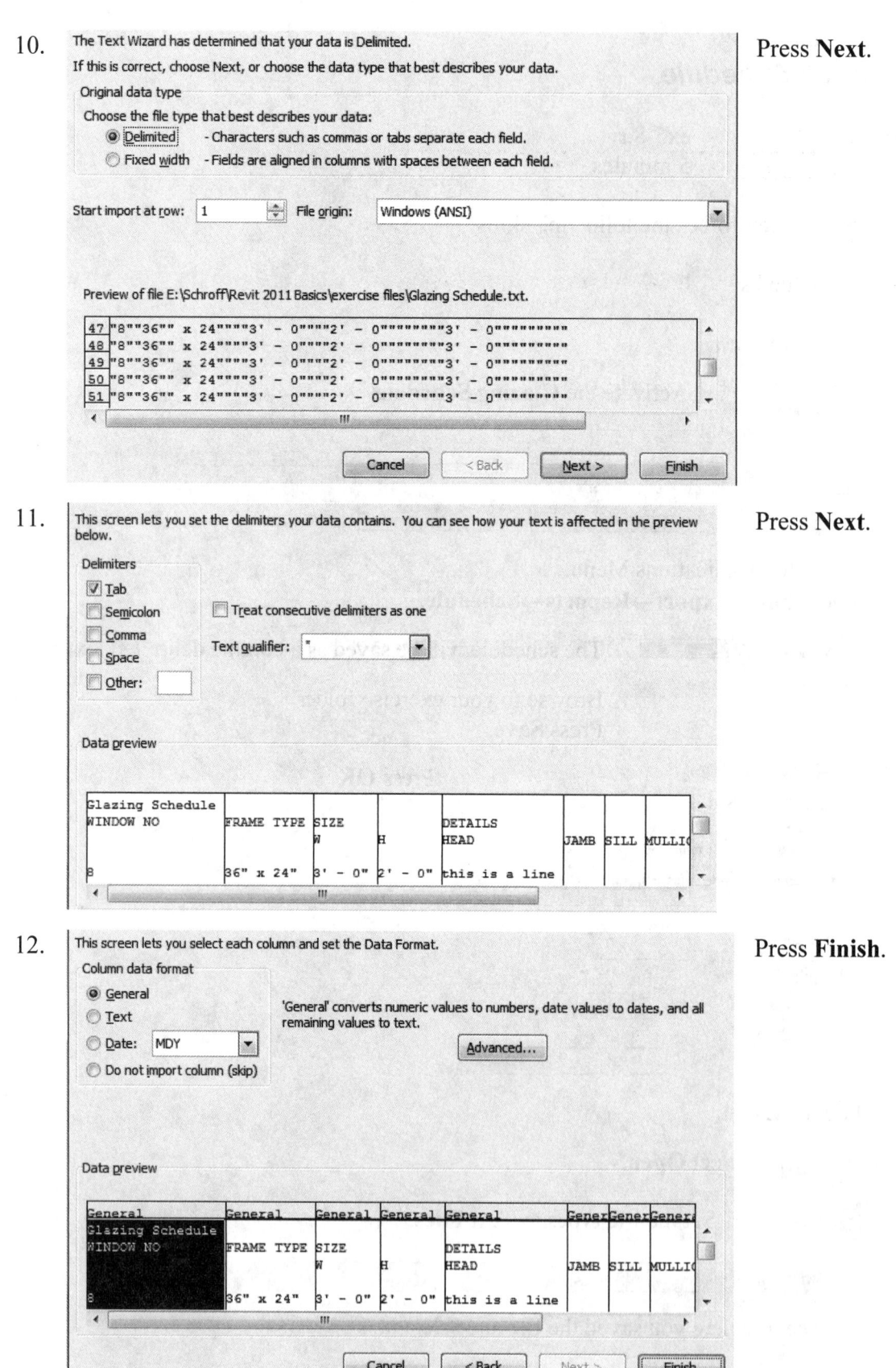

11. This screen lets you set the delimiters your data contains. You can see how your text is affected in the preview below.

Press **Next**.

12. This screen lets you select each column and set the Data Format.

Press **Finish**.

13.

1	Glazing Schedule						
2	WINDOW	FRAME TYPE	SIZE		DETAILS		
3			W	H	HEAD	JAMB	SILL
4							
5	8	36" x 24"	3' - 0"	2' - 0"			2' - 9"
6	8	36" x 24"	3' - 0"	2' - 0"			2' - 9"
7	8	36" x 24"	3' - 0"	2' - 0"			4' - 0"
8	8	36" x 24"	3' - 0"	2' - 0"			4' - 0"
9	8	36" x 24"	3' - 0"	2' - 0"			4' - 0"

The spreadsheet opens.

14. Close the Revit and Excel files without saving.

Notes:

Additional Projects

		FINISH SCHEDULE													
	ROOM	FLOOR		BASE		NORTH WALL		EAST WALL		SOUTH WALL		WEST WALL		CLG	
NO	NAME	MAT	FIN	MAT	FIN	MAT	FIN	MAT	FIN	MAT	FIN	MAT	FIN	MAT	FIN	REMARKS

1)   Using Shared Parameters, create a Finish Schedule for the lavatories.

Door Schedule - Ver 2			
Mark	Type	Count	Remarks
1	36" x 84"	1	Single-Flush
2	36" x 84"	1	Single-Flush
3	36" x 84"	1	Single-Flush
4	36" x 84"	1	Single-Flush
5	72" x 78"	1	Double-Exterior
6	72" x 78"	1	Double-Exterior
7	36" x 84"	1	Single-Flush
8	36" x 84"	1	Single-Flush
9	36" x 84"	1	Single-Flush
10	36" x 84"	1	Single-Flush
	Curtain Wall Dbl Glass	1	Double Glazed

2)   Create a door schedule

Door Schedule 2							
			Rough Opening				
Mark	Type	Level	Rough Height	Rough Width	Material	Lock Jamb	Swing
1	36" x 84"	Level 1			ULTEX/WOOD	CENTER	RIGHT
2	36" x 84"	Level 1			ULTEX/WOOD	THROW	RIGHT
3	36" x 84"	Level 1			ULTEX/WOOD	THROW	LEFT
4	36" x 84"	Level 1			ULTEX/WOOD	THROW	LEFT
5	72" x 78"	Level 1			ULTEX/WOOD	THROW	CENTER
6	72" x 78"	Level 1			ULTEX/WOOD	THROW	CENTER
	Curtain Wall Dbl	Level 1			ULTEX/WOOD	THROW	CENTER
7	36" x 84"	Level 2			ULTEX/WOOD	THROW	LEFT
8	36" x 84"	Level 2			ULTEX/WOOD	THROW	RIGHT
9	36" x 84"	Level 2			ULTEX/WOOD	THROW	RIGHT
10	36" x 84"	Level 2			ULTEX/WOOD	THROW	RIGHT

3)   Create this door schedule.

Notes:

Lesson 5 Quiz

True or False

1. A schedule displays information about elements in a building project in a tabular form.
2. Each property of an element is represented as a field in a schedule.
3. If you replace a model element, the schedule for that element will automatically update.
4. Shared parameters are saved in an Excel spreadsheet.
5. A component schedule is a live view of a model.

Multiple Choice

6. Select the three types of schedules you can create in Revit:

    A. Component
    B. Multi-Category
    C. Key
    D. Symbol

7. Keynotes can be attached to the following:
   Select THREE answers.

    A. Model elements
    B. Detail Components
    C. Materials
    D. Datum

8. Select the tab which is not available on the Schedule Properties dialog:

    A. Fields
    B. Filter
    C. Sorting/Grouping
    D. Formatting
    E. Parameters

9. Schedules are exported in this file format:

    A. Excel
    B. Comma-delimited text
    C. ASCII
    D. DXF

10. To export a schedule:

    A. Right click on a schedule and select **Export**.

    B. Place a schedule on a sheet, select the sheet in the Project Browser, right click and select Export.

    C. Go to the Manage ribbon and select the Export Schedule tool.

    D. On the Application Menu, go to File→Export→Reports→Schedule.

ANSWERS:

    1) T; 2) T; 3) T; 4) F; 5) T; 6) A, B, and C; 7) A, B, and C; 8) E; 9) B; 10) D

Lesson 6
Roofs

Revit provides three methods for creating Roofs: By extrusion or footprint or by face. The extrusion method requires you to sketch an open outline. The footprint method uses exterior walls or a sketch. The face method requires a mass.

Exercise 6-1
Creating a Roof Using Footprint

Drawing Name: ex5-8.rvt
Estimated Time: 15 minutes

This exercise reinforces the following skills:

- ❑ Level
- ❑ Roof
- ❑ Roof Properties
- ❑ Roof Options
- ❑ Isolate Element
- ❑ Select All Instances
- ❑ 3D View

1.   Open *ex5-8.rvt*.

2.   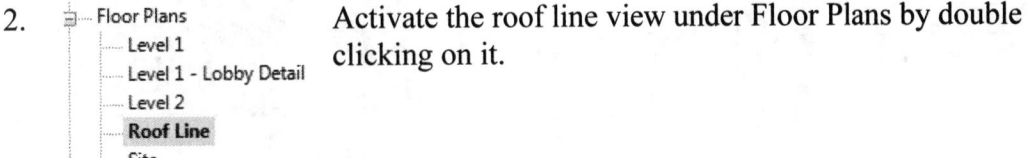   Activate the roof line view under Floor Plans by double clicking on it.

3.   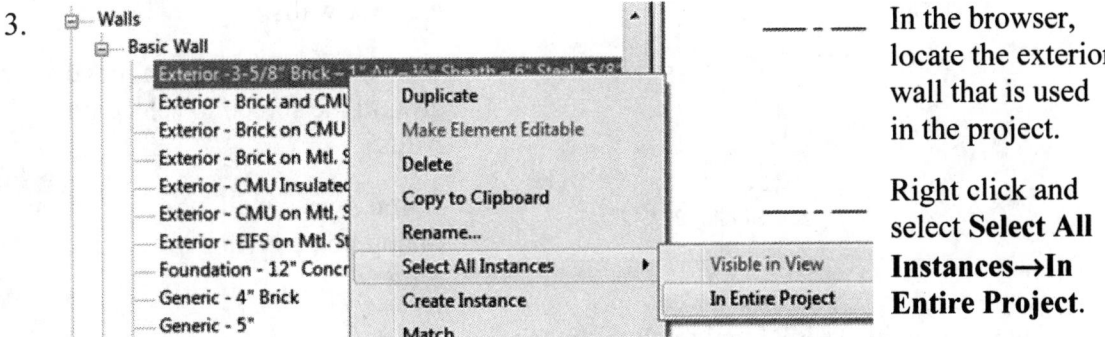   In the browser, locate the exterior wall that is used in the project.

Right click and select **Select All Instances→In Entire Project**.

4.

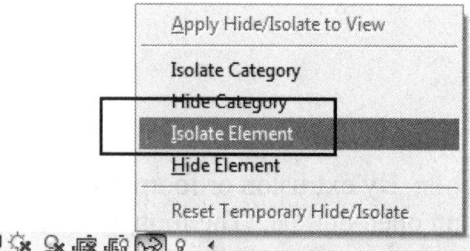

On the status bar:

Select **Isolate element**.

This will turn off the visibility of all elements except for the exterior walls. This will make selecting the walls easier.

You should see the top view of your model with only the exterior walls visible.

You won't see the curtain wall because it is a different wall style.

5.

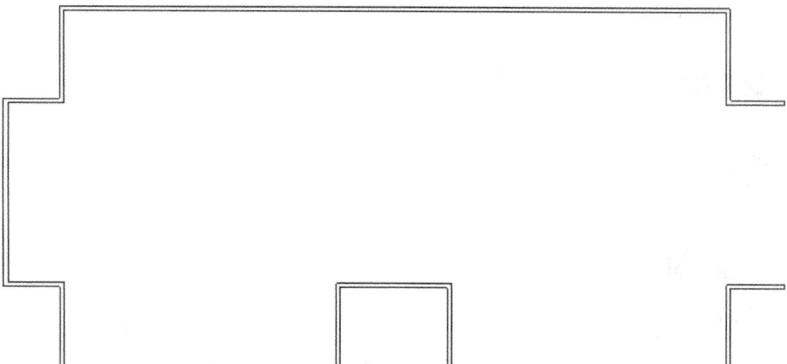

Select **Build→Roof→Roof by Footprint** from the Home ribbon.

Notice that **Pick Walls** is the active mode.

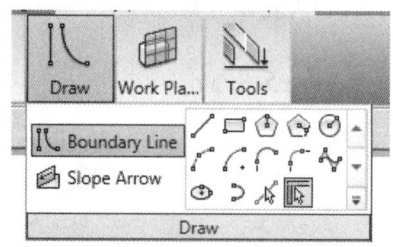

6. You can zoom in and select the exterior walls.

You can pan or scroll to move around the screen to select the walls.

If you miss a wall, you will get a dialog box advising you of the error.

You can use the ALIGN tool to align the roof edge with the exterior side of the wall.

7. ☑ Defines slope   Overhang: 0' 6"   ☑ Extend to wall core

On the options bar, enable **Defines slope**.
Set the Overhang to **6″ [600 mm]**.
Enable **Extend to wall core**.

It is very important to enable the **Extend into wall (to core)** if you want your roof overhang to reference the structure of your wall.

For example, if you want a 2'-0" overhang from the face of the stud, not face of the finish, you want this box checked. The overhang is located based on your pick point. If your pick point is the inside face, the overhang will be calculated from the interior finish face.

The angle symbols indicate the roof slope.

8. 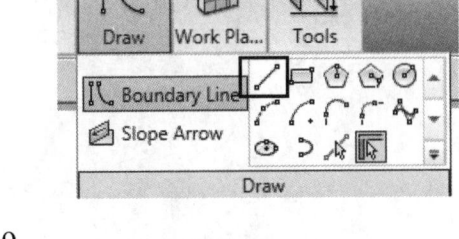 Select the **Line** tool from the Draw panel.

9.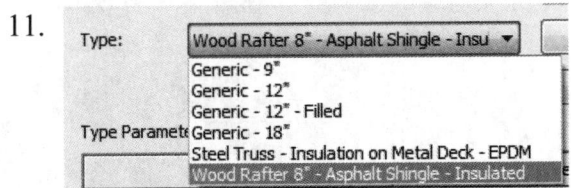

Draw a line to close the sketch.

Check the sketch to make sure there are no gaps or intersecting lines.

10. Edit Type   Select **Edit Type** from the Properties pane.

11. Type: Wood Rafter 8" - Asphalt Shingle - Insu
Generic - 9"
Generic - 12"
Generic - 12" - Filled
Type Parameter Generic - 18"
Steel Truss - Insulation on Metal Deck - EPDM
Wood Rafter 8" - Asphalt Shingle - Insulated

Select the **Wood Rafter 8" – Asphalt Shingle – Insulated [Warm Roof - Timber]** under Type.

Press **OK**.

12. Mode   Select **Green Check** under Mode.

13.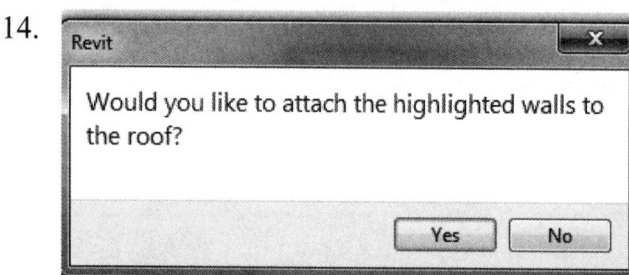

This dialog will appear if you missed a wall.

You can press the **Show** button and Revit will highlight the wall you missed.

14.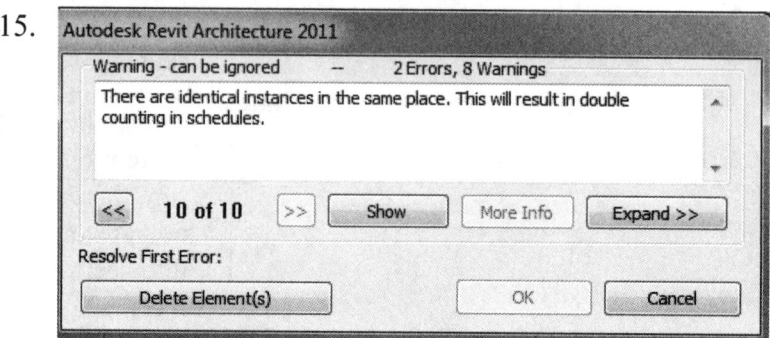

A dialog will appear. Press **Yes**.

15.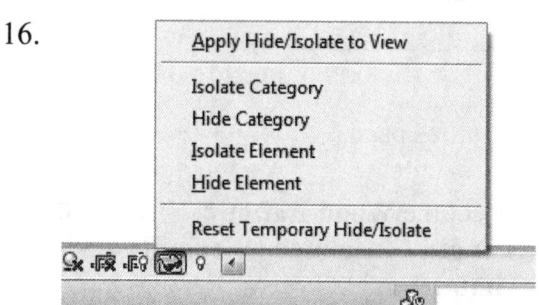

If you get an error message like this, press **Delete Elements** to delete any conflicting elements.

16.

> Apply Hide/Isolate to View
>
> Isolate Category
> Hide Category
> Isolate Element
> Hide Element
>
> Reset Temporary Hide/Isolate

On the Display bar:

Select **Reset Temporary Hide/Isolate**.

17. Go to **3D View**.

18.

> Wireframe
> Hidden Line
> Shaded
> Shaded with Edges
> Consistent Colors
> Realistic
>
> 1/8" = 1'-0"

Enable **View→Realistic**.

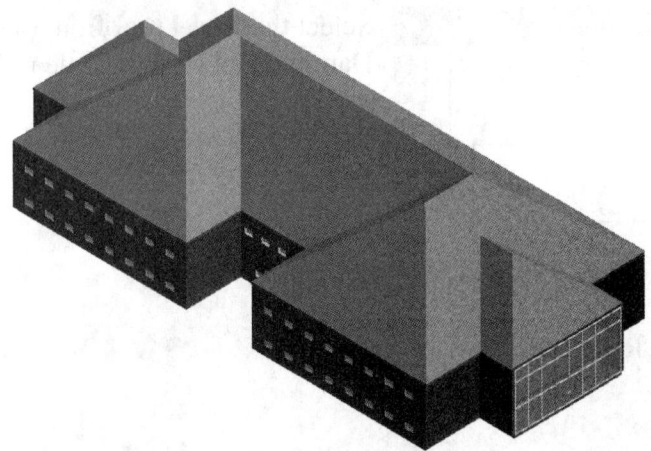

We can now inspect our roof.

19. Save as *ex6-1.rvt*.

TIP: The **Cutoff Level Property** defines the distance above or below the level at which the roof is cut off.

Roofs (1)	
Constraints	
Base Level	Roof Line
Room Bounding	☑
Related to Mass	☐
Base Offset From Level	0' 0"
Cutoff Level	None
Cutoff Offset	0' 0"

Exercise 6-2
Modifying a Roof

Drawing Name: ex6-1.rvt
Estimated Time: 10 minutes

This exercise reinforces the following skills:

- Modifying Roofs
- Edit Sketch
- Align Eaves
- Roof
- Work Plane

1. Open or continue working in *ex6-1.rvt*.

2. Elevations (Building Elevation) Activate the East elevation.
   - **East**
   - North
   - South
   - South - Lobby
   - West

3. 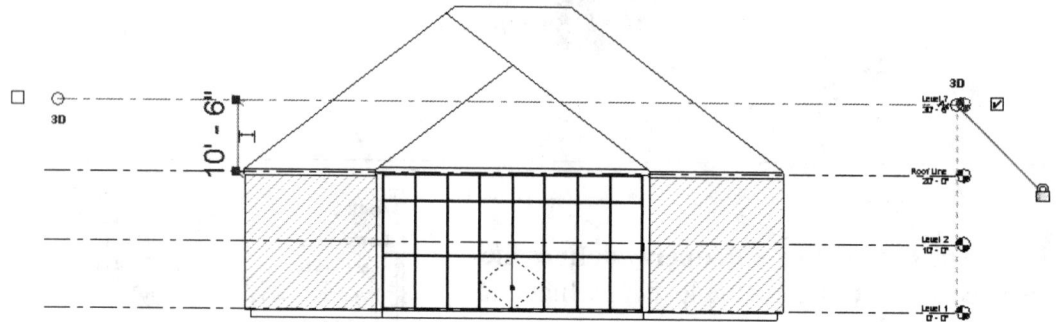 Select the **Level** tool from the Datum panel on the Home ribbon.

4. Add a level 10′ 6″ above the Roof Line level.

5. 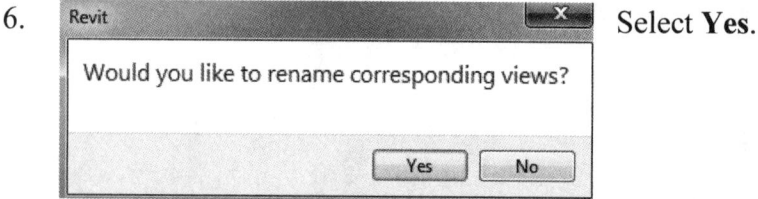 Rename the Level **Roof Cutoff**.

6. 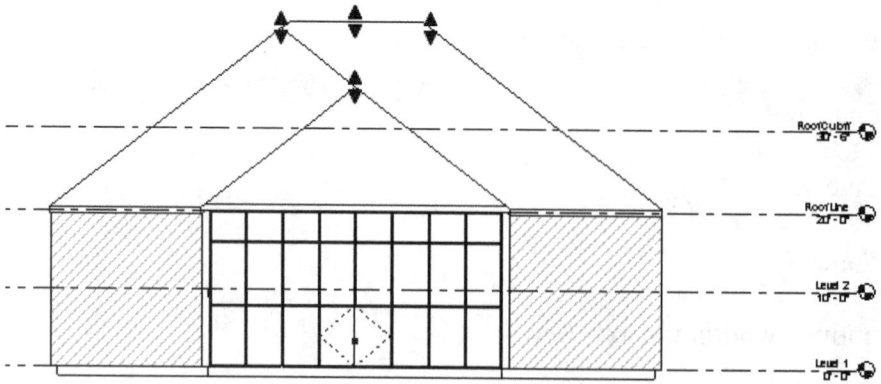 Select **Yes**.

Would you like to rename corresponding views?

7. Select the roof so it is highlighted.

8.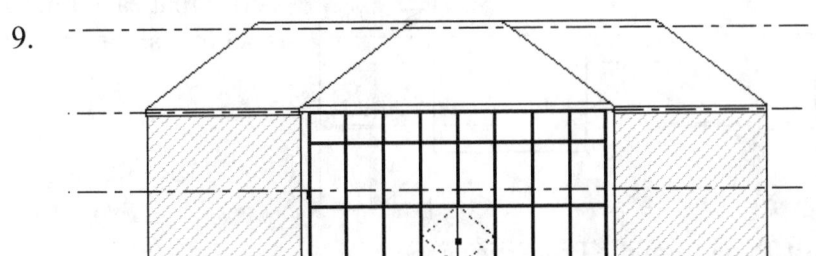

On the Properties pane:

Set the Cutoff Level to **Roof Cutoff**.

9.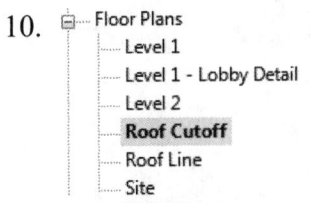

Note how the roof adjusts.

10.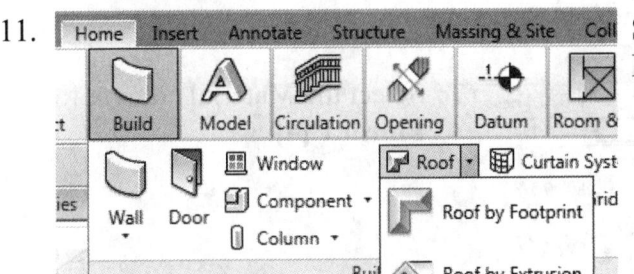

Activate the **Roof Cutoff** view under Floor Plans.

11.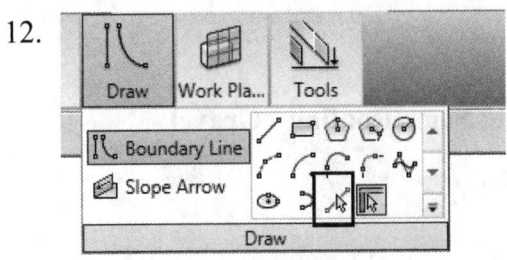

Select **Build→Roof→Roof by Footprint** from the Home ribbon.

12.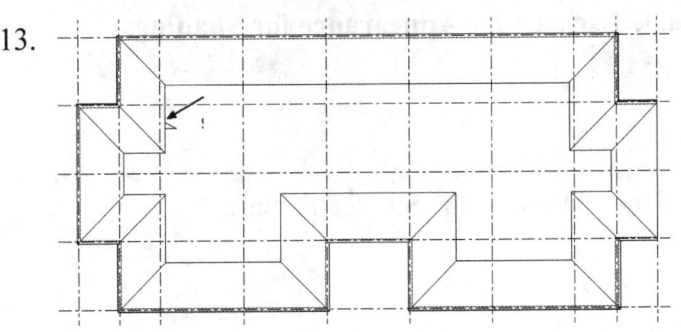

Select **Pick Lines** from the Draw panel.

13.

Pick an edge.

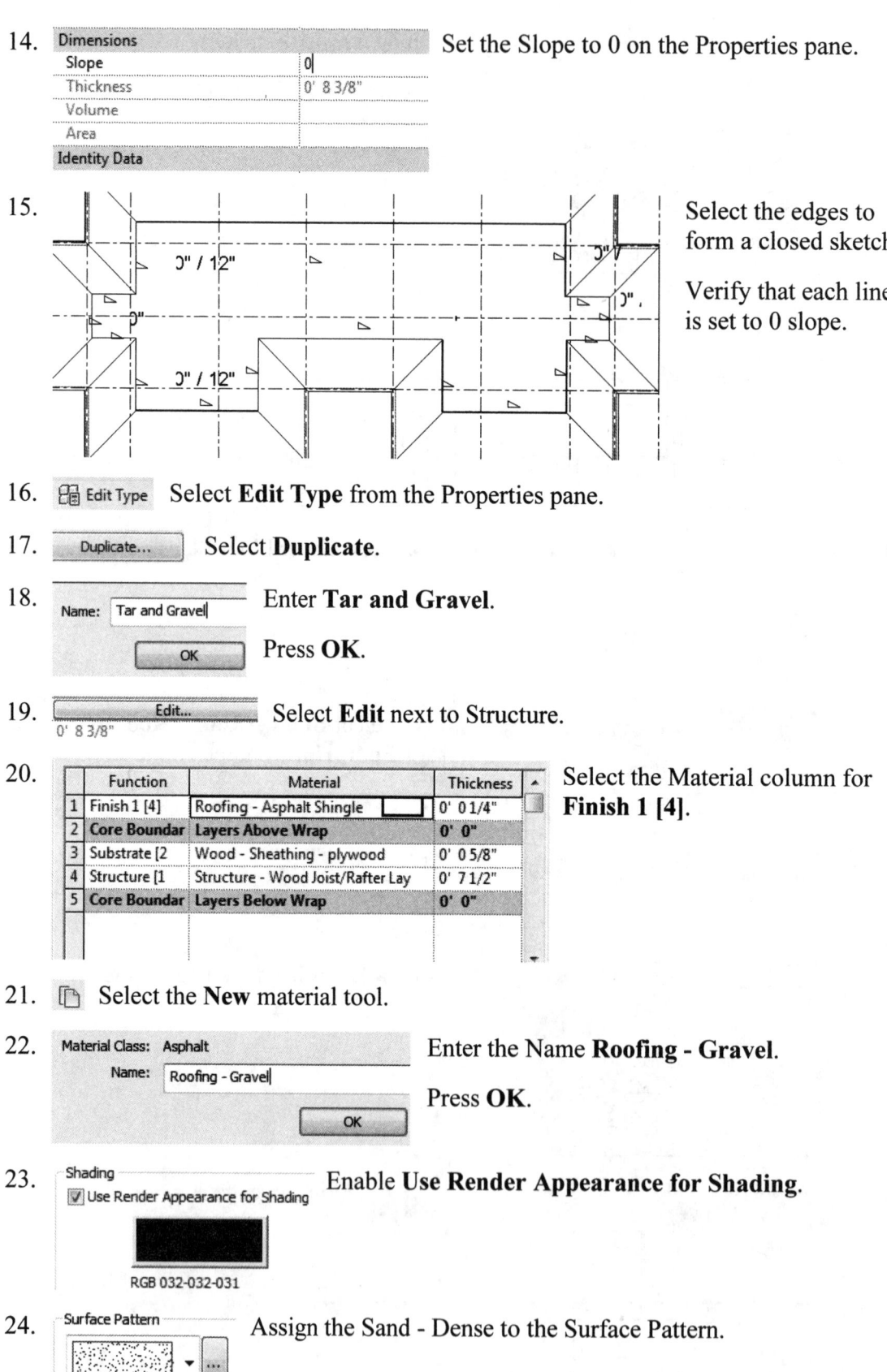

14. Set the Slope to 0 on the Properties pane.

15. Select the edges to form a closed sketch.

Verify that each line is set to 0 slope.

16. Select **Edit Type** from the Properties pane.

17. Select **Duplicate**.

18. Enter **Tar and Gravel**.

Press **OK**.

19. Select **Edit** next to Structure.

20. Select the Material column for **Finish 1 [4]**.

	Function	Material	Thickness
1	Finish 1 [4]	Roofing - Asphalt Shingle	0' 0 1/4"
2	Core Boundar	Layers Above Wrap	0' 0"
3	Substrate [2	Wood - Sheathing - plywood	0' 0 5/8"
4	Structure [1	Structure - Wood Joist/Rafter Lay	0' 7 1/2"
5	Core Boundar	Layers Below Wrap	0' 0"

21. Select the **New** material tool.

22. Enter the Name **Roofing - Gravel**.

Press **OK**.

23. Enable **Use Render Appearance for Shading**.

24. Assign the Sand - Dense to the Surface Pattern.

25.

Render Appearance Based On:	
Aggregate - High	Replace...

Select the Render Appearance tab.

Select the **Replace** button.

26.

Gravel - Mix...

Select the **Gravel - Mixed** material.

27.

Division 31		Earthwork
	31 05 00	Common Work Results for Earthwork
	31 23 00	Excavation and Fill
	31 23 00.A1	Undisturbed Soil
	31 23 00.A2	Compacted Soil
	31 23 00.B1	Gravel
	31 23 00.B2	Compacted Gravel Sub-Base
	31 23 00.B3	Crushed Stone

Select the Identity tab.

Assign **Gravel** to the keynote.

28.

Annotation Information	
Keynote:	31 23 00.B1
Mark:	G

Enter **G** for the Mark.

Press **OK**.

29.

	Function	Material	Thickness
1	Finish 1 [4]	Roofing - Gravel	0' 0 1/4"
2	Core Boundar	Layers Above Wrap	0' 0"
3	Membrane	Roofing - EPDM Membrane	0' 0"
4	Substrate [2	Wood - Sheathing - plywood	0' 0 5/8"
5	Structure [1	Structure - Wood Joist/Rafter Lay	0' 7 1/2"
6	Core Boundar	Layers Below Wrap	0' 0"

Add a layer for the Membrane.

Set the Material to **Roofing - EPDM Membrane**.

Set the Membrane thickness to **0"**.

Press **OK**.

30.

Graphics	
Coarse Scale Fill Pattern	Sand - Dense
Coarse Scale Fill Color	Black

Assign the **Sand - Dense** to the Coarse Scale Fill Pattern.

Press **OK**.

31.  Select the **Green Check** under the Model panel to **Finish Roof**.

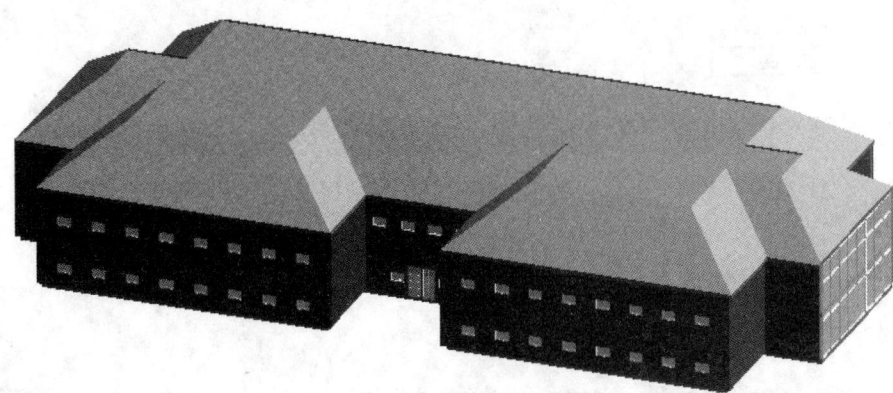

32. Save as *ex6-2.rvt*.

Exercise 6-3
Adding Roof Components

Drawing Name: ex6-2.rvt
Estimated Time: 10 minutes

This exercise reinforces the following skills:

- ❑ Window
- ❑ Load from Library
- ❑ Array

1.   Open or continue working in *ex6-2.rvt*.

2.
```
Floor Plans
    Level 1
    Level 1 - Lobby Detail
    Level 2
    Roof Cutoff
    Roof Line
    Site
```
Activate **Roof Cutoff** view.

3.   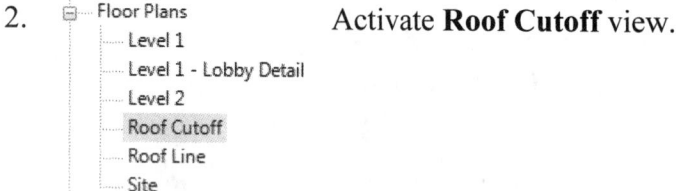   Activate **Window** mode from the Build panel on the Home ribbon.

4.   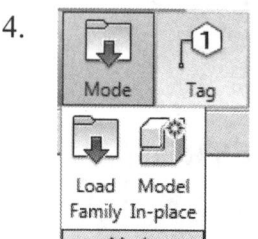   Select **Load Family** from the Mode panel.

5.   Browse to the *Windows* folder.

6.
File name: Skylight.rfa
Files of type: Family Files (*.rfa)

File name: M_Skylight.rfa
Files of type: Family Files (*.rfa)

Locate the *Skylight.rfa [M_Skylight.rfa]* file. Press **Open**.

7.   Select **Skylight.rfa: 28″ x 38″ [M_Skylight: 1180 x 1170mm]** from the type drop-down.

Skylight
28" x 38"

8. 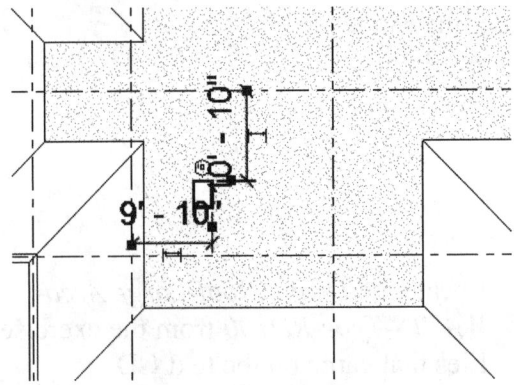 Place the skylight on the section of top roof.

9. 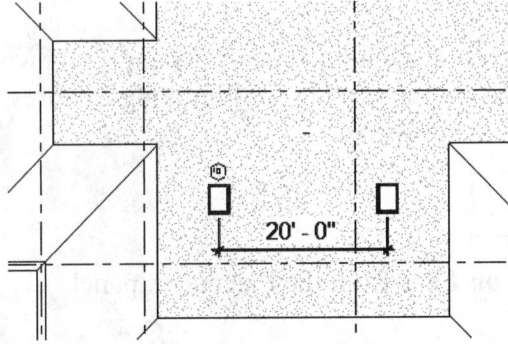 Using the **ARRAY** tool, place a total of two skylights.

Locate the skylights so they are **20′ [6096mm]** apart.

10. Mirror the skylights to the other side of the roof.

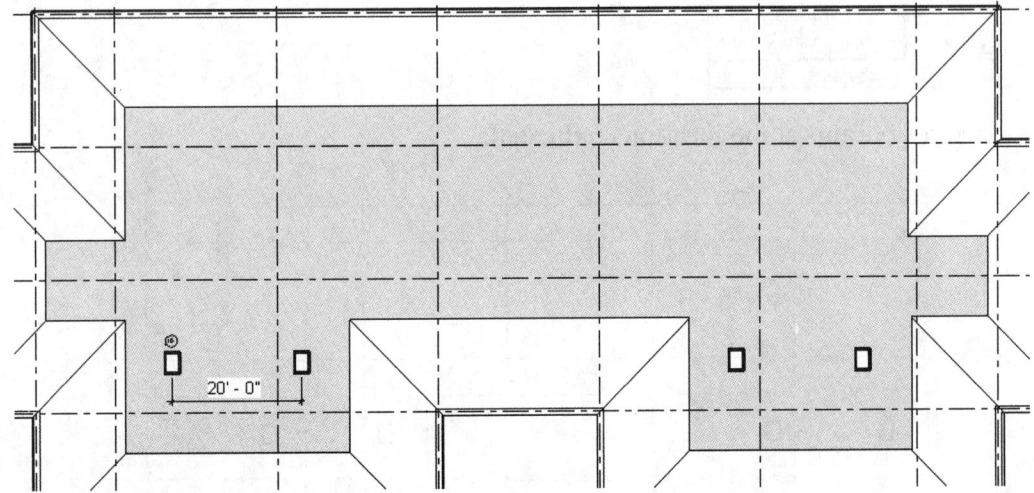

11. 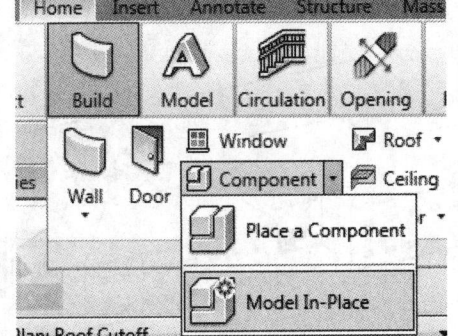 Select **Place a Component** from the Build panel on the Home ribbon.

12. 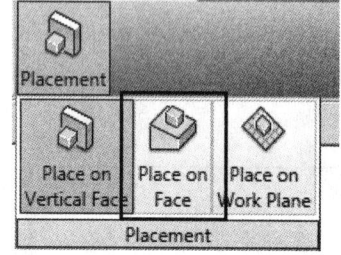 Select **Load Family** under the Mode panel.

13.

File name:	Drain-Roof-Large_Area-WATTS-Type_RD100
Files of type:	All Supported Files (*.rfa, *.adsk)

Locate the *Drain- Roof-Large Area- WATTS-Type-RD100* from the exercise files that came on the text CD.

Press **Open**.

14.

There is no tag loaded for Plumbing Fixtures. Do you want to load one now?

Yes   No

If a dialog appears asking if you want to load a tag for Plumbing Fixtures, press **No**.

15. Select **Place on Face** from the Placement panel.

16. Place roof drains at the locations indicated.

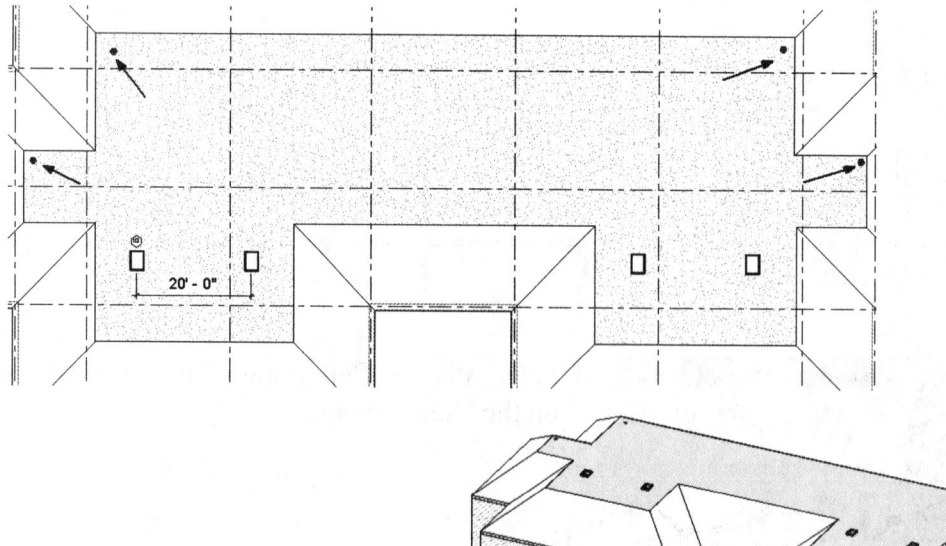

17. Save the file as *ex6-3.rvt*.

Exercise 6-4
Creating a Gable

Drawing Name: ex6-3.rvt
Estimated Time: 60 minutes

This exercise reinforces the following skills:

- Edit Elevation Profile
- Work Plane
- Create Roof from Extrusion
- Detach/Attach Walls to Roof
- Join/Unjoin Roof
- Window
- Load from Library

1. Open or continue working in *ex6-3.rvt*.

2. Elevations (Building Elevation)
     East
     North
     South
     South - Lobby
     West

    Select the **South** Elevation.

3.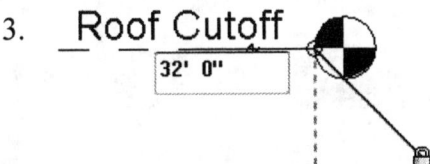

    Change the Roof Cutoff Elevation to **32'-0"**.

4. Go to **3D View**.

    Go to **Rotate the view to a Southeast view**.

5. Pick the wall indicated so it highlights.

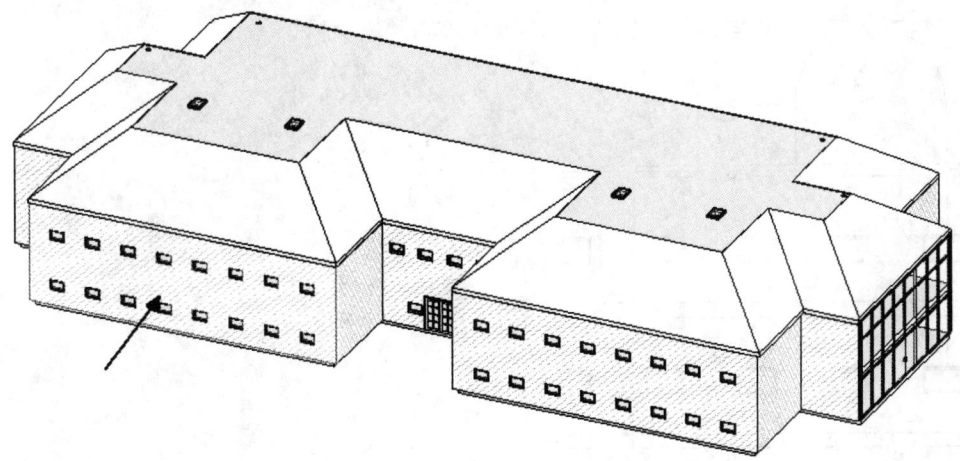

6. 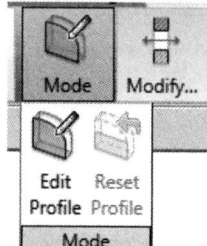 Select **Edit Profile** under the Mode panel.

7. 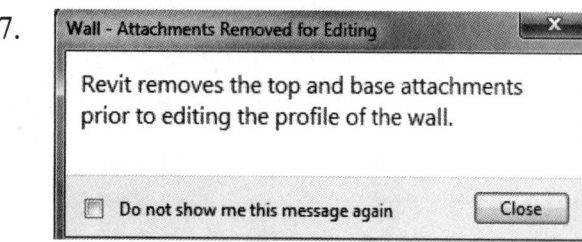 A message will appear.

Press **Close**.

8. Elevations (Building Elevation)
   - East
   - North
   - **South**
   - South - Lobby
   - West

Activate the **South** Elevation.

9. Select the **Line** and **Arc** tools from the Draw panel to modify the profile.

10. Sketch an arc with a **12′ [3000 mm]** diameter on the top of the wall. Set the vertical line to be **5′ [1524 mm]**.

Be sure to delete any line segments that may be self-intersecting.

11.

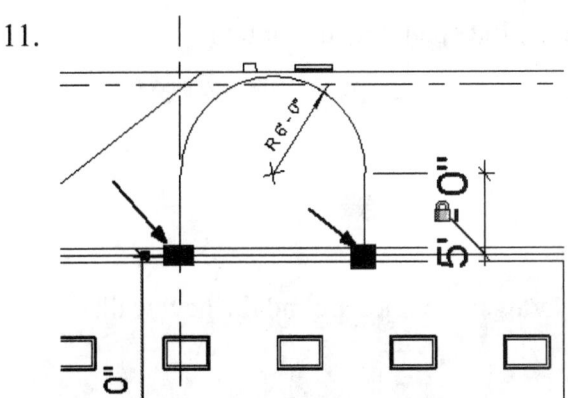

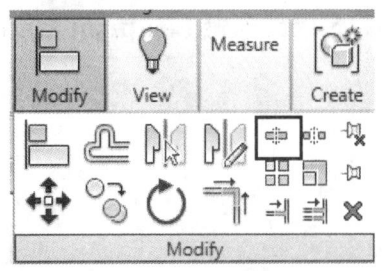

To do this, use the SPLIT tool to divide the top wall line at the intersecting points and then delete the short line.

12. 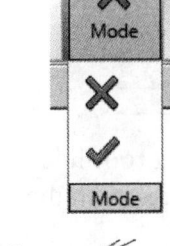 Select the **Green Check** on the Mode panel to **Finish Wall**.

13.

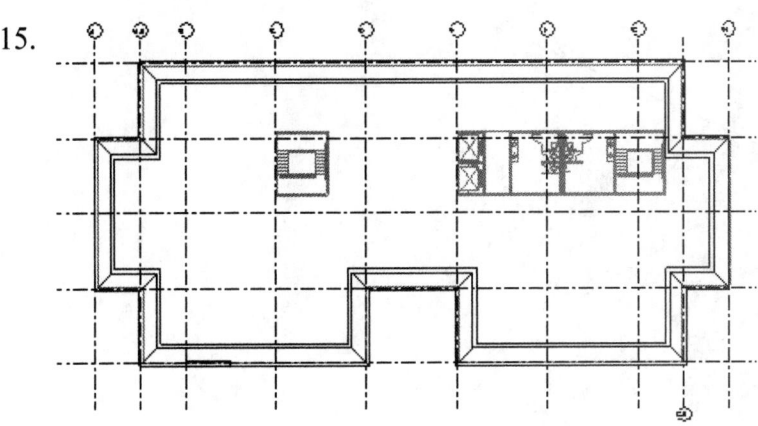

We see the modified wall.

We need to modify the roof slightly to accommodate the new wall.

14.

Floor Plans
- Level 1
- Level 1 - Lobby Detail
- Level 2
- Roof Cutoff
- Roof Line
- Site

Switch to **Roof Line** Floor Plan.

15.

Select the roof so it highlights.

16.  Select **Edit Footprint** from the Mode panel on the ribbon.

17. 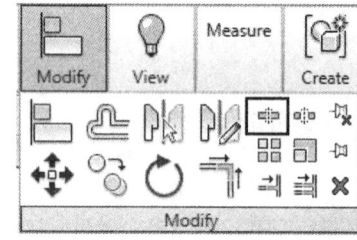 Draw three lines around the new wall.

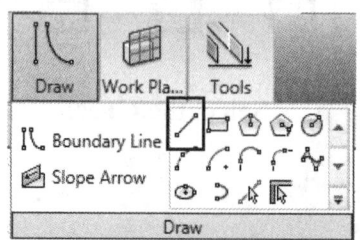

18.  Use the SPLIT tool to modify the existing roof line. Then delete the small section that interferes with the wall.

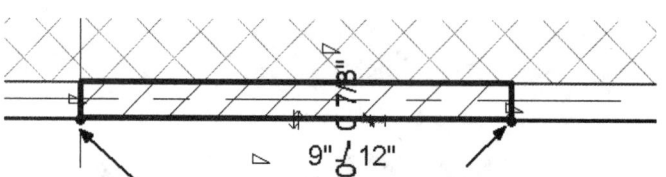

19. Select the **Green Check** on the Mode panel to **Finish Roof**.

20. 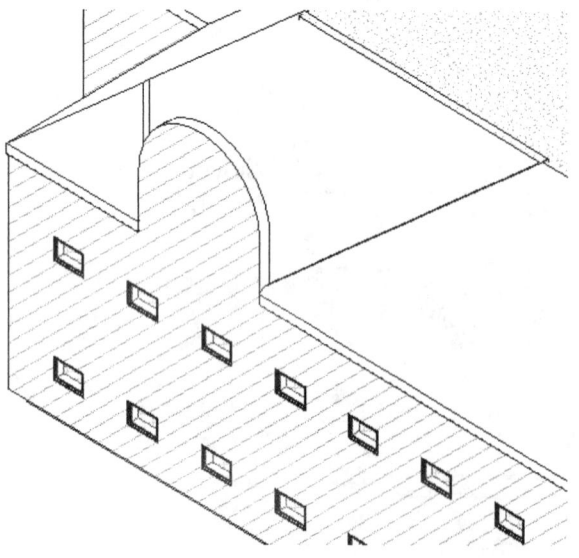 Now there is no interference between the roof and the wall.

21. Switch to **Roof Line** Floor Plan.

```
Floor Plans
    Level 1
    Level 1 - Lobby Detail
    Level 2
    Roof Cutoff
    Roof Line
    Site
```

22.

```
Basic Wall
Exterior -3-5/8" Brick – 1" Air – ½" Sheath – 6" Steel- 5/8"
Gypsum
```

Set the wall type to the **Exterior -3- 5/8″ Brick - 1″ Air - 1/2″ Sheath = 6″ Steel = 5/8″ Gypsum** using the Properties pane.

23.

```
Height: Uncon ▼  5' 0"    |    Location Line: Finish Face: Int ▼    ▢
```

On the Options bar:
Set the Height to 5′ 0″ [**1524mm**].
Set the Location Line to **Finish Face: Interior**.

24. Draw two walls.
Align with the new wall ends.

25. Switch back to a **3D View**.

26.  Use the ALIGN tool if needed to align the walls.

27. Select a wall so it highlights in red.

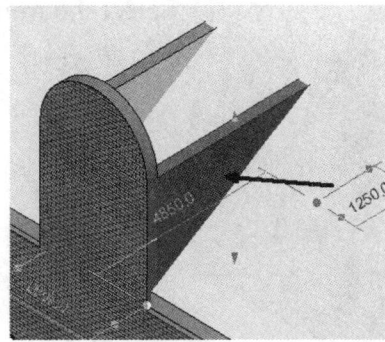

28. 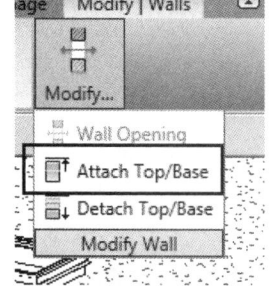 Select the **Attach** tool on the Modify Wall panel on the ribbon.

29. 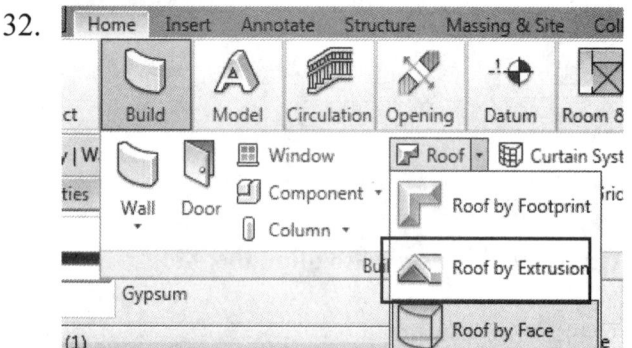 Select the **Base** option on the lower left status bar.

30. Select the Roof face where the roof attaches.

31. 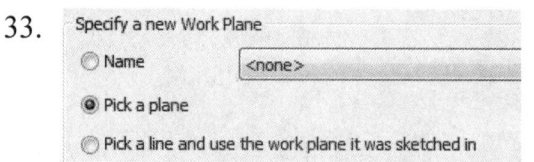 The gable wall trims so it meets the roof properly.

    Repeat for the other wall.

32. On the Home ribbon, select **Build→Roof→Roof by Extrusion**.

33. Enable **Pick a Plane**.

    Press **OK**.

34. 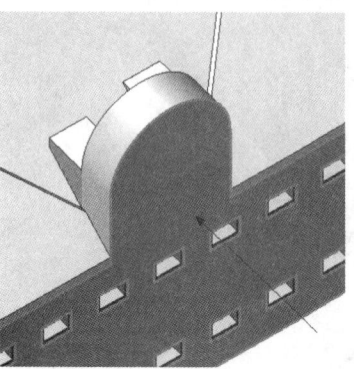 Select the front of the arched wall as the work plane.

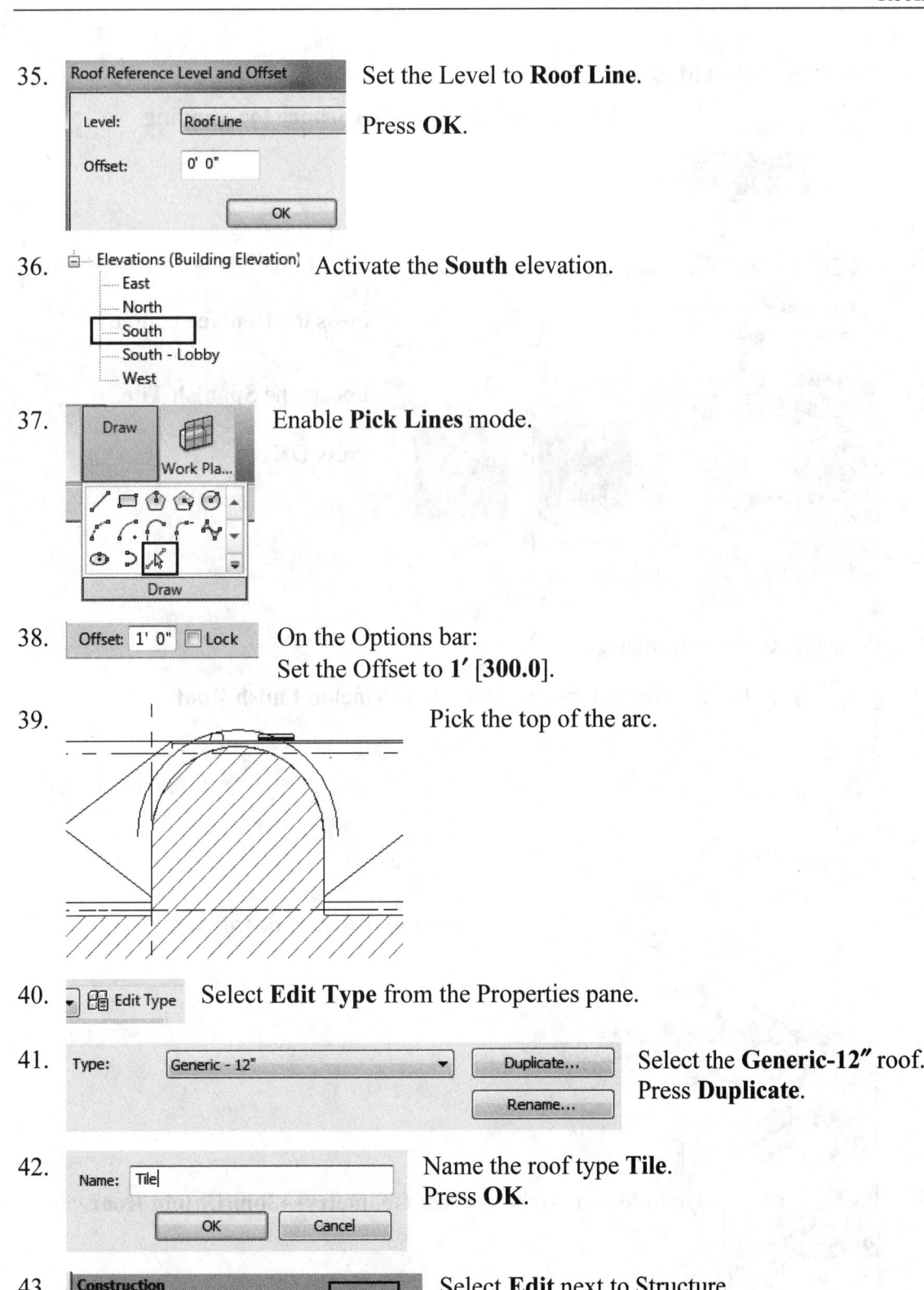

35. Set the Level to **Roof Line**.

Press **OK**.

36. Activate the **South** elevation.

37. Enable **Pick Lines** mode.

38. On the Options bar:
Set the Offset to **1′ [300.0]**.

39. Pick the top of the arc.

40. Select **Edit Type** from the Properties pane.

41. Select the **Generic-12″** roof.
Press **Duplicate**.

42. Name the roof type **Tile**.
Press **OK**.

43. Select **Edit** next to Structure.

44. Select the **Material** column next to Structure.

45.  Select **Masonry - Tile**.

46. Shading
☑ Use Render Appearance for Shading   Enable **Use Render Appearance for Shading**.

RGB 084-083-086

47. | Graphics | Render Appearance | Identity | Physical |

Render Appearance Based On:
Spanish Tile - Red 3   [Replace...]

Select the Render Appearance tab.
Press the **Replace** button.

48.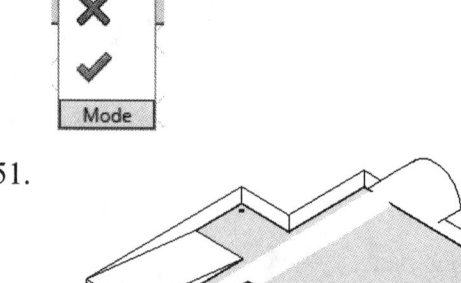

Plastic
Roofing
Siding
Sitework
Stone
Stone - Granite
Stone - Marble
Stucco
Wall Covering

Spanish Tile...   Standing Se...

[88] ▾   Swatch Size

Locate the **Spanish Tile**.

Press **OK**.

49. Press **OK** to close the dialog.

50. 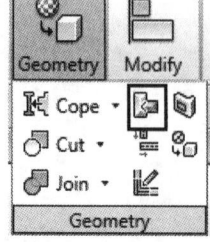 Select the **Green Check** on the Mode panel to **Finish Roof**.

51. 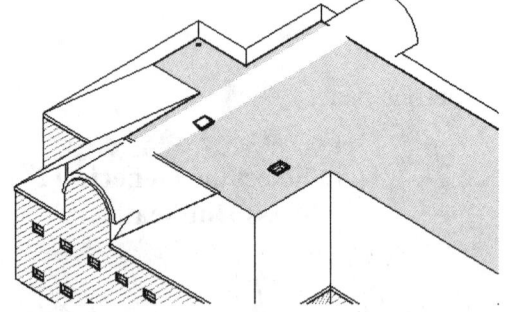   The roof needs to be trimmed.

52. Go to **Modify** ribbon, select **Geometry→Join/Unjoin Roof**.

Geometry   Modify

Cope ▾
Cut ▾
Join ▾

Geometry

In the lower left corner of your screen you will see a prompt instructing you to select the edge of the roof to trim.

53.

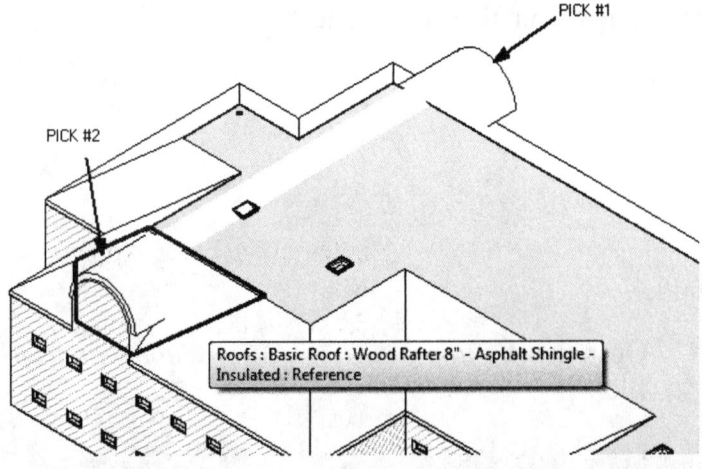

Pick the edge of the roof that is extending too far.

PICK #1

PICK #2

Roofs : Basic Roof : Wood Rafter 8" - Asphalt Shingle - Insulated : Reference

54. Select the face on another roof or a wall to which you want the first roof to be joined.

In the lower left corner of your screen you will see a prompt instructing you to select the face of the roof to be used as the cutting edge.

55. Select the face of the sloped roof.

56.

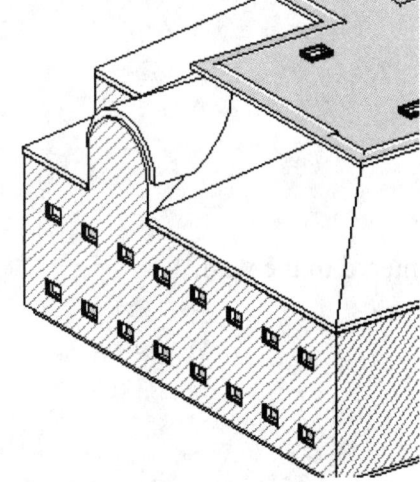

The roof is trimmed properly now for the gable.

TIP: The **Join/Unjoin Roof** command can not be used to join or unjoin a wall to a roof. Use the Attach/Detach tool for that operation. The Join/Unjoin Roof command is used to join one roof to another roof.

57.

Select the **Window** tool from the Build panel on Home ribbon.

58. 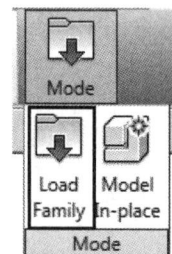 Select **Load Family** from the Mode panel.

59. Browse to the *Windows* folder.

60.  Open the *Archtop with Trim [M_Archtop with trim]* file.

61. Select the **36″ x 48″ [1220 x 2438mm]** size from the drop-down list.

```
16" x 24"
16" x 48"
16" x 72"
24" x 24"
24" x 48"
24" x 72"
36" x 24"
36" x 48"
36" x 72"
```

62.  Place the window so it is centered in the wall.

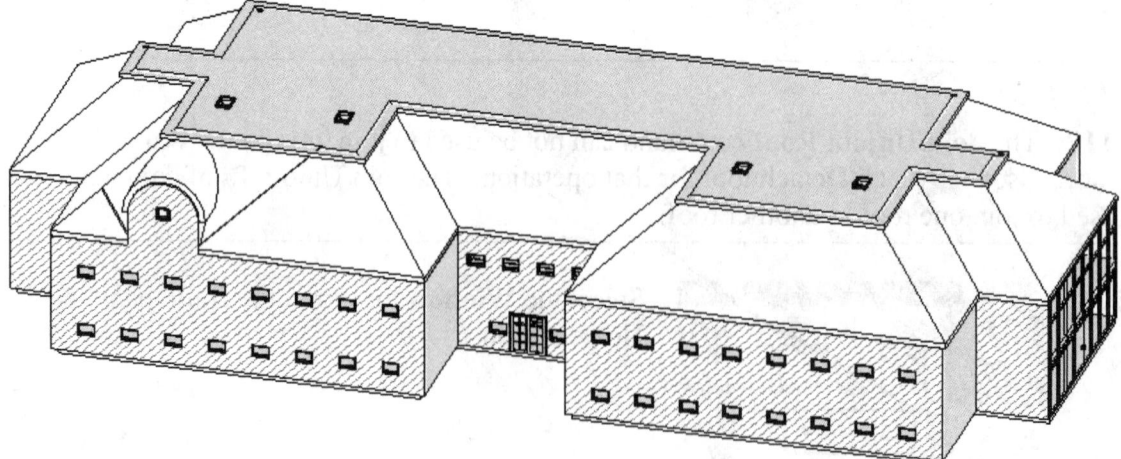

63. Save the file as *ex6-4.rvt*.

Lesson 6 Quiz

True or False

1. A roof footprint is a 2-D sketch.
2. When creating a roof by extrusion, the sketch must be closed.
3. When placing a roof by footprint, you must specify the work plane to place the sketch.
4. When you create a roof by extrusion, you can extend the extrusion toward or away from the view.
5. The Join/Unjoin Roof tool can be used to join two roofs together.

Multiple Choice

6. Roofs can be created using the following options:
   Select three:

   A. Roof by footprint
   B. Roof by extrusion
   C. Roof by face
   D. Roof by sketch

7. The Join/Unjoin roof tool is located:

   A. On the Modify panel of the Modify ribbon.
   B. On the Build panel of the Home ribbon.
   C. On the Geometry panel of the Modify ribbon.
   D. On the right shortcut menu when the roof is selected.

8. When creating a roof sketch you can use any of the following EXCEPT:

   A. Pick wall.
   B. Lines
   C. Arcs
   D. Circles

9. In order to attach a wall to a roof which is above the wall, you should use this option:

   A. Base Attach
   B. Top Attach
   C. Edit Profile
   D. Join/Unjoin

10. The Properties pane for a roof displays the roof:

        A. Area
        B. Weight
        C. Elevation
        D. Function

ANSWERS:
   1) T; 2) F; 3) F; 4) T; 5) T; 6) A, B, & C; 7) C; 8) D; 9) B; 10) A

Lesson 7
Elevations & Plans

Exercise 7-1
Creating Elevation Documents

Drawing Name: 6-4.rvt
Estimated Time: 10 minutes

This exercise reinforces the following skills:

- Sheet
- Add View
- Changing Visibility

1. 📂 Open *ex6-4.rvt*.

2. View Activate the **View** ribbon.

3. Select **Sheet** from Sheet Composition panel to add a new sheet.

4. File name: D 22 x 34 Horizontal.rfa Select the **D 22 x 34 Horizontal [A3 metric]** title block.

   File name: A3 metric.rfa

5. Select a titleblock
   D 22 x 34 Horizontal
   E1 30 x 42 Horizontal : E1 30x42 Horizontal

   Select **D 22 x 34 Horizontal [A3 metric]** titleblock. Press **OK**.

6. | Sheet Number | A105 |
   | Sheet Name | Exterior Elevations |
   | Sheet Issue Date | 07/20/10 |

   In the Properties pane:

   Change the Sheet Name to **Exterior Elevations**.

7. Elevations (Building Elevation)
   East
   North
   South
   South - Lobby
   West

   Locate the North and South Elevations in the Project Browser.

8.

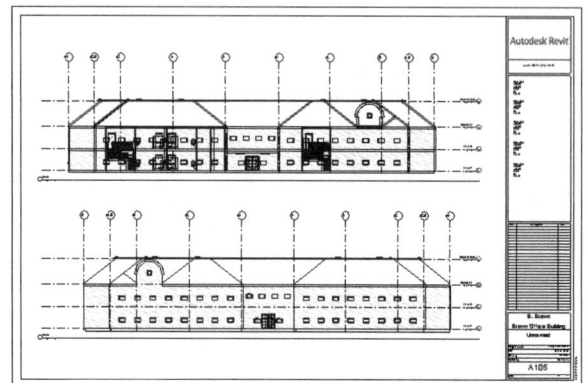

Drag and drop the North and South Elevations from the browser onto the sheet.
The top elevation will be the North elevation.
The bottom elevation will be the South Elevation.

You may notice that some entities are visible in the view, which you do not want to see, like the stairs inside.

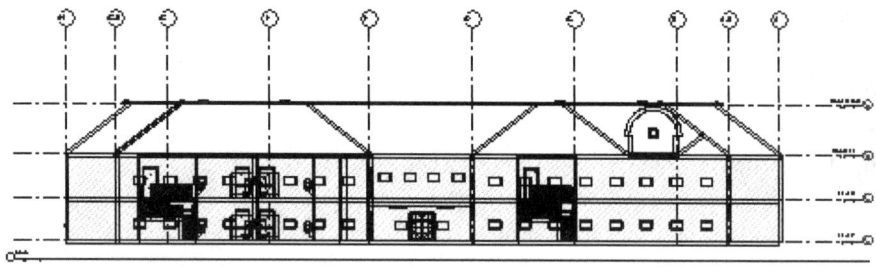

Let's look at the **North** Elevation first.

9.

Detail Number	1
Rotation on Sheet	None
Visibility/Graphics Overrides	Edit...
Visual Style	Wireframe
Graphic Display Options	Wireframe
Hide at scales coarser than	Hidden Line
Discipline	Shaded
Color Scheme Location	Shaded with Edges
Color Scheme	Consistent Colors
	Realistic

Select the **North** Elevation View on the sheet.

In the Properties pane:
Set the Visual Style to **Hidden Line**.

10.

Rotation on Sheet	None
Visibility/Graphics Overrides	Edit...
Visual Style	Hidden Line
Graphic Display Options	Edit...
Hide at scales coarser than	1" = 400'-0"

Select **Edit** next to Visibility/Graphics Overrides.

11.

☑ Generic Model Tags
☐ Grids
☑ Levels

Under Annotation Categories, disable Grids and Sections.

Press **OK**.

12.

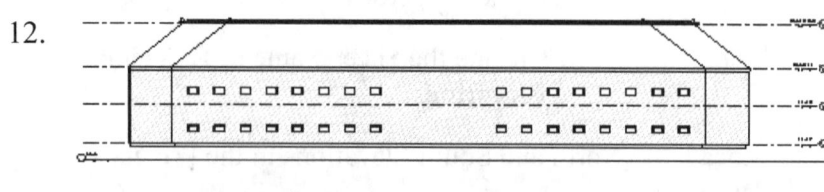

The North Elevation now looks more appropriate.

13.

Repeat for the other elevation view.

14. Save as *ex7-1.rvt*.

Exercise 7-2
Using Line Work

Drawing Name: 7-1.rvt
Estimated Time: 15 minutes

This exercise reinforces the following skills:

-   Activate View
-   Linework tool
-   Line Styles
-   Line Weight

1.   Open *ex7-1.rvt.*

2.
Sheets (all)
    A101 - First Level Floor Plan
    A102 - Door Schedule
    A103 - Glazing Schedule
    A104 - Finish Schedule
    A105 - Exterior Elevations
       Activate the **Exterior** Elevations sheet.

3.   Activate View   Select the top elevation view (**North**).
Right click and select **Activate View**.

Activate View works similarly to Model Space/Paper Space mode in AutoCAD.

4.   Modify   Select the **Modify** ribbon.

5.   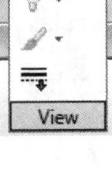 Massing & Site   Select the **Linework** tool from the View panel.

6. 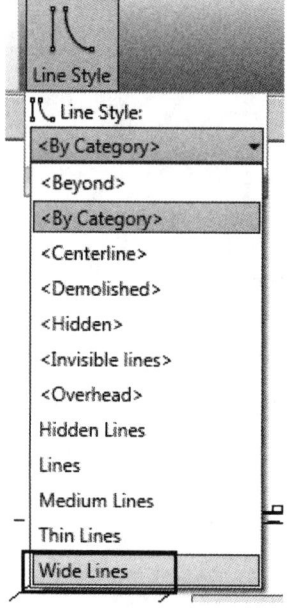 Select **Wide Lines** from the Line Style panel on the ribbon.

7. 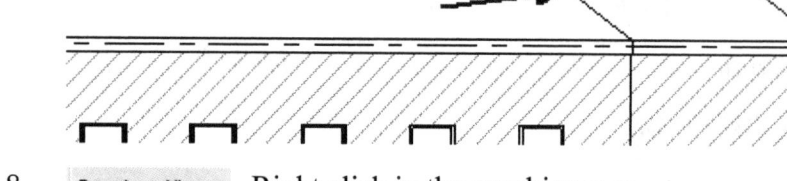 Select the Roof lines.

8. Deactivate View   Right click in the graphics area.
   Select **Deactivate View**.

9. Manage   Activate the **Manage** ribbon.

10. 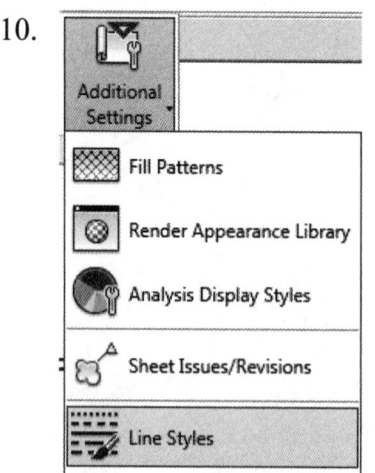 Go to **Settings→Additional Settings→Line Styles**.

   Move the dialog out of the way so you can see what happens when you apply the new line weight.

11.
Medium Lines	3
Thin Lines	1
Wide Lines	16

   Set the Line Weight for Wide Lines to **16**.
   Press **Apply**.

12. 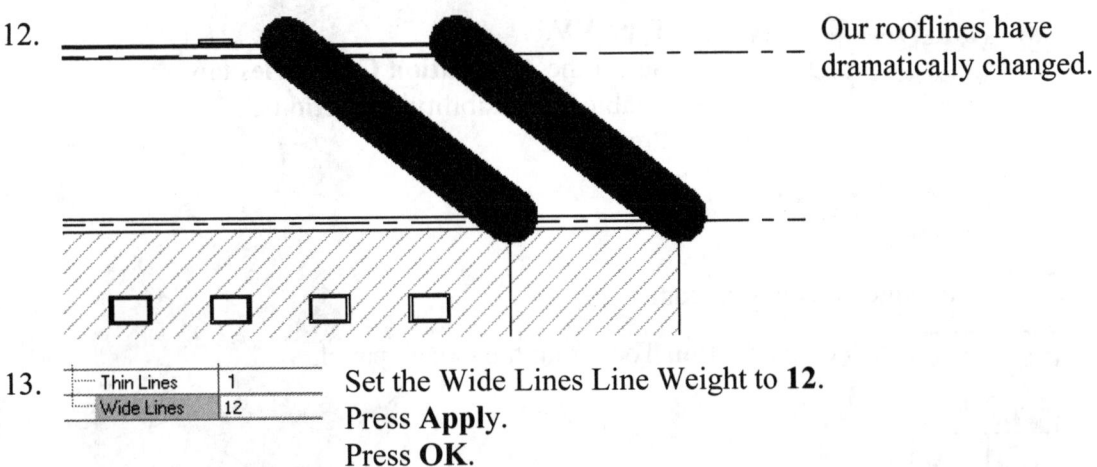 Our rooflines have dramatically changed.

13. | Thin Lines | 1 |
| Wide Lines | 12 |

Set the Wide Lines Line Weight to **12**.
Press **Apply**.
Press **OK**.

14. Save the file as *ex7-2.rvt*.

TIP:
You can use invisible lines to hide any lines you don't want visible in your view.
Linework is specific to each view. If you duplicate the view, any linework edits you
applied will be lost.

Exercise 7-3
Creating a Section View

Drawing Name: 7-2.rvt
Estimated Time: 15 minutes

This exercise reinforces the following skills:

- Activate View
- Add Section Symbol

1.   Open *ex7-2.rvt*.

2.   Sheets (all)
        A101 - First Level Floor Plan
        A102 - Door Schedule
        A103 - Glazing Schedule
        A104 - Finish Schedule
        A105 - Exterior Elevations

Activate the **Exterior** Elevations sheet.

3.   Activate View   Select the bottom (**South**) elevation view.
                   Right click and select **Activate View**.

4. Type **VV**.
   Select the **Annotation Categories** tab.
   Enable the Visibility of **Sections**.
   Press **OK**.

5. Activate the **View** ribbon.

6. Select the **Section** Tool from the Create panel.

7. Place the section symbol at the middle of the building.

   Use the arrows to flip the symbol arrow to the right.

   Note you can use the arrow grips to control the section depth.

8. On the Properties pane:

   Enable **Crop View**.
   Enable **Crop Region Visible**.

9. Set the Far Clip Offset to **80′ [2800 mm]**.
   Left click anywhere in the window.

10. The new section appears in your Project Browser.

11. Type **VV** and turn off visibility of sections.

12. Right click and select **Deactivate View**.

13. Activate the **View** ribbon.

14. Select **New Sheet** from the Sheet Composition panel.

15. Select **D 22 x 34 Horizontal [A1 Metric]** title block.
Press **OK**.

Select a Titleblock

Select a titleblock

D 22 x 34 Horizontal
E1 30 x 42 Horizontal : E1 30x42 Horizontal

16.

Approved By	M. Instructor
Designed By	Designer
Checked By	Checker
Sheet Number	A106
Sheet Name	East Elevation
Sheet Issue Date	07/20/10
Appears In Sheet List	☑
Revisions on Sheet	Edit...
Other	
File Path	
Drawn By	J. Student
Guide Grid	<None>

In the Properties pane:

Change the Sheet Name to **East Section**.

Modify the Drawn By field with your name.

Modify the Approved By field with your instructor's name.

17. Drag and drop the section view onto the sheet.

18.

Viewports (1)	
View Scale	1/4" = 1'-0"
Scale Value 1:	48
Display Model	Normal

Select the view.
In the Properties pane:
Set the View Scale to **1/4″ = 1′-0″**.

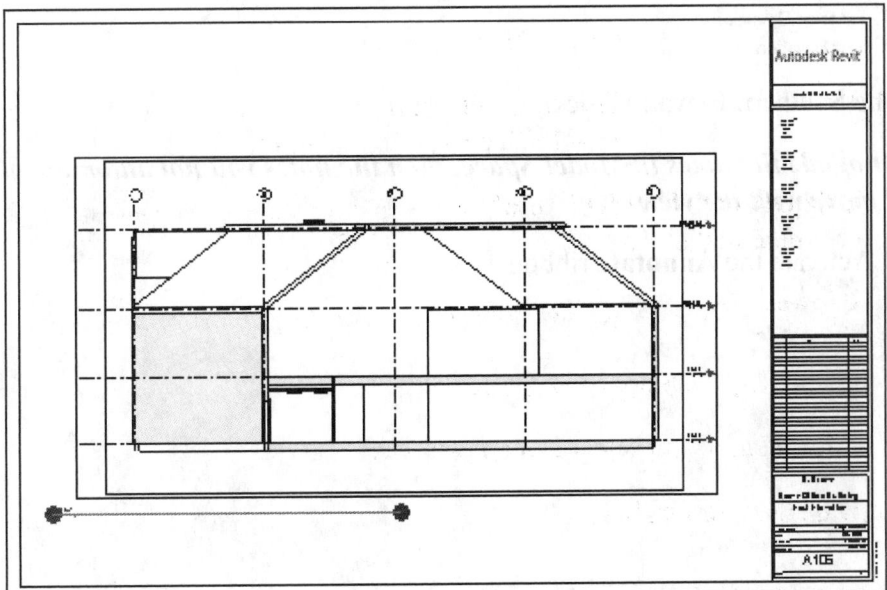

19. Save the file as *ex7-3.rvt*.

TIP:
Any blue symbol will behave like a hyperlink on a web page and can be double clicked to switch to the referenced view. (Note: The blue will print black on your plots if you want it to.)

Exercise 7-4
Adding Keynotes

Drawing Name: 7-3.rvt
Estimated Time: 15 minutes

This exercise reinforces the following skills:

❑ Keynotes
❑ Materials

1.   Open or continue working in *ex7-3.rvt*.

2. Sheets (all)
    A101 - First Level Floor Plan
    A102 - Door Schedule
    A103 - Glazing Schedule
    A104 - Finish Schedule
    A105 - Exterior Elevations
    A106 - East Elevation
      Activate the **Exterior Elevations** sheet.

3. Activate the Southern Elevation view.

    If you do not add the notes in Model Space, then the notes will not automatically scale and move with the view.

4. Annotate   Activate the **Annotate** ribbon.

5. 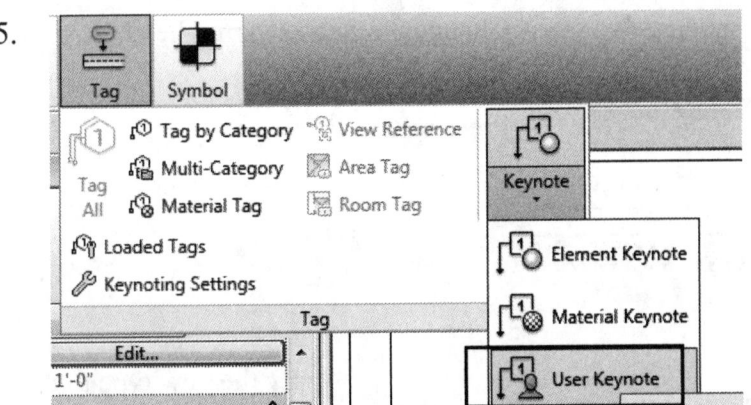 Select the **User Keynote** tool from the Tag panel.

Note: Revit only uses fonts available in the Windows fonts folder. If you are an AutoCAD user with legacy shx fonts, you need to locate ttf fonts that are equivalent to the fonts you want to use and load them into the Windows font folder. To convert shx fonts over to ttf, check with www.tcfonts.com.

6. 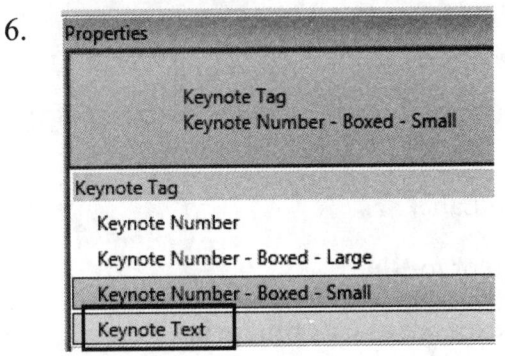 Select **Keynote Text** from the Properties pane Type Selector.

7. 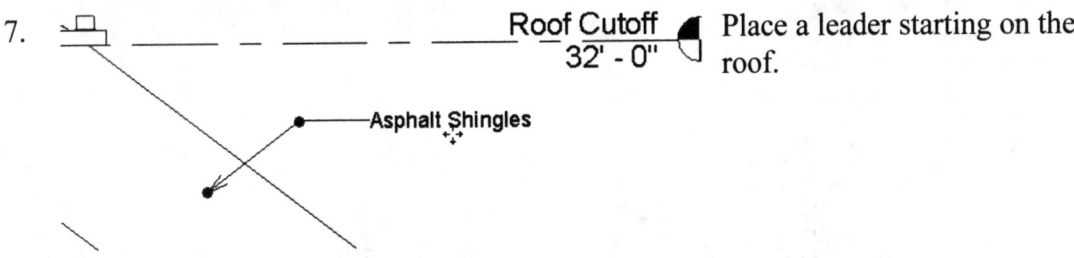 Place a leader starting on the roof.

8. ⊞—07 26 00   Vapor Retarders   Locate the **Asphalt Shingles** material.
   ⊟—07 31 00   Shingles and Shakes
        07 31 00.A1   Asphalt Shingles   Press **OK**.
        07 31 00.B1   15# Felt

Architects are particular about the size of text, and often about the alignment. Notes should not interfere with elevations, dimensions, etc. You can customize the appearance of keynotes.

9. Edit Type   Select **Edit Type** from the Properties panel.

10. Duplicate...   Select **Duplicate**.

11. Name: Keynote Text - Custom   Enter **Keynote Text - Custom**.

     OK   Press **OK**.

12.

Type Parameters	
Parameter	Value
Graphics	
Keynote Text	☑
Keynote Number	☐
Boxed	☐
Leader Arrowhead	Arrow Filled 30 Degree
Dimensions	
Box Size	0' 0 15/16"

Change the Leader Arrowhead to **Arrow Filled 30 Degree**.

Press **OK**.

13.

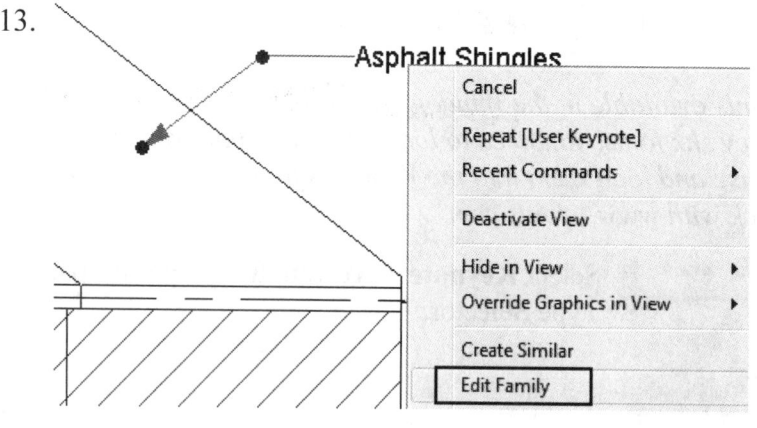

Apply the new type to the keynote.

Select the keynote.
Right click and select **Edit Family**.

14. | Label | Edit... | Select **Edit** next to Label.

15.

Type Parameters	
Parameter	
Graphics	
Color	■ Blue
Line Weight	1
Background	Opaque
Show Border	☐
Leader/Border Offset	5/64"
Text	
Text Font	CityBlueprint
Text Size	3/32"
Tab Size	1/2"
Bold	☐
Italic	☐
Underline	☐
Width Factor	1.000000

Change the Color to **Blue**.

Change the Text Font to **CityBlueprint**.

16.

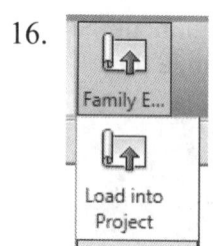

Save the file.

Select Load into Project under the Family Editor panel.

17.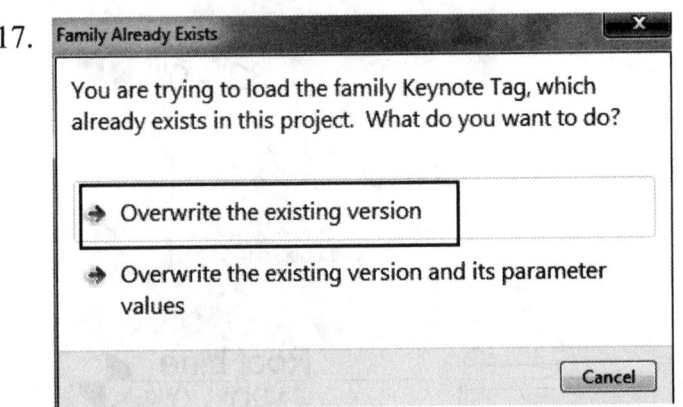

Select **Overwrite the existing version**.

18. 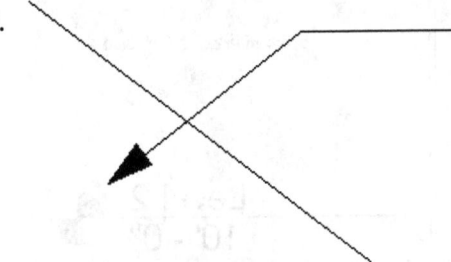 Asphalt Shingles   The keynote font updates.

19.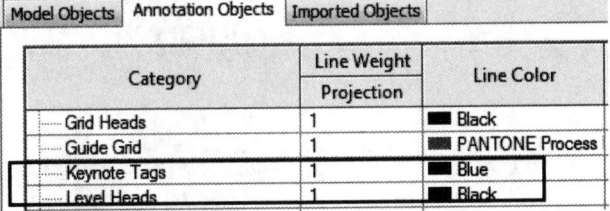

Activate the Manage ribbon.

Select **Object Styles** under Settings.

20.

Category	Line Weight Projection	Line Color
Grid Heads	1	▪ Black
Guide Grid	1	▪▪ PANTONE Process
Keynote Tags	1	▪ Blue
Level Heads	1	▪ Black

Select the Annotation Objects tab. Set the Line Color for Keynote Tags to **Blue**.

Press **OK**.

21. 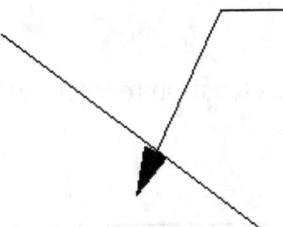 Asphalt Shingles   The leader changes to blue.

22. Add the material notes.

Material indications for brick should mention the pattern (running bond, soldier course, etc.)

Another typical material note would be the roofing material (asphalt shingle, tile, etc.)

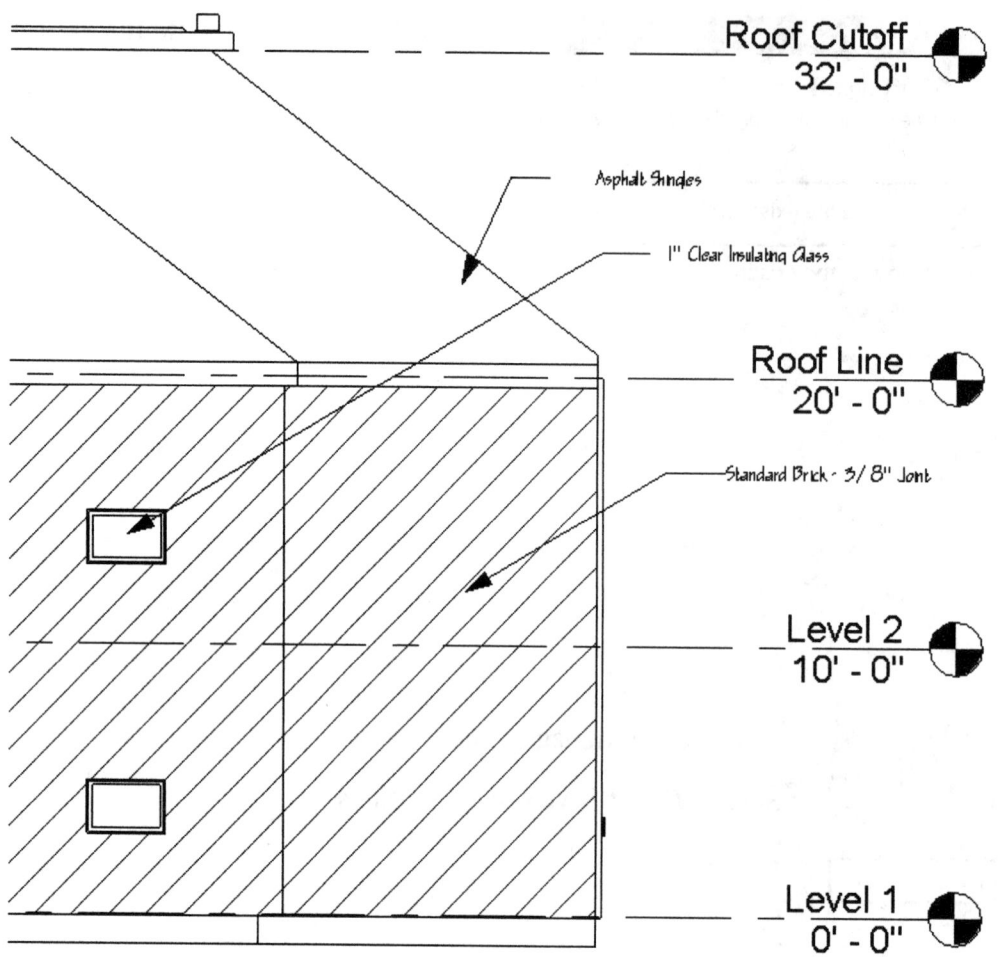

23. Deactivate the view.

24. Save the file *ex7-4.rvt*.

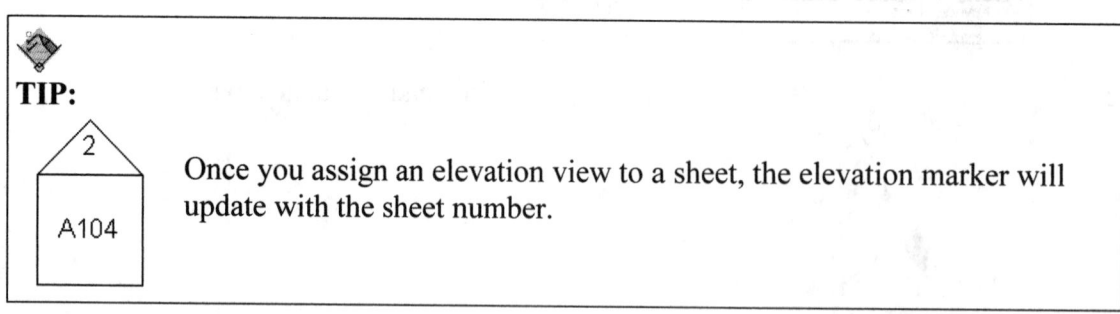

TIP:

Once you assign an elevation view to a sheet, the elevation marker will update with the sheet number.

Exercise 7-5
Adding Window Tags

Drawing Name: 7-4.rvt
Estimated Time: 5 minutes

This exercise reinforces the following skills:

- Tag All Not Tagged
- Window Schedules
- Schedule/Quantities
- Schedule Properties

1. Open *e7-4.rvt*.

2. Activate the **Exterior Elevations** sheet.

    Sheets (all)
    - A101 - First Level Floor Plan
    - A102 - Door Schedule
    - A103 - Glazing Schedule
    - A104 - Finish Schedule
    - **A105 - Exterior Elevations**
    - A106 - East Elevation

3. Select the top (**North**) elevation view.
    Right click and select **Activate View**.

    Activate View

4. Activate the **Annotate ribbon**.

5. Select the **Tag All** tool from the Tag panel.

    Tag Symbol

    Tag by Category   View Reference
    Multi-Category   Area Tag
    Tag All Material Tag   Room Tag
    Loaded Tags
    Keynoting Settings

6. Highlight the **Window Tags**.

    Press **OK**.

Room Tags	Room Tag : Room
Window Tags	Window Tag

Category	Loaded Tags
Door Tags	M_Door Tag
Room Tags	M_Room Tag : Room Tag
Room Tags	M_Room Tag : Room Tag With Area
Room Tags	M_Room Tag : Room Tag With Volume
Window Tags	M_Window Tag

7.

Tags will appear on all the windows.

Deactivate View

Deactivate the view.

8.   Save the file as *ex7-5.rvt*.

Exercise 7-6
Changing Window Tags from Type to Instance

Drawing Name: 7-5.rvt
Estimated Time: 20 minutes

This exercise reinforces the following skills:

    ❑   Family Types
    ❑   Parameters
    ❑   Tags

In Exercise 7-5, we added a window tag that was linked to window type. So, all the tags displayed the same number for all windows of the same type. Some users want their tags to display by instance (individual placement). That way they can specify in their schedule the location of each window as well as the type. In this exercise, you learn how to modify Revit's window tag to link to an instance instead of a type.

1.   ☞ Open *ex7-5.rvt*.

2.   ⊞── A104 - Roof Plan   Activate the **Exterior Elevations** sheet.
       ⊞── A105 - First Level Reflected Ceiling Plan
       ⊞── **A106 - Exterior Elevations**

3.   Activate View   Select the top (**North**) elevation view.
                               Right click and select **Activate View**.

4.   Select one of the window tags.

       Make sure you don't select a window.

       The Window Tag will display in the Properties pane if it is selected.

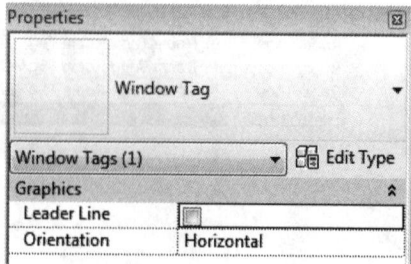

7-14

5. 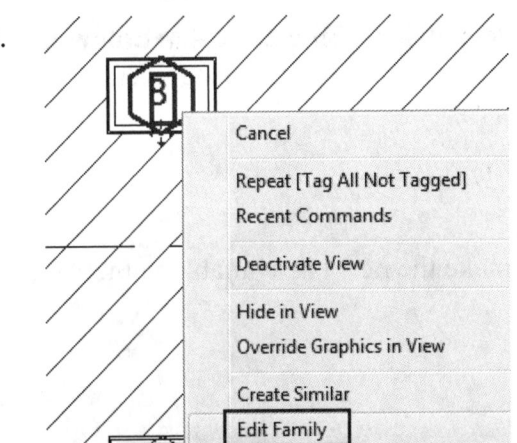 Right click and select **Edit Family**.

6. 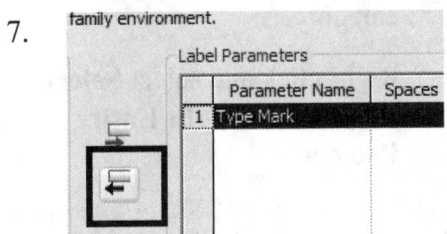 Select the label/text located in the center of the tag.
Select **Edit Label** on the ribbon bar.

7. 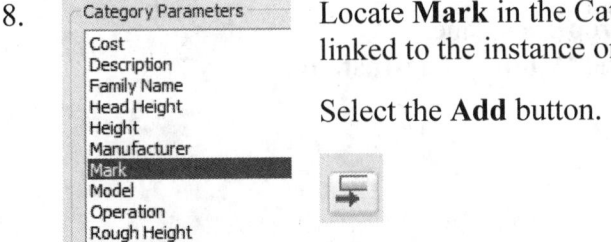 Highlight the Type Mark listed as the Label Parameters.

This is linked to the type of window placed.

Select the **Remove** button.

8. 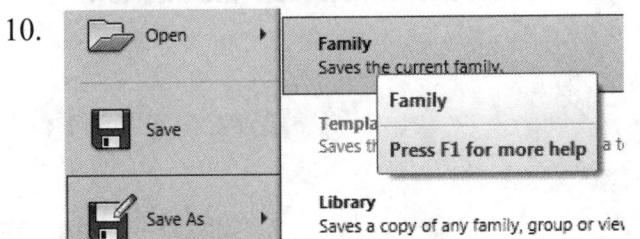 Locate **Mark** in the Category Parameters list. This parameter is linked to the instance or individual window.

Select the **Add** button.

9. You should see the Mark parameter listed.

Press **OK**.

10. On the Applications Menu:

Go to **File→Save As→Family**.

11.

File name: Window Tag_Instance.rfa

Files of type: Family Files (*.rfa)

Save the file with a new file name – **Window Tag_Instance** – in your class work folder.

File name: M_Window Tag_Instance.rfa

Files of type: Family Files (*.rfa)

12.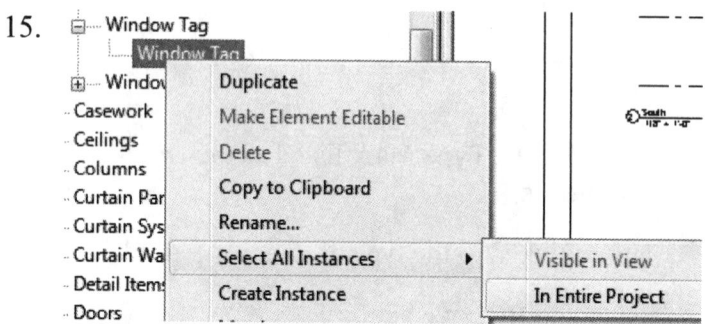

Family E...

Load into Project

Family Editor

Select **Load into Project** to make the new tag available in the building model.

13. Close the window tag file.

14. Switch back to the *ex7-5.rvt* file.

15. Window Tag
Window Tag
Windo   **Duplicate**
Casework   Make Element Editable
Ceilings   Delete
Columns
Curtain Par   Copy to Clipboard
Curtain Sys   Rename...
Curtain Wa   Select All Instances   ►   Visible in View
Detail Items   Create Instance   In Entire Project
Doors

In the Project Browser:
Locate the **Window Tag** under the Annotation Symbols category.

Right click and select **Select All Instances→In Entire Project**.

16. Properties

Window Tag

Window Tag
Window Tag
Window Tag-Instance
Window Tag-Instance ◄——

The window tags will be selected in all views.

In the Properties Pane:
Select the **Window Tag-Instance**.

17.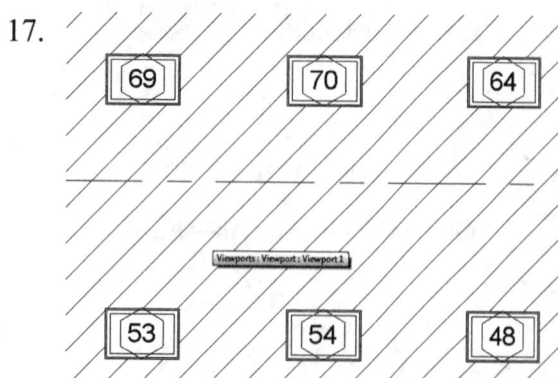

69   70   64

Viewports : Viewport : Viewport 1

53   54   48

Zoom in to see that the windows are now renumbered.

Right click and **Deactivate** the view.

18. Save as *7-6.rvt*.

Exercise 7-7
Creating a Plan Region View

Drawing Name: plan region view.rvt (this is downloaded from the publisher's website)

Estimated Time: 20 minutes

Thanks to John Chan, one of my Revit students at SFSU for this project!

This exercise reinforces the following skills:

- ❑ Plan Region View
- ❑ Split Level Views
- ❑ Linework

Some floor plans are split levels. In those cases, users need to create a Plan Region View in order to create a good floor plan.

1. 📂 Open *plan region view.rvt*.

2. If you switch to a 3D view, you see that this is a split-level floor plan.

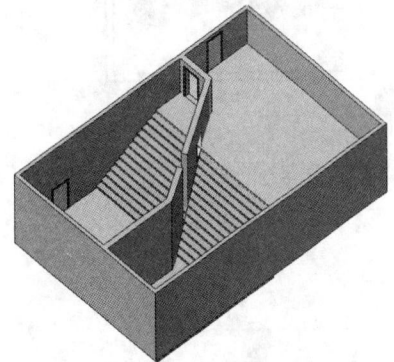

3. Floor Plans
    1/F Level 1
    1/F Level 2
    2/F
    Site

    Activate the **1/F Level 1** view under floor plans.

    You see the door and window tags, but no doors or windows.

4. View   Activate the **View** ribbon.

5.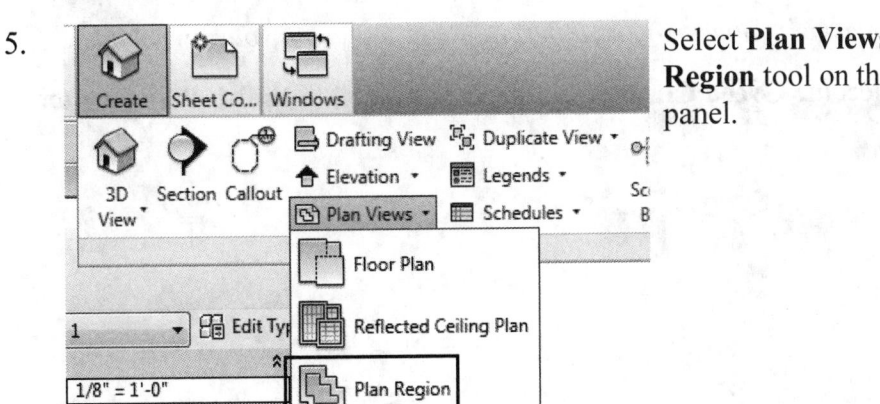

    Select **Plan Views→Plan Region** tool on the Create panel.

6. 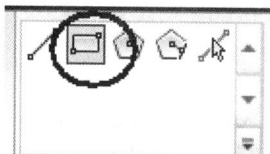 Select the **Rectangle** tool from the ribbon.

7. 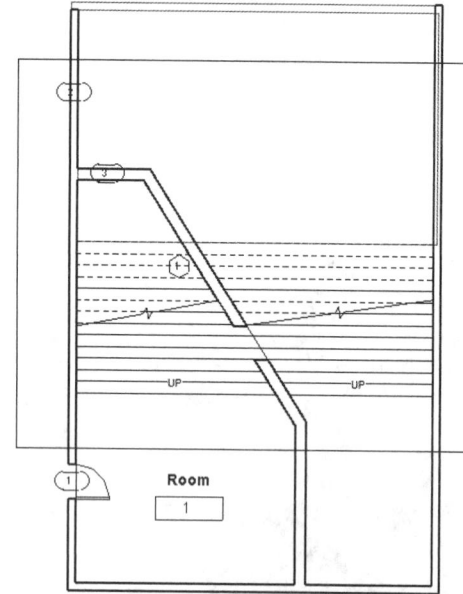 Draw a rectangle around the region where you want the doors and windows to be visible.

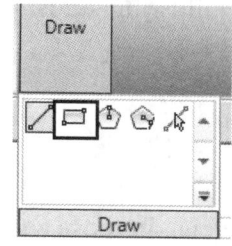

Be sure to extend the rectangle across the entire plan or the stairs may not appear properly.

8. 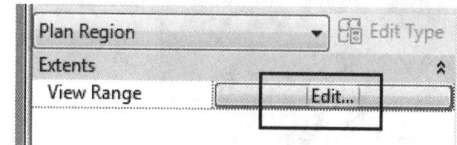 Select the **Edit** button next to View Range on the Properties pane.

9. 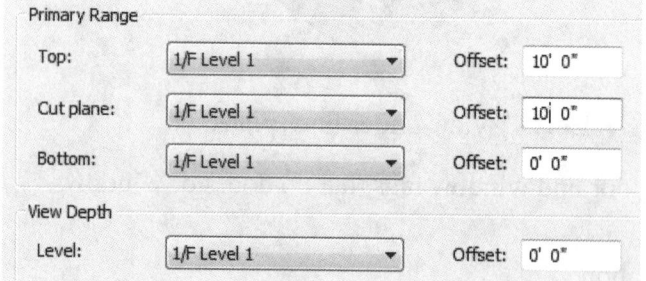 Set the Offset for the Top plane to **10′ 0″**.
Set the Cut Plane Offset to **10′ 0″**.

Press **OK**.

Note: Your dimension values may be different if you are using your own model.

10. Select the **Green Check** under the Mode panel to **Finish Plan Region**.

11.

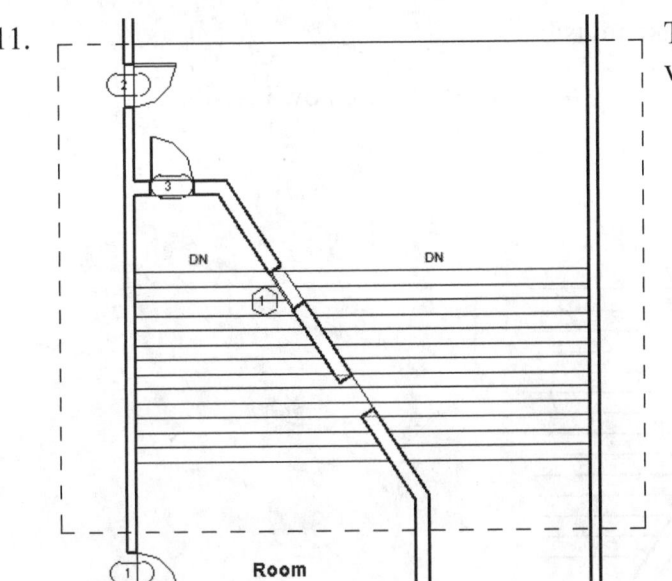

The doors and window are now visible.

12.

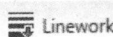

To turn off the visibility of the Plan Region rectangle in the view, type **VG**.
Select the Annotations tab.
Disable **Plan Region**.
Press **OK**.

13.

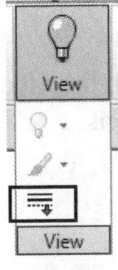

There is a line where the two stairs connect.

Linework

We can use the Linework tool to make this line invisible.

14. Modify   Activate the Modify ribbon.

15.

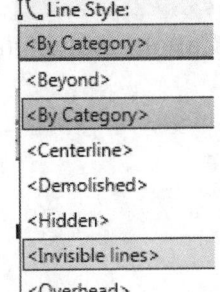

Select the **Linework** tool under the View panel.

16. Line Style:

Select **Invisible Lines** from the Line Style drop-down list.

<By Category>
<Beyond>
<By Category>
<Centerline>
<Demolished>
<Hidden>
<Invisible lines>
<Overhead>

17. Select the lines you wish to make invisible.

18.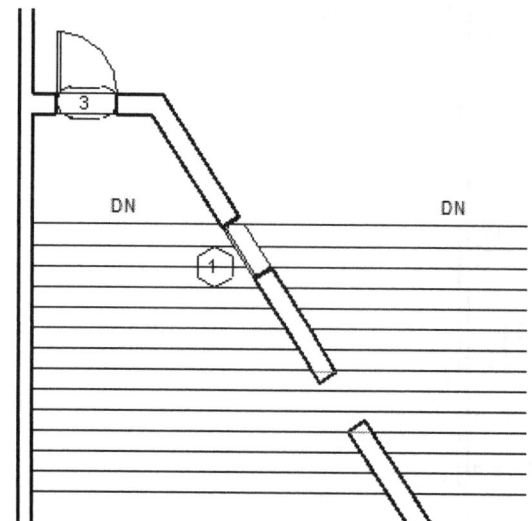
    The lines are now invisible.

19. Close without saving.

Exercise 7-8
Creating a Detail View

Drawing Name: ex7-6.rvt
Estimated Time: 20 minutes

This exercise reinforces the following skills:

□   Detail Components
□   Notes

To create a detail view, you use the model as an underlay for the detail. You then load and add the desired detail components. Finally, add any notes and dimensions.

1.   Open *ex7-6.rvt*.

2.   Sections (Building Section)   Activate Section 1 in the browser.
          Section 1

3.   On the View ribbon, select the **Callout** tool on the Create panel.

4. Set the type of Callout to **Wall Section** on the Properties pane.

5. Select the Scale for the Detail View on the Options bar.

Set it to **1/4″ = 1′-0″ [1:50]**.

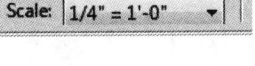

6. Enable **Reference other view:** and set to **New Drafting View** on the status bar.

7. Place the callout on the east wall.

Use the grips to position the Detail Callout.

The detail number and sheet number will be filled out when you place the view on a sheet automatically.

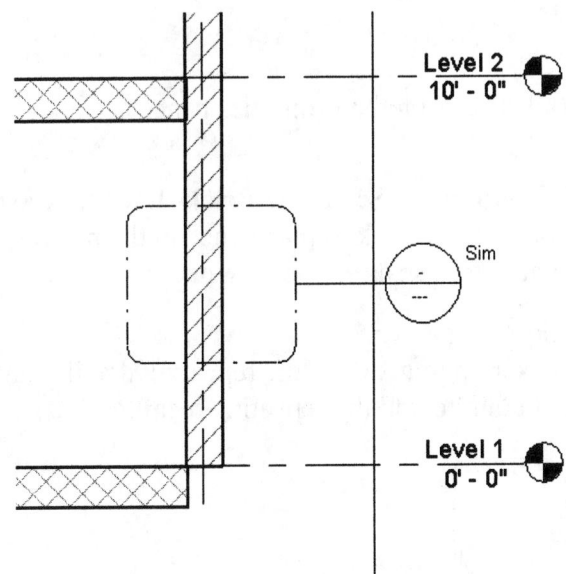

8. The Callout is now listed in the browser.

Activate the Callout view.

9. Activate the **Callout of Section 1** view.

10.

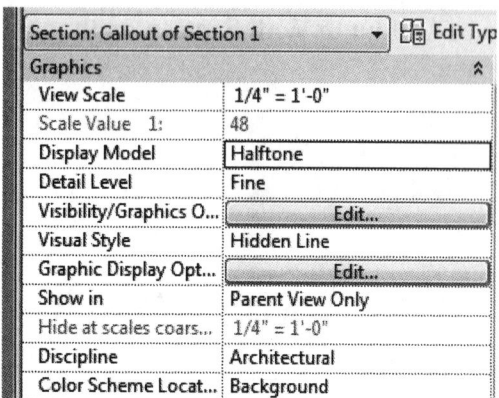

On the Properties pane:

For Display Model, set to **Halftone**.
Set the Detail Level to **Fine**.

11. [Annotate] Activate the **Annotate** ribbon.

12. Select **Detail→Component→Repeating Detail** from the ribbon.

13. [Repeating Detail Brick] Select **Repeating Detail: Brick** on the Properties pane.

If this is not available, select **Detail Component**. Select the **Brick- UK Standard: Soldier & Plan** from the Options drop-down. Click to place once in the project, then delete it. This will make it available for use as a repeating detail.

14.

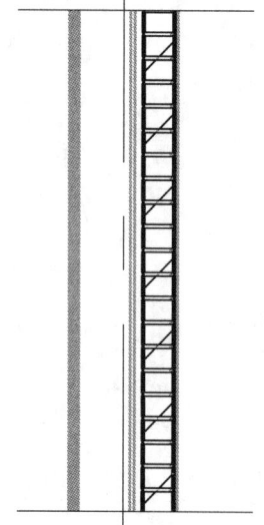

Select the start point as shown.
Then drag the cursor up to generate the repeating detail.
Select the second point to end the repeating detail.

15. 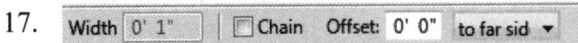 Select the **Detail→Insulation** tool.

16. Pick to select the start and end points for the insulation.

17. Width 0' 1" ☐ Chain Offset: 0' 0" to far sid ▼

You can control the width and the placement of the insulation detail on the status bar located on the lower left of the screen.

18. 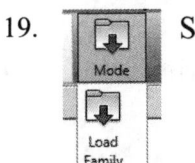 Select **Detail Component** from the Detail panel on the Annotation ribbon.

19. 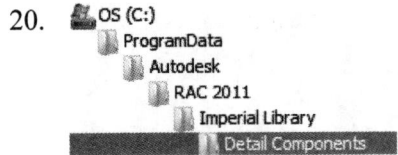 Select **Load Family** under the Mode panel.

20. Browse to the **Detail Components** folder.

21. Browse down to the **06160-Sheathing** folder.

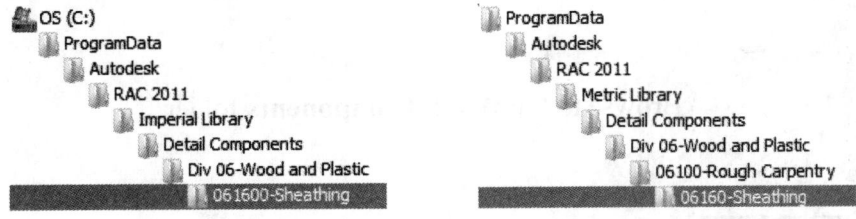

22. 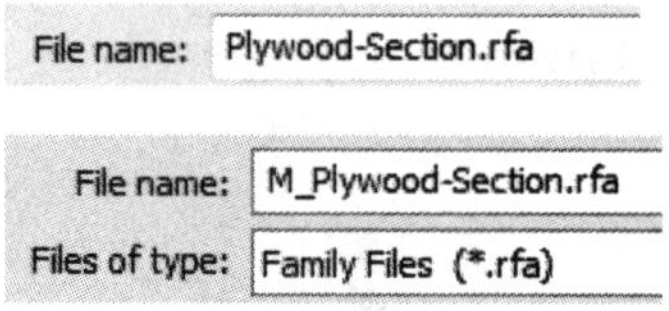 File name: Plywood-Section.rfa

Locate the *Plywood-Section* [*M_Plywood-Section.rfa*] file.

File name: M_Plywood-Section.rfa

Files of type: Family Files (*.rfa)

Press **Open**.

23. 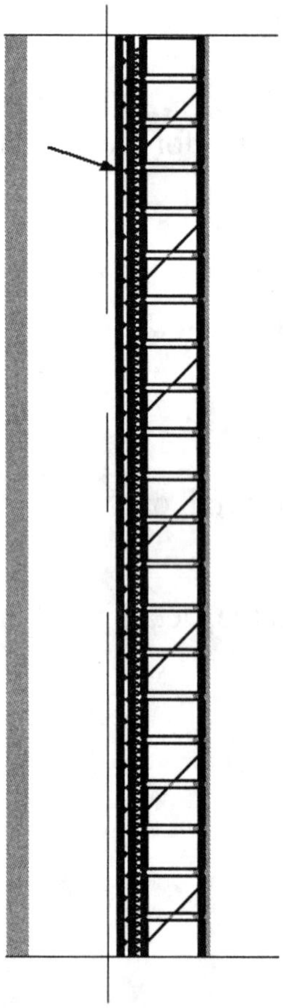 Place the detail component behind the insulation.

You can use the arrow keys to flip it if you need to reorient the placement.

24. 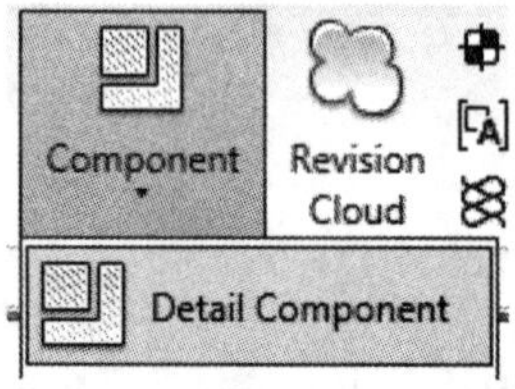 Component   Revision Cloud

Detail Component

Select **Detail Component** from the Annotation ribbon.

25. 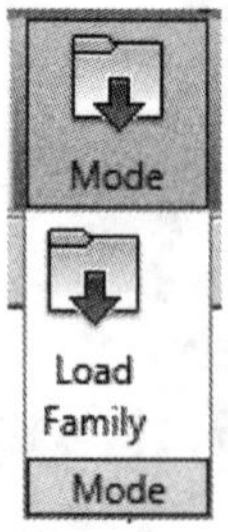 Mode

Load Family

Mode

Select **Load Family** under the Mode panel.

26. 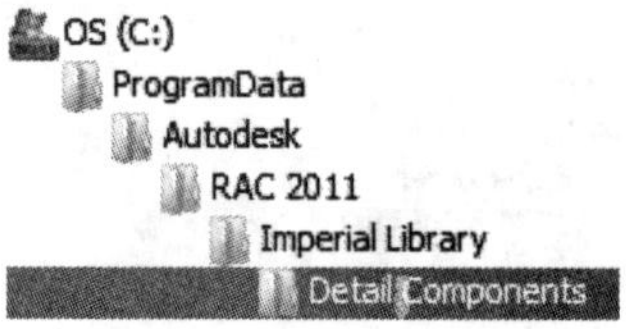 OS (C:)
    ProgramData
    Autodesk
    RAC 2011
    Imperial Library
    Detail Components

Browse to the **Detail Components** folder.

27. Browse down to the **092900-Gypsum Board [09250-Gypsum Wallboard]** folder.

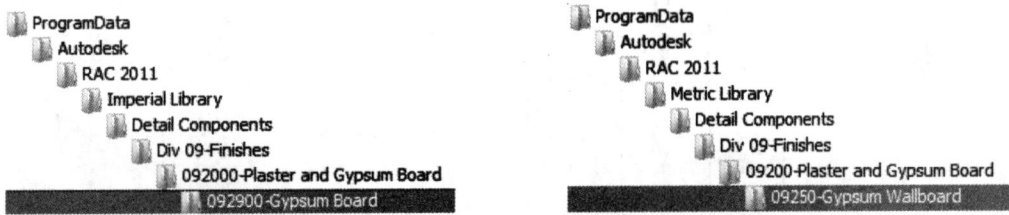

28. | File name: | Gypsum Wallboard-Section.rfa |

Locate the *Gypsum Wallboard-Section [M_Gypsum Wallboard-Section.rfa]* file.

| File name: | M_Gypsum Wallboard-Section.rfa |
| Files of type: | Family Files (*.rfa) |

Press **Open**.

29.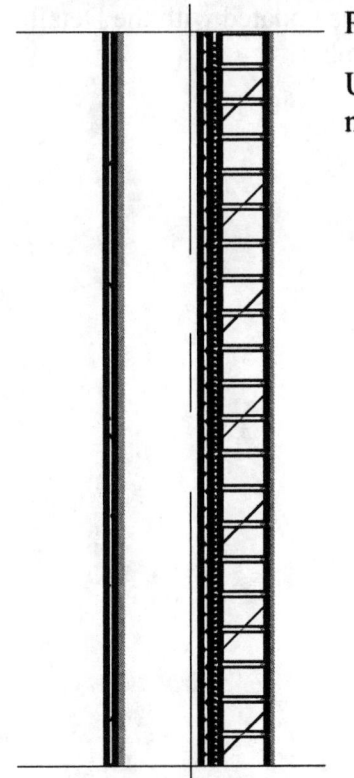

Place the gypsum wallboard on the left side of the wall.

Use the arrows to flip the orientation of the wallboard if necessary.

30. Room Style Schedule

Sheets (all)

A10   New Sheet...

A10

A10   Type Properties...

Highlight Sheets in the browser.

Right click and select **New Sheet**.

31. Select titleblocks:

D 22 x 34 Horizontal

E1 30 x 42 Horizontal : E1 30x42 Horizontal

None

Press **OK**.

32. | Sheet Number | A107 |
Sheet Name	Detail Views
Sheet Issue Date	07/20/10
Appears In Sheet List	☑

On the Properties pane:

Change the Sheet Name to **Detail Views**.

33. 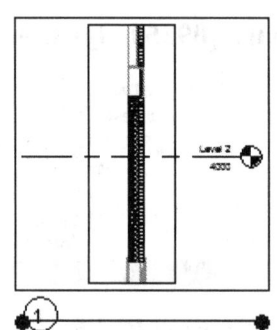 Drag and drop the Callout view onto the sheet.

Callout of Section 1
1 : 50

34. 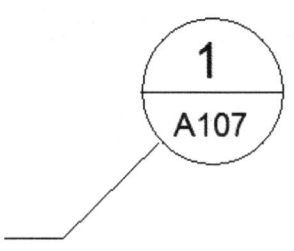 Activate **Section 1** in the browser.

35. _____ _____ ⌐∿ Note that the callout has updated with the Detail number and Sheet Number.

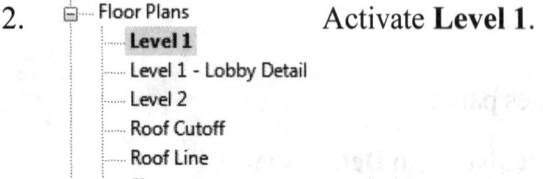

36. Save as *ex7-8.rvt*.

Exercise 7-9
Using a Matchline

Drawing Name: ex7-8.rvt
Estimated Time: 20 minutes

This exercise reinforces the following skills:

□ Matchline
□ Sheets
□ Views

1. 📂 Open *ex7-8.rvt*.

2.   Floor Plans   Activate **Level 1**.
       Level 1
       Level 1 - Lobby Detail
       Level 2
       Roof Cutoff
       Roof Line
       Site

3.  Right click on **Level 1** in the browser.

Select **Duplicate View→ Duplicate with Detailing**.

4. Rename the view **Level 1-East Wing**.

Press **OK**.

5. 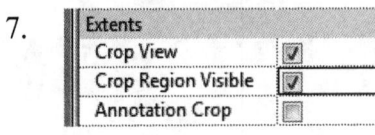 Right click on **Level 1** in the browser.

Select **Duplicate View→ Duplicate with Detailing**.

6. Rename the view **Level 1-West Wing**.

Press **OK**.

7. Activate the view **Level 1-West Wing** floor plan.

In the Properties pane:
Enable **Crop View**.
Enable **Crop Region Visible**.

8. 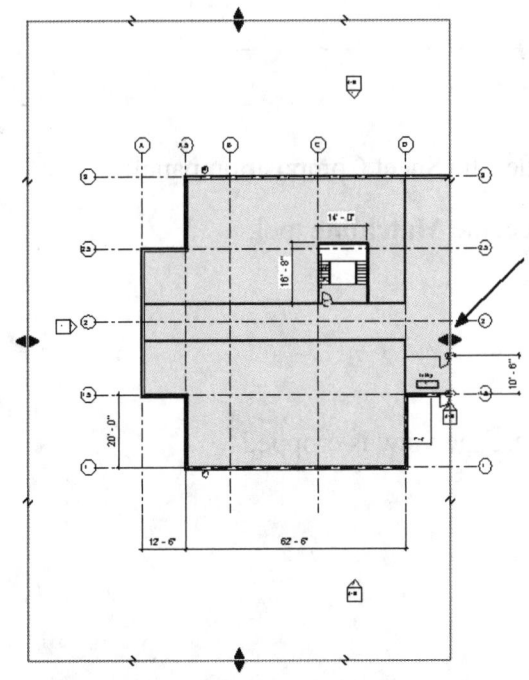 Use the grips on the crop region to only show the west side of the floor plan.

9. Activate **Level 1 - East Wing**.

10. 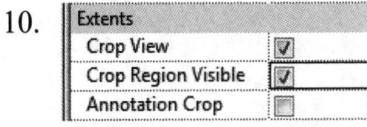 In the Properties pane:
Enable **Crop View**.
Enable **Crop Region Visible**.

11.   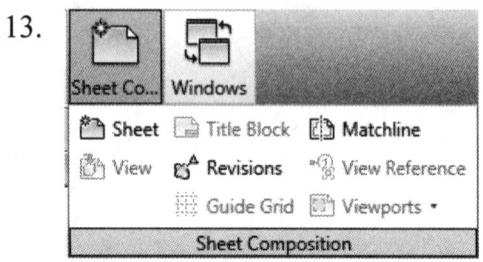   Use the grips on
                                  the crop region
                                  to only show
                                  the east side of
                                  the floor plan.

12. [View] Activate the **View** ribbon.

13. 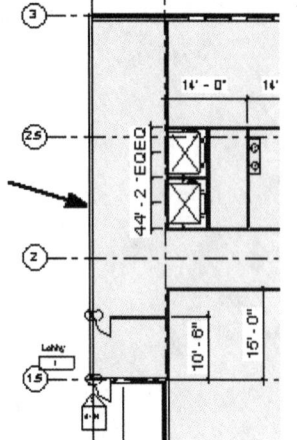 Under the Sheet Composition panel:

Select the **Matchline** tool.

14. Draw a line where the view is cropped.

15. 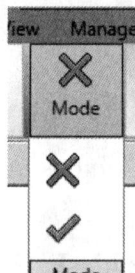 Select the **Green Check** under Mode to finish the matchline.

16. 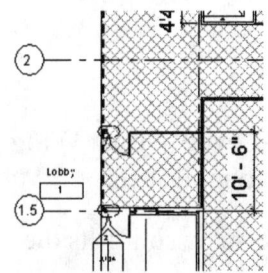 Adjust the crop region so that you see the match line.

17.

Extents	
Crop View	☑
Crop Region Visible	☐
Annotation Crop	☐

Disable **Crop Region Visible** in the Properties pane.

18. Level 1 - Lobby Detail
Level 1 - West Wing
Level 1- East Wing

Activate the **Level 1 - West Wing** floor plan.

19. You should see a match line in this view as well.

20.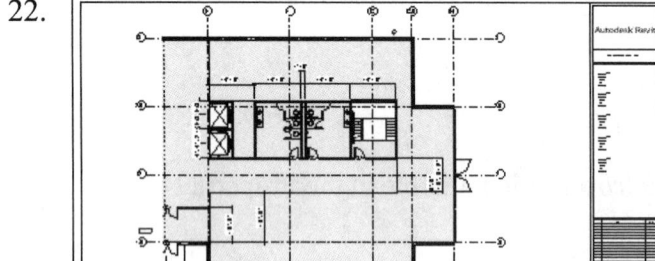

Disable **Crop Region Visible** in the Properties pane.

21.

Add a new **Sheet** using the Sheet Composition panel on the View ribbon.

Press **OK** to accept the default title block.

22.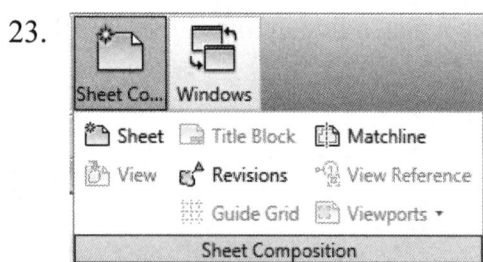

Place the **Level 1- East Wing** floor plan on the sheet.

Adjust the scale so it fills the sheet.

Turn off the visibility of the elevation markers.

Name the sheet **Level 1 - East Wing**.

23.

Add a new **Sheet** using the Sheet Composition panel on the View ribbon.

Press **OK** to accept the default title block.

24.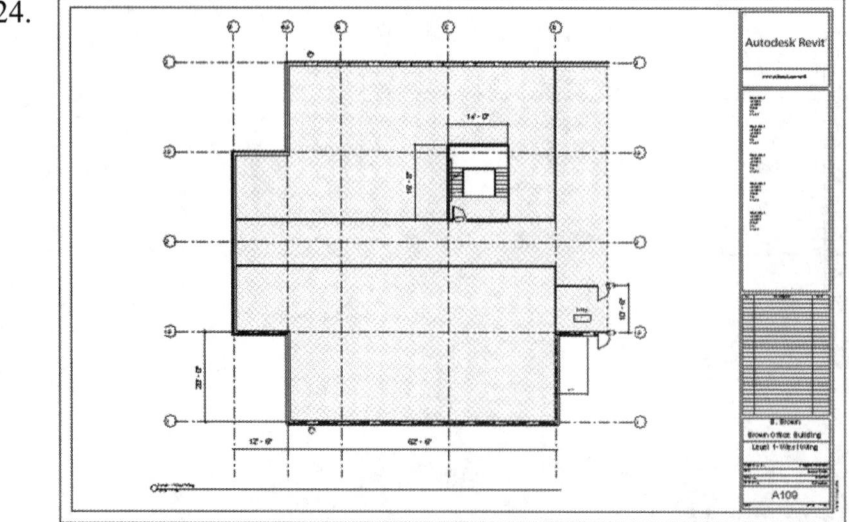

Place the **Level 1- West Wing** floor plan on the sheet.

Adjust the scale so it fills the sheet.

Turn off the visibility of the elevation markers.

Name the sheet **Level 1 -West Wing**.

25. Save the file as *ex7-9.rvt.*

Additional Projects

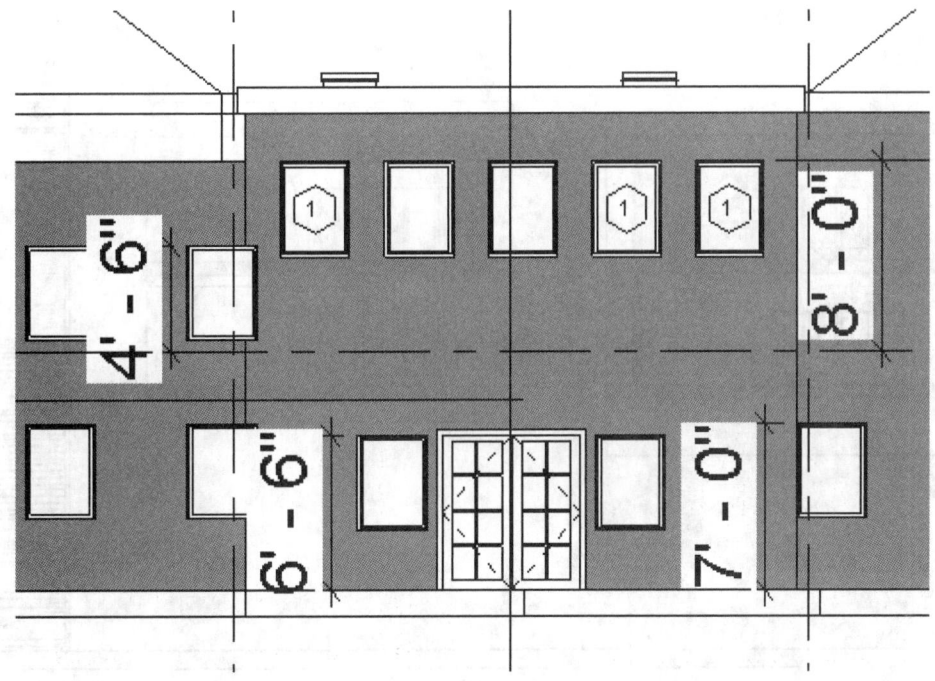

1)   Add dimensions to the North-South Elevation sheet.

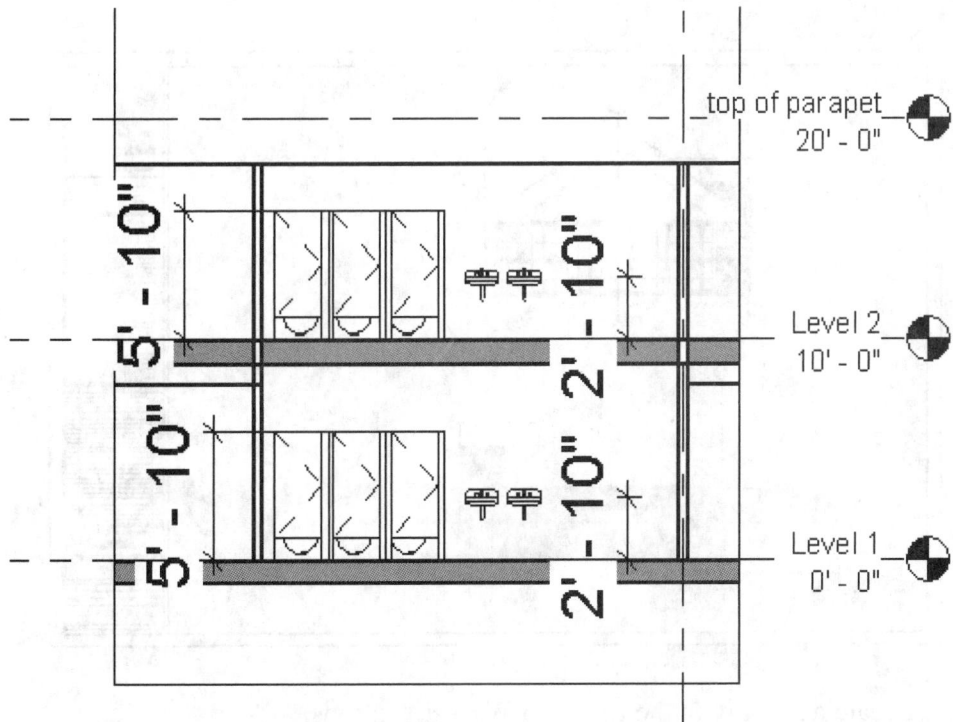

2)   Create a section view of the women's lavatory
         Add it to a sheet and dimension

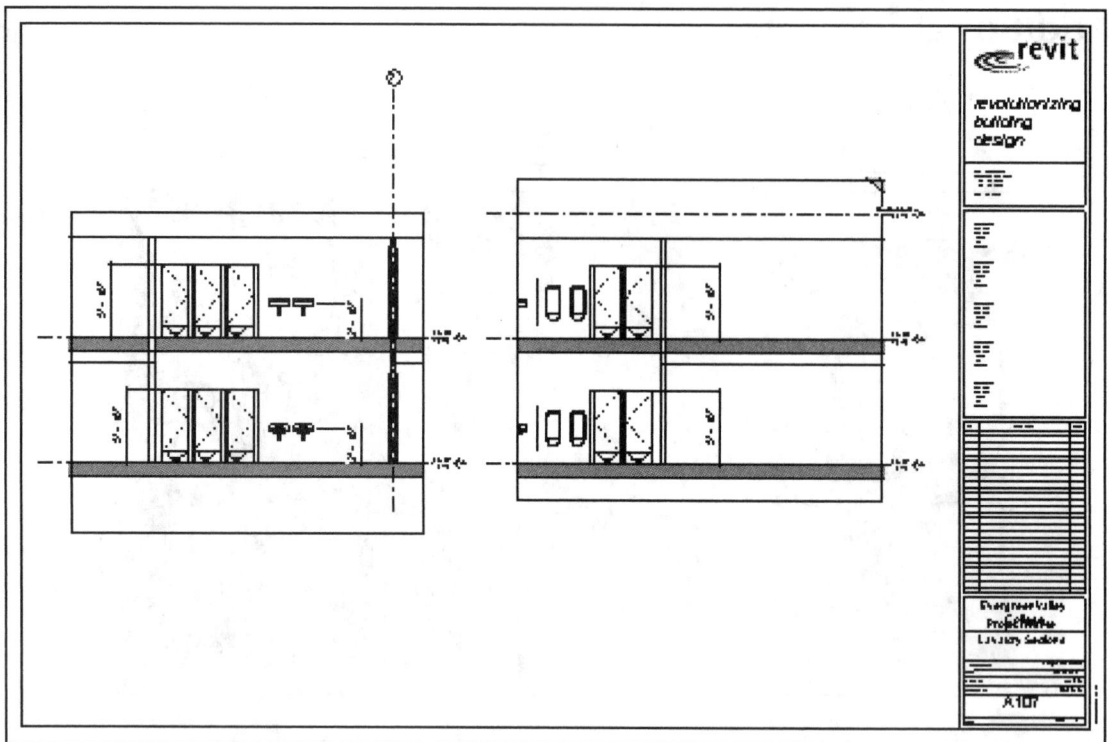

3) Add a section view of the men's lavatory to the sheet.
Dimension that section view.

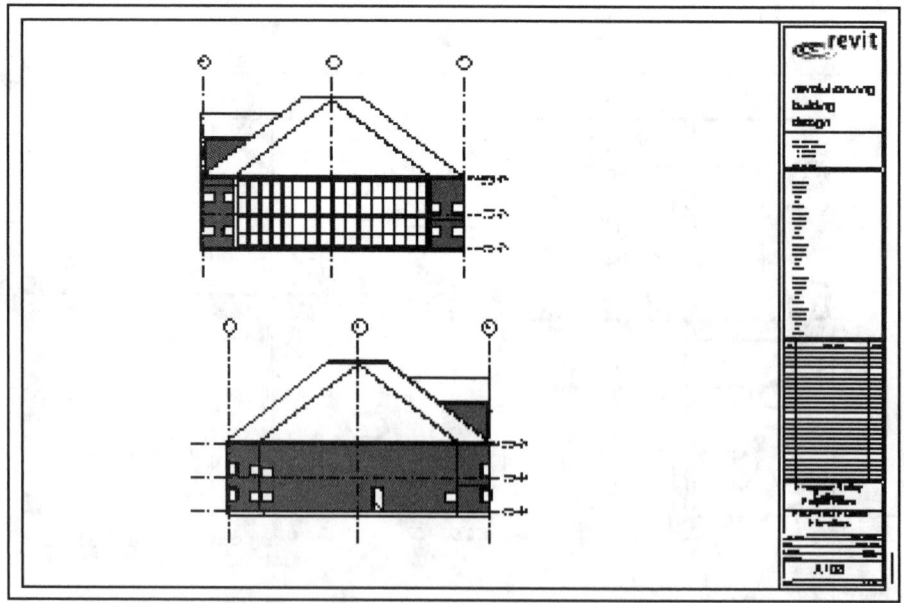

4) Create a sheet with the East and West Elevations.
You may have to adjust the East and West Elevation arrow symbols locations
and cut depth.

Lesson 7 Quiz

True or False

1. You have to deactivate a view before you can activate a different view.
2. When adding dimensions to an elevation, you add horizontal dimensions, not vertical dimensions
3. The Linework tool is used to change the line style of a line in a view
4. If you change the line style of a line in one view, it will automatically update in all views.
5. Double clicking on a blue symbol will automatically activate the view linked to that symbol.

Multiple Choice

6. To add a view to a sheet, you can:

    A. Drag and drop the view name from the browser onto the sheet
    B. Go to View→New→Add View
    C. Select 'Add View' from the View Design Bar
    D. All of the above

7. To add a sheet, you can:

    A. Select the New Sheet tool from the View ribbon.
    B. Right click on a sheet and select New Sheet.
    C. Highlight Sheets in the Browser, right click and select 'New Sheet'.
    D. Go to File→New Sheet.

8. To control the depth of an elevation view (visible objects behind objects):

    A. Change to Hidden Line mode
    B. Adjust the location of the elevation clip plane
    C. Adjust the Section Box
    D. Change the View Underlay

9. The keyboard shortcut key for Linework is:

    A. L
    B. LW
    C. LI
    D. LK

10. The text leader option NOT available is:

    A. Leader with no shoulder
    B. Leader with shoulder
    C. Curved Leader
    D. Spline Leader

11. The number 1 in the section symbol shown indicates:

    A. The sheet number
    B. The sheet scale
    C. The elevation number
    D. The detail number on the sheet

12. The values in the section symbol are automatically linked to:

    A. The browser
    B. The sheet where the section view is placed
    C. The text entered by the user
    D. The floor plan

13. To control the line weight of line styles:

    A. Go to Settings→Line Styles
    B. Go to Line Styles→Properties
    C. Pick the Line, right click and select 'Properties'.
    D. Go to Tools→Line Weights

ANSWERS:

    1) T; 2) F; 3) T; 4) F; 5) T; 6) D; 7) A & C; 8) B; 9) B; 10) D; 11) D; 12) B; 13) A

Lesson 8
Rendering

Rendering is an acquired skill. It takes practice to set up scenes to get the results you want. It is helpful to become familiar with photography as many of the same lighting and shading theory is applicable. Getting the right scene is a matter of trial and error. It is a good idea to make small adjustments when setting up a scene as you often learn more about the effects of different settings.

Exercise 8-1
Adding Scenery

Drawing Name: 7-9.rvt
Estimated Time: 30 minutes

This exercise reinforces the following skills:

- ❑ Site
- ❑ Toposurface
- ❑ Site Component

Before we can create some nice rendered views, we need to add some background scenery to our model.

1. 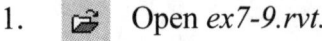 Open *ex7-9.rvt*.

2. 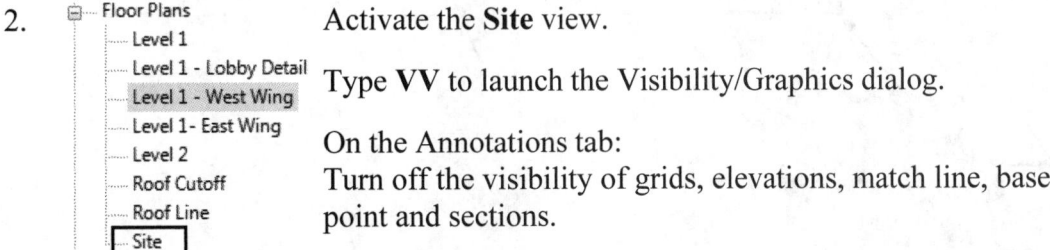 Activate the **Site** view.

Type **VV** to launch the Visibility/Graphics dialog.

On the Annotations tab:
Turn off the visibility of grids, elevations, match line, base point and sections.

3. 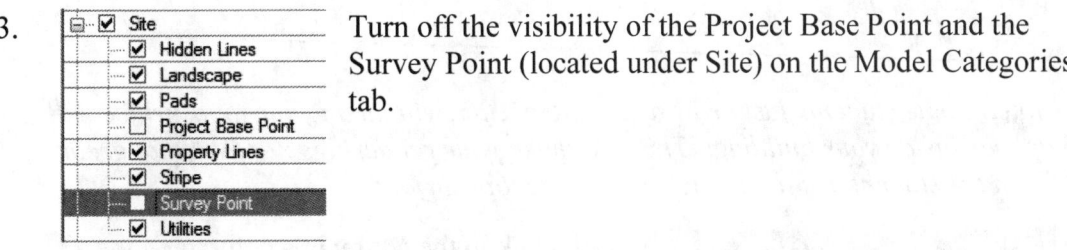 Turn off the visibility of the Project Base Point and the Survey Point (located under Site) on the Model Categories tab.

4. Massing & Site Activate the **Massing & Site** ribbon.

5. Select the **Toposurface** tool from the Model Site panel.

6. Use the **Point** tool from the Tools panel to create an outline of a lawn surface.

7. Pick the points indicated to create a lawn expanse.
    You can grab the points and drag to move into the correct position.

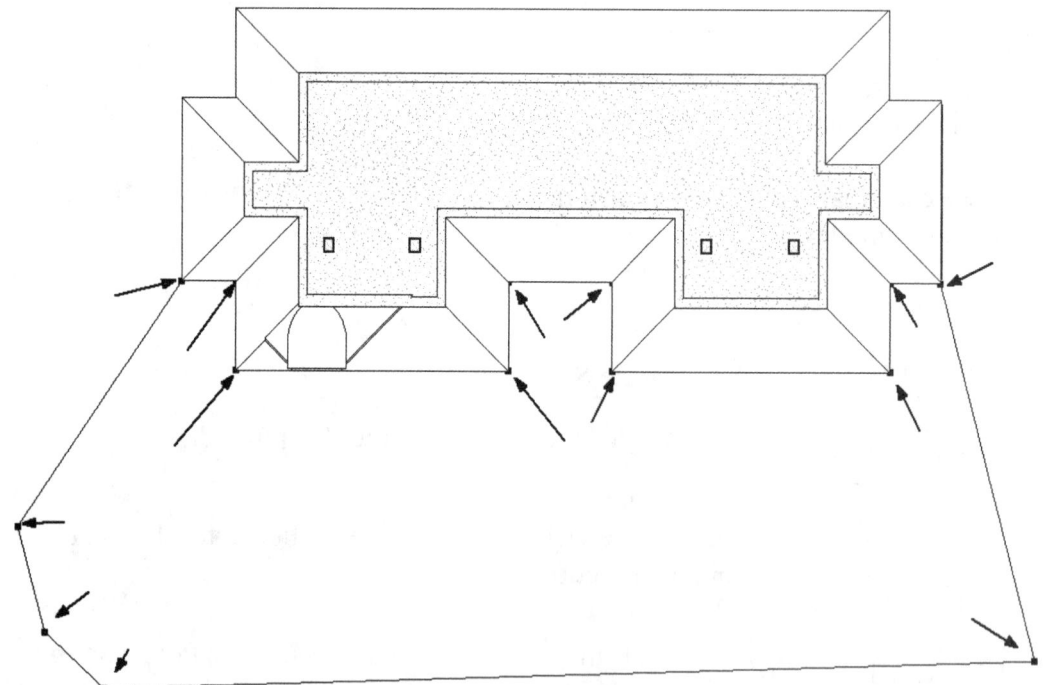

Note: Some students just draw a rectangle…this will mean your toposurface will appear inside your building. This will make your renderings not look that great. Then the student has to go back and fix the toposurface.

8. Left click in the **Materials** column on the Properties pane.

9. 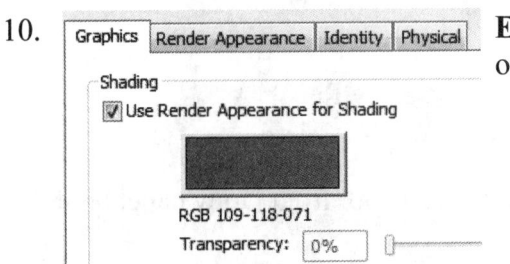 Under Materials, select **Site-Grass** from the dialog.
   Press **OK** to close the Properties dialog.

10. 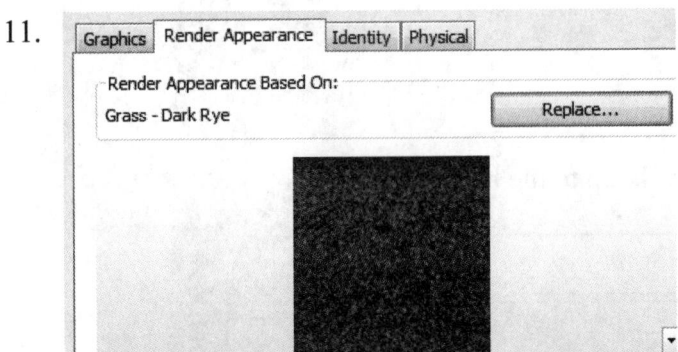 **Enable Use Render Appearance for Shading** on the Graphics tab.

11.  Select the Render Appearance tab.

    Press the **Replace** button.

12. 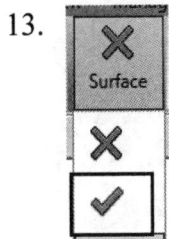 Select the **Grass-Bluegrass** of your choice.

    Press **OK** twice to exit the dialog.

13. 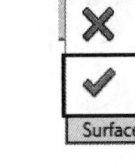 Select the **Green Check** on the Surface panel to **Finish Surface**.

14. 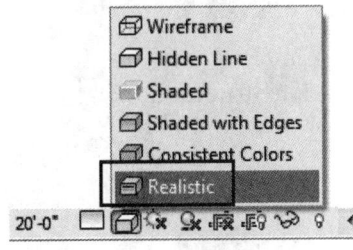 Switch to **Realistic** to see the grass material.

15. 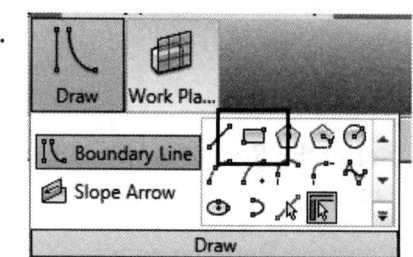 Select the **Building Pad** tool on the Model Site panel.

16. Select the **Rectangle** tool from Draw panel on the ribbon.

17. Use **Rectangle** to create a sidewalk up to the building.

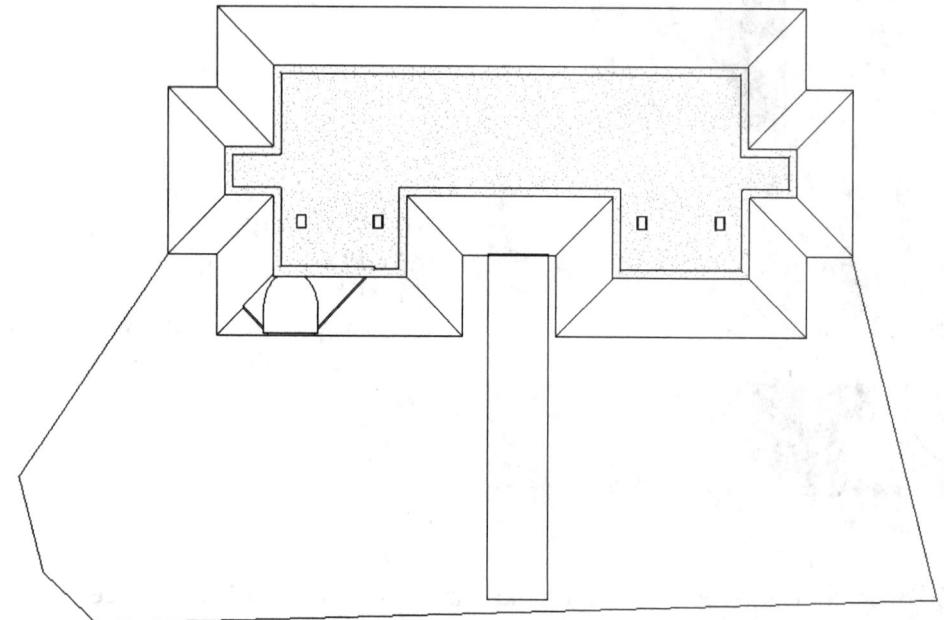

18. Select **Edit Type** on the Properties pane.

19. Select **Duplicate**.

20. Enter **Walkway** in the Name field.
     Press **OK**.

21. Select **Edit** under Structure.

22. 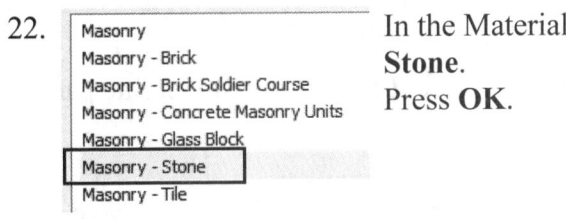 In the Material dialog for Structure [1], select **Masonry - Stone**.
Press **OK**.

23. 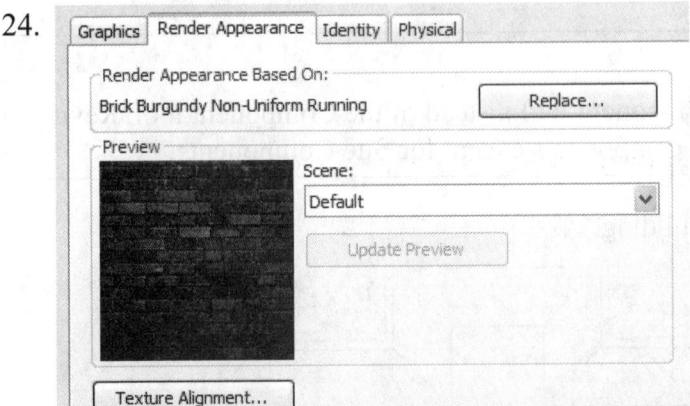 Enable **Use Render Appearance for Shading**.

24. Select the Render Appearance tab and there will be a preview of how the walkway should appear in the rendering.

Press **OK** multiple times to close all dialogs.

25. 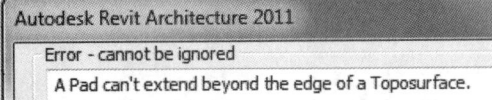 Select the **Green Check** on the Surface panel to **Finish Building Pad**.

If you see this error, you need to adjust the rectangle sketch so it is entirely on the toposurface.

26. Switch to a **3D** View.

27. 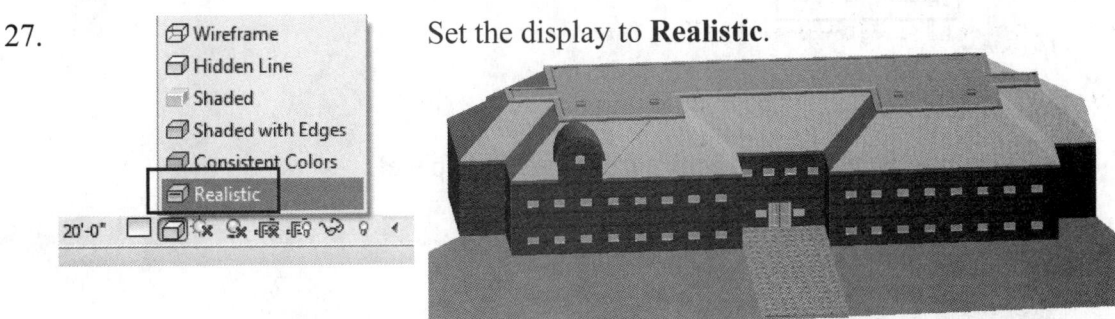 Set the display to **Realistic**.

28. Switch to the **Site** View.

29. Activate the **Massing & Site** ribbon.

30. 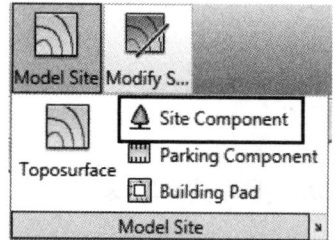 Select the **Site Component** tool on the Model Site panel.

31. RPC Tree - Deciduous Red Maple - 30' Select **Red Maple - 30′** [**Red Maple - 9 Meters**] from the Properties pane.

TIP: When you select the Site Component tool instead of the Component tool, Revit automatically filters out all loaded components except for Site Components.

---

32. Place the trees in front of the building.

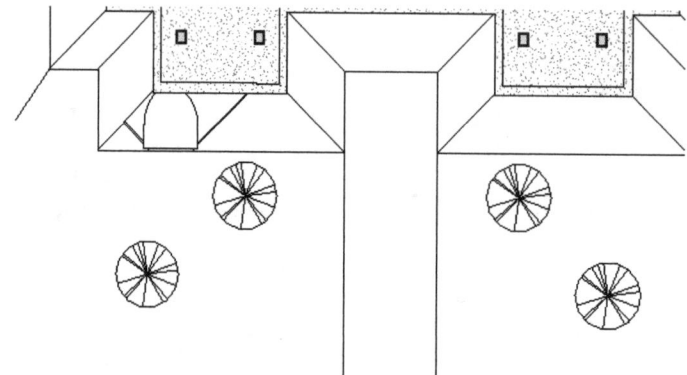

Many designers like to place people in their renderings to provide a sense of scale.

There are several people files available in the Revit software for you to place in the model.

33. 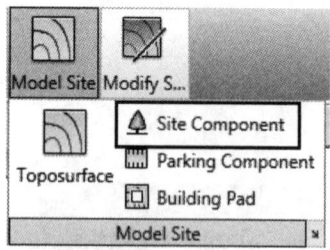 Select the **Site Component** tool on the Model Site panel.

34. 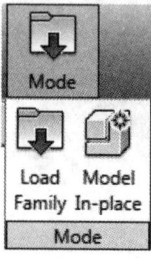 Select **Load Family** from the Mode panel.

35. Browse to the *Entourage* folder.

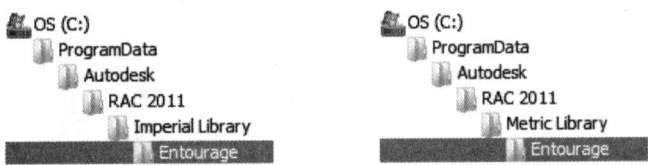

36. 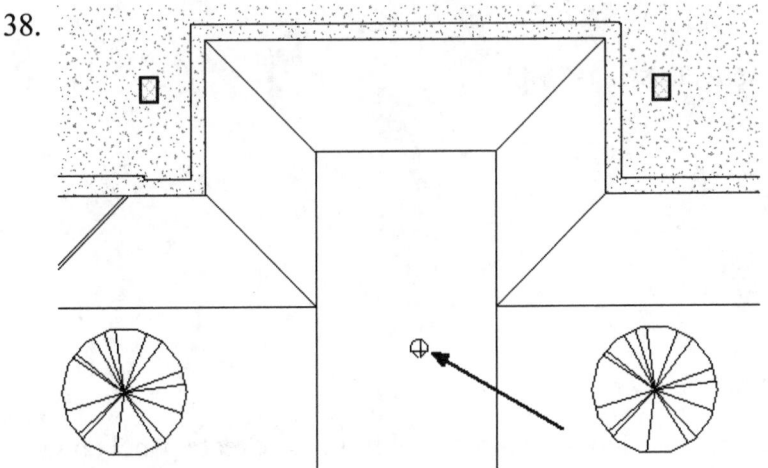 Locate the **RPC Female [M_RPC Female.rfa]** file.

Press **Open**.

37. RPC Female Cathy Set the Female to **Cathy** on the Properties pane.

38. Place the person on the walkway.

38. If you zoom in on the person, you only see a symbol – you don't see the real person until you perform a Render. You may need to switch to Hidden Line view to see the symbol for the person.

The point indicates the direction the person is facing.

39. 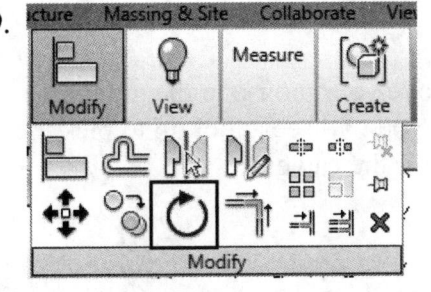 Rotate your person, so she is facing the building.

40. Save the file as *ex8-1.rvt*.

TIP: Make sure Level 1 or Site is active or your trees could be placed on Level 2 (and be elevated in the air). If you mistakenly placed your trees on the wrong level, you can pick the trees, right click, select Properties, and change the level.

Exercise 8-2
Defining Camera Views

Drawing Name: 8-1.rvt
Estimated Time: 15 minutes

This exercise reinforces the following skills:

- ❑ Camera
- ❑ Rename View
- ❑ View Properties

1.   📂 Open *ex8-1.rvt.*

2.   Activate **Site** floor plan.

    Views (all)
        Floor Plans
            Level 1
            Level 1 - Lobby Detail
            Level 1 - West Wing
            Level 1- East Wing
            Level 2
            Roof Cutoff
            Roof Line
            Site

3.   View Activate the **View** ribbon.

4.   Select the **3D View→Camera** tool from the Create panel on the View ribbon.

    Create Sheet Co... W

    3D View Section Callout

    Default 3D View

    Camera

5.   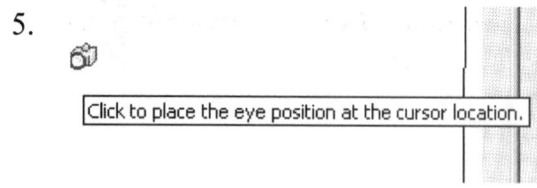

    Click to place the eye position at the cursor location.

If you move your mouse in the graphics window, you will see a tool tip to pick the location for the camera.

6. 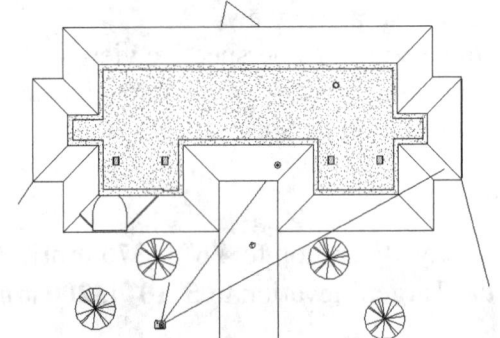   Aim the camera towards the front entrance to the building.

7. A window opens with the camera view of your model.

   The person and the tree appear as stick figures because the view is not rendered yet.

8. 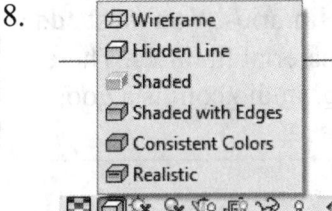   Change the Model Graphics Style to **Realistic**.

9.    Our view changes to a realistic display.

   The people and trees will appear like cardboard cutouts unless they are rendered. This is to conserve system resources.

10. 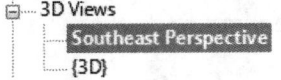   If you look in the browser, you see that a view has been added to the 3D Views list.

11. Highlight the **3D View 1**.

    Right click and select **Rename**.

    Rename to **Southeast Perspective**.

The view we have is a perspective view – not an isometric view.
Isometrics are true scale drawings. The Camera View is a perspective view with vanishing points. Isometric views have no vanishing points. Vanishing points are the points at which two parallel lines appear to meet in perspective.

12.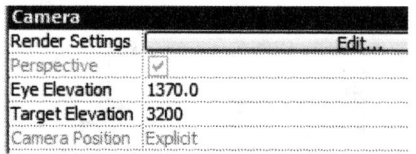

In the Properties pane:

Change the Eye Elevation to **4'6"** [**1370 mm**].
Change the Target Elevation to **5' 10"** [**3200 mm**].
Press **OK**.

Your view shifts slightly.

13. Save the file as *ex8-2.rvt*.

TIP: Additional material libraries can be added to Revit. You may store your material libraries on a server to allow multiple users access to the same libraries. You must add a path under Settings→Options to point to the location of your material libraries. There are many online sources for photorealistic materials; www.accustudio.com is a good place to start.

Exercise 8-3
Assigning Settings

Drawing Name: 8-2.rvt
Estimated Time: 20 minutes

This exercise reinforces the following skills:

- Rendering
- Settings
- Save to Project

You can also assign a specific time, date, location, lighting, and environment to your model.

1. Open *ex8-2.rvt*.

2. 3D Views
   Southeast Perspective
   {3D}
   Activate the **Southeast Perspective** view.

3. In the Properties pane:

Under Camera:
Select **Edit** for Render Settings.

Camera	
Rendering Settings	Edit...
Perspective	☑
Eye Elevation	4' 6"
Target Elevation	5' 10"
Camera Position	Explicit

4. Set the Quality Setting to **Medium**.

Press **OK**.

Rendering Settings

Quality
Setting: Medium

Lighting
Scheme: Exterior: Sun only
Sun Settings: Sunlight from Top Right
Artificial Lights...

Background
Style: Sky: Few Clouds

Clear   Hazy
Haze: ▯

Image
Adjust Exposure...

5. Activate the **Manage** ribbon.

Select **Location** on the Project Location panel.

Project L...   Design O...
- Location
- Coordinates ▾
- Position ▾
Project Location

6. Set the Project Address to 850 Market St. San Francisco, CA

The map will update to the location.

Press **OK**.

Location Weather and Site

Location | Site

Define Location by:
Internet Mapping Service

Project Address:
850 Market St, San Francisco, CA 94103, USA   Search

Map | Satellite | Hybrid | Terrain

Project Address: 850 Market St, San Francisco, CA 94103, USA
Latitude: 37.7850073
Longitude: -122.4068187
Enter an address or drag to move it.

7. Select the **Rendering** tool located on the bottom of the screen.

Perspective

8.  Select the **Render** button.

9. Your window will be rendered.

10. Select **Save to Project**.

11. 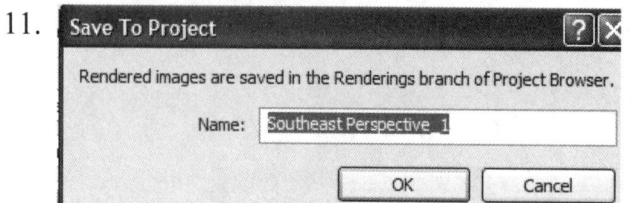 Press **OK** to accept the default name.

Save To Project

Rendered images are saved in the Renderings branch of Project Browser.

Name: Southeast Perspective_1

OK   Cancel

12. Renderings
    Southeast Perspective_1

Under Renderings, we now have a view called **Southeast Perspective_1**.

You can then drag and drop the image onto a sheet.

13. Display
    Show the model

Select the **Show the Model** button.
Close the Rendering dialog.

14. Our window changes to Shading – not Rendered mode.

15. Save the file as *ex8-3.rvt*.

Exercise 8-4
Interior Scenes

Drawing Name: 8-3.rvt
Estimated Time: 60 minutes

This exercise reinforces the following skills:

- ❑ Component
- ❑ Camera
- ❑ Dynamic 3D View
- ❑ Rendering Settings
- ❑ Walkthrough

- ❑ Section Box
- ❑ Lighting Fixtures
- ❑ Decals
- ❑ Sections
- ❑ Elevations

1.  Open *ex8-3.rvt.*

2. 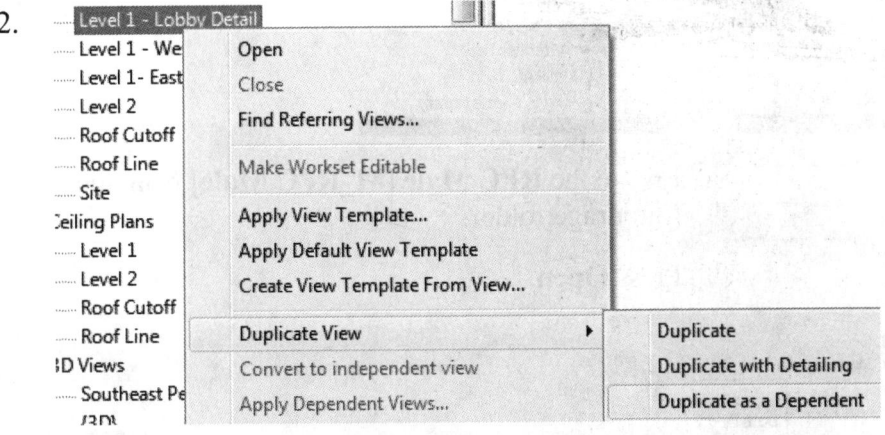 Select the **Level 1- Lobby Detail** Floor Plan. Right click and select **Duplicate View→ Duplicate**.

3. 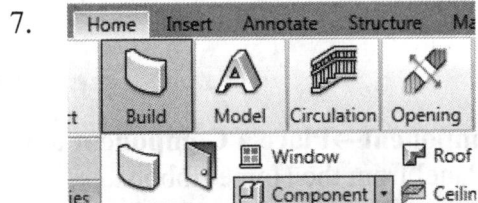 Rename the new view **Level 1 - Lobby Space Planning**.

4. On the Properties pane:

   Select **Edit** under Visibility/Graphics Overrides.

Detail Level	Medium
Visibility/Graphics O...	Edit...
Visual Style	Hidden Line
Graphic Display Opt...	Edit...

5. Uncheck **Ceilings** and **Floors** in the Model Categories tab.

   ☑ Casework
   ☐ Ceilings

6. Uncheck **Dimensions, Grids, Matchline** and **Sections** under the Annotations Categories tab.

   ☑ Generic Mo
   ☐ Grids

   ☑ Scope Boxes
   ☐ Sections
   ☑ Site Tags

7. Select the **Component→Place a Component** tool on the Build Panel from the Home ribbon.

8. 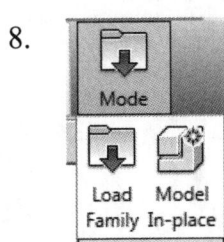 Select **Load** Family from the Mode panel.

9. Browse to the *Entourage* folder.

10.

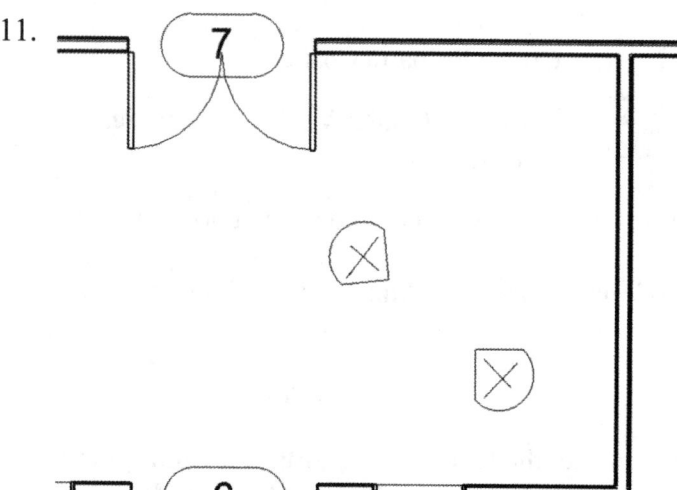

Locate the **RPC Male [M_RPC Male]** from the Entourage folder.

Press **Open**.

11.

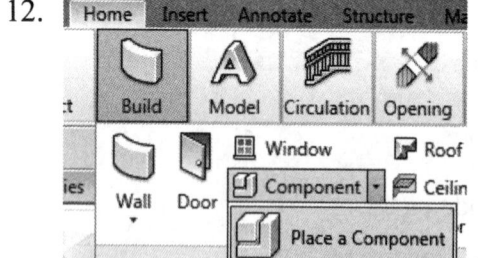

Place **RPC Male [M_RPC Male]: Dwayne** and **RPC Female [M_RPC Female:] Tina** in the waiting room area.

Use the Rotate tool to place them so they are facing each other.

12.

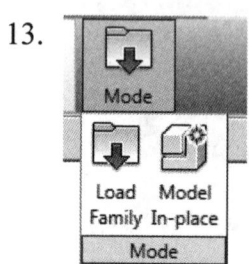

Select the **Component→Place a Component** tool on the Build Panel from the Home ribbon.

13. Select **Load** Family from the Mode panel.

14.

Hold down the **control** key to select the *Chair-Corbu, Television_Frame* and the *Table-Coffee* from the *Exercise Files* folder on the CD that came with the textbook.

Press **Open**.

Similar families are available in the Furniture folder that comes with Revit. However, the author has "tweaked" these families to display materials so that they look better in a rendering.

TIP:
> The point in the person symbol indicates the front of the person. To position the person, rotate the symbol using the Rotate tool.
> Add lights to create shadow and effects in your rendering. By placing lights in strategic locations, you can create a better photorealistic image.

15.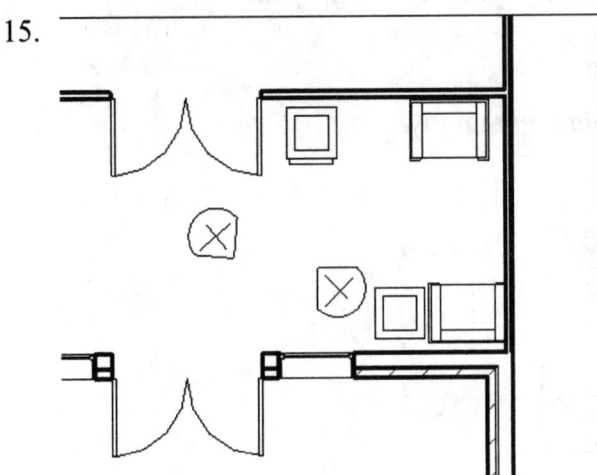

Place the chair and table in the waiting area.

If you press the SPACE bar before you click to place you can rotate the object.

16.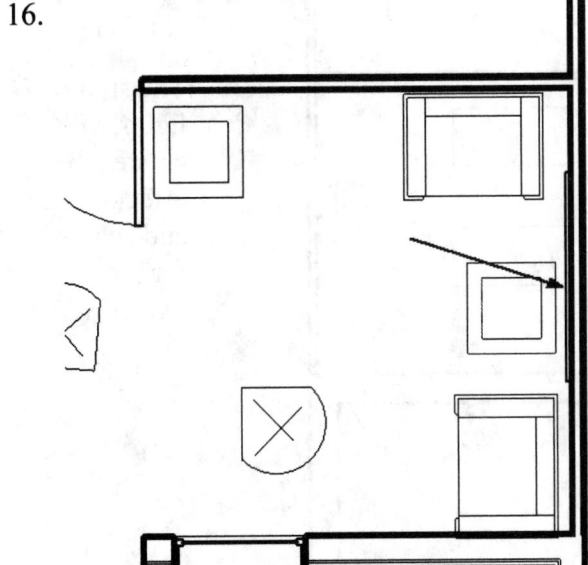

Place the *Television_Frame* on the East wall.

Constraints	
Level	Level 1
Elevation	3' 6"
Identity Data	
Comments	

In the Properties pane:
Set the Elevation to **3' 6"**.
This will locate the frame 3' 6" above Level 1.

17. 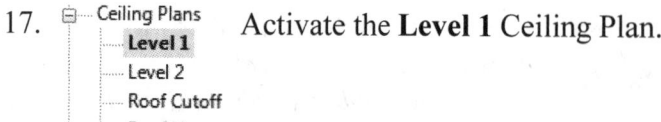 Activate the **Level 1** Ceiling Plan.

18. 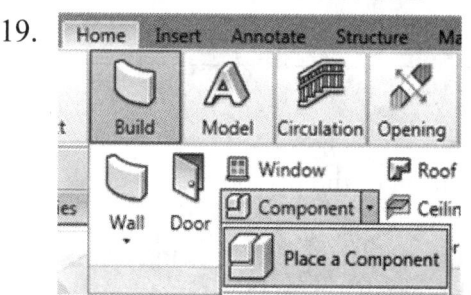 Type VV to launch the Visibility/Graphics dialog.
Disable the visibility of Matchline.
Press **OK**.

19. Select the **Component→Place a Component** tool on the Build Panel from the Home ribbon.

20. Select **Load** Family from the Options panel.

21. Browse to the *Lighting Fixtures* folder.

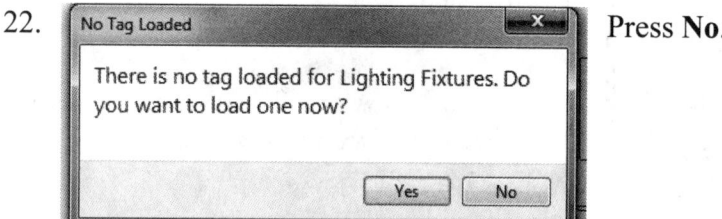 Locate the *Studio Light* family.

Press **Open**.

22. Press **No**.

No Tag Loaded

There is no tag loaded for Lighting Fixtures. Do you want to load one now?

Yes   No

23.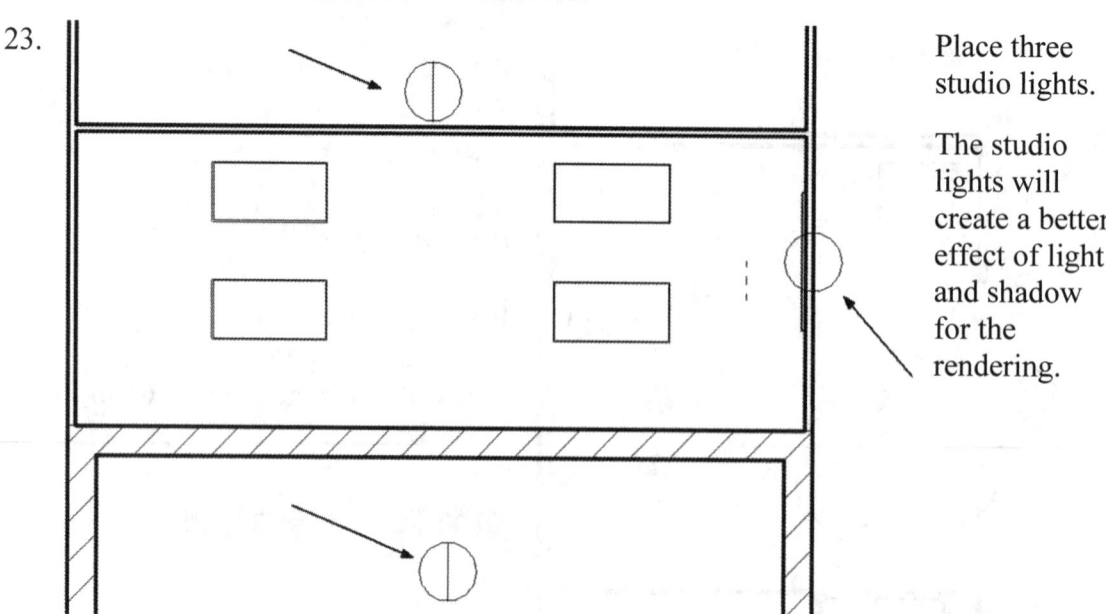

Place three studio lights.

The studio lights will create a better effect of light and shadow for the rendering.

24. 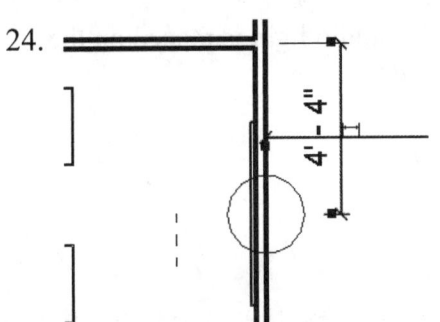 Select the Studio Light placed on the picture frame.

Set the Offset to **3′ 6″** in the Properties pane.

Constraints	
Level	Level 1
Host	Level : Level 1
Offset	3' 6"
Moves With Nearby Ele...	☐

25. Level 1 - Lobby Detail
Level 1 - Lobby Space Planning
Level 1 - West Wing
Level 1 - East Wing

Activate the **Level 1 - Lobby Space Planning** floor plan.

26. ⌐View⌐ Activate the **View** ribbon.

27. Select **Create→Section**.

28. 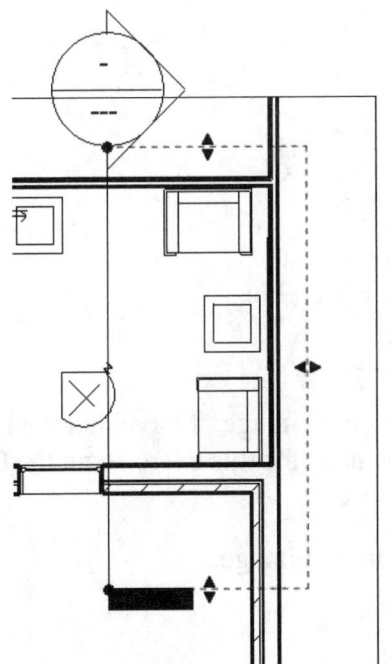 Place a section so it is looking at the wall with the picture frame.

29. Sections (Wall Section)
— Callout of Section 1
— Lobby Elevation

Rename the Section **Lobby Elevation**.

30. Sections (Wall Section)
— Callout of Section 1
— **Lobby Elevation**

Activate the **Lobby Elevation** section.

31. Note that the studio light is placed on the picture frame.

32. 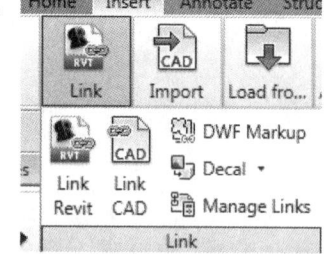 Activate the **Insert** ribbon.

33. Select **Decal→Decal Types**.

34. Select **New Decal** from the bottom left of the dialog box.

35. Type a name for your decal.

The decal will be assigned an image. I have included three images that can be used for this exercise on the CD: baseball, jockey, and soccer.

You can select the image of your choice or use your own image.

Press **OK**.

36. Select the Search button to select the image.

37.  Browse to where your exercise files are located.

Select the baseball/jockey/soccer image file.
Press **Open**.

38. 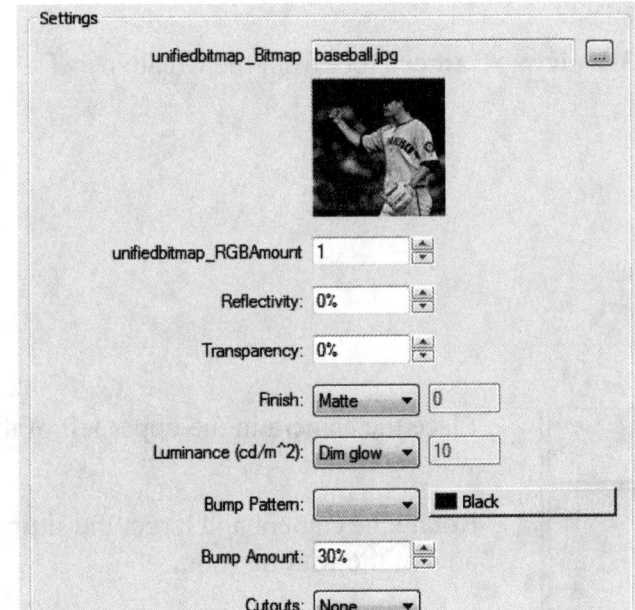 You will see a preview of the image.
Set the Finish to **Matte**.
Set the Luminance **to Dim glow**.

Press **OK**.

39. 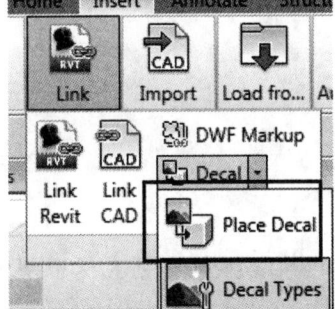 Select **Decal→Place Decal**.

40. On the Options bar: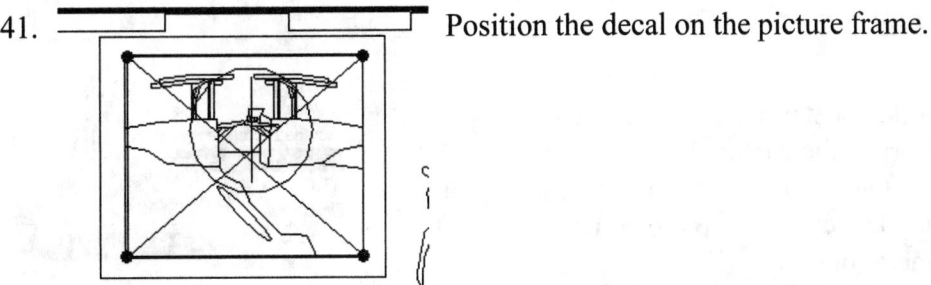

Disable **Lock Proportions**.
Set the Width to **3′ 10″**.
Set the Height to **3′ 2″**.

41. Position the decal on the picture frame.

42.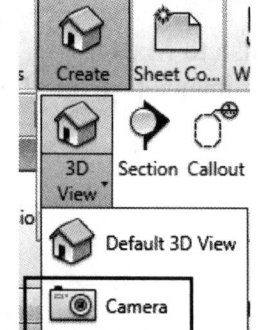

Floor Plans
Level 1
Level 1 - Lobby Detail
Level 1 - Lobby Space Planning
Level 1 - West Wing
Level 1- East Wing

Activate the **Level 1 - Lobby Space Planning** floor plan.

43. [View] Activate the **View** ribbon.

44. Select the **3D View→Camera** tool from the Create panel.

45.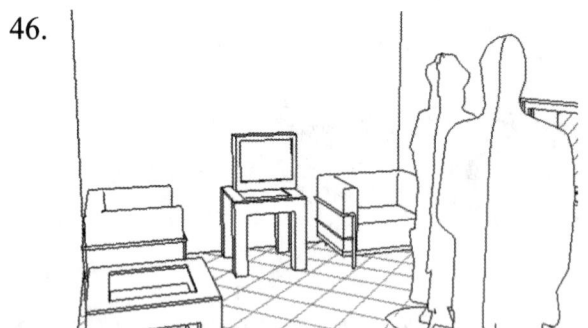

Place the camera in the upper left of the waiting room.

Rotate the camera and target the sitting area of the waiting room.

46. A window will appear with our interior scene.

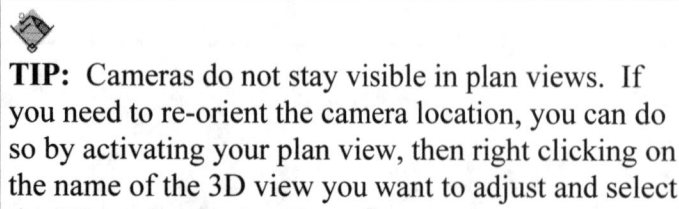

TIP: Cameras do not stay visible in plan views. If you need to re-orient the camera location, you can do so by activating your plan view, then right clicking on the name of the 3D view you want to adjust and select the 'Show Camera' option.

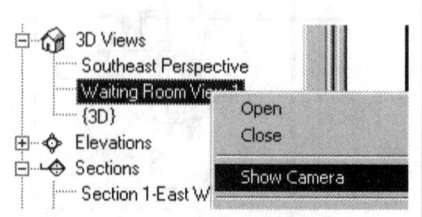

47. 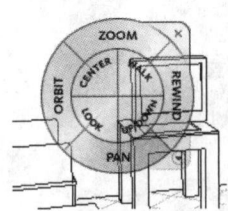 Rename the view **Lobby**.

48. Select **Mini Tour Building Wheel** from View toolbar.

Use the Navigation Wheel to adjust your scene. Try the LOOK and WALK buttons.

49. 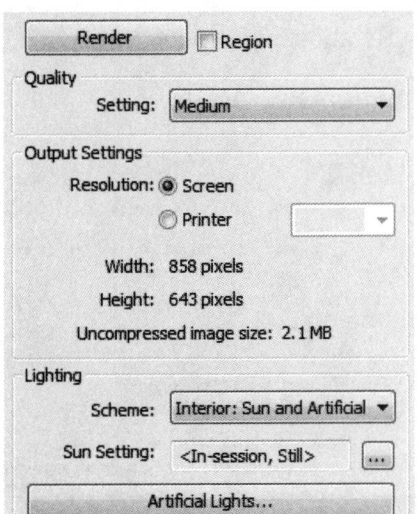 Change the camera view until you see your people.

You also see that you can use this tool to 'walk through your model'.

50. Activate the **Southeast Perspective** view.
Our previous shaded exterior view is restored.
Activate the **Lobby** view.

51. Turn **Sun Path ON**.
Turn Shadows ON.

52. Activate the **Rendering** dialog.

53. Set the Quality Setting to **Medium**.

Set the Lighting Scheme to **Interior: Sun and Artificial Light**.

Press **Render**.

54. The interior scene is rendered.

55.    Select the **Adjust Exposure** button on the Rendering Dialog.

56.   If necessary:

Adjust the controls and select **Apply**.

Readjust and select **Apply**.

Press **OK**.

57. Save to Project...   Press **Save to Project**.

58. Save To Project

     Rendered images are saved in the Renderings branch of Project Browser.

     Name: Lobby_1

       OK   Cancel   Press **OK**.

59. Close the Rendering Dialog.

60. Save the file as *ex8-4.rvt*.

Exercise 8-5
Placing a Rendering on a Sheet

Drawing Name: 8-4.rvt
Estimated Time: 5 minutes

This exercise reinforces the following skills:

- ❑ View Properties
- ❑ View Titles

1.   Open *ex8-4.rvt*.

2. Sheets (all)
   A101 - First Level Floor Plan
   A102 - Door Schedule
   A103 - Glazing Schedule
   A104 - Finish Schedule
   A105 - Exterior Elevations
   A106 - East Elevation
   A107 - Detail Views

    In the browser, activate the **Exterior Elevations** sheet.

3. Viewports (1)   Edit Type

Graphics	
View Scale	1/8" = 1'-0"
Scale Value 1:	3/16" = 1'-0"
Display Model	1/8" = 1'-0"
Detail Level	1" = 10'-0"
Detail Number	3/32" = 1'-0"
	1/16" = 1'-0"
Rotation on Sheet	1" = 20'-0"
Visibility/Graphics Overr...	3/64" = 1' 0"...
Visual Style	Hidden Line

In the Properties pane:

Set the View Scale to **1/16″ = 1′-0″ [1:200]**.

Press **OK**.

4. Repeat for the South Elevation.

5.

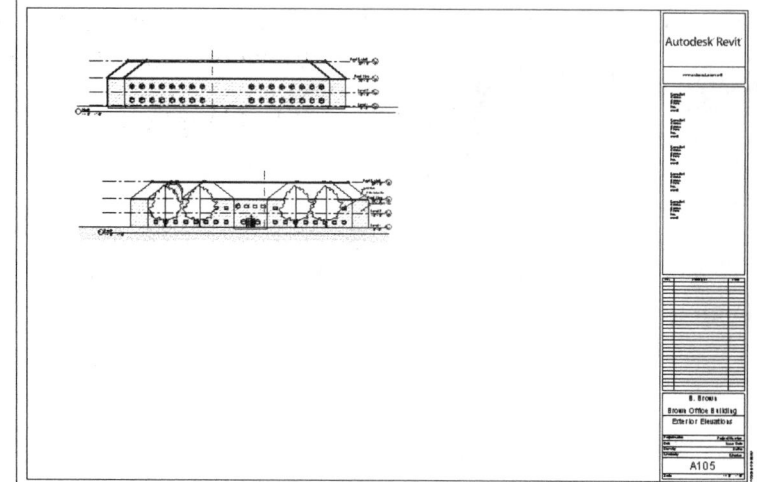

Zoom to Fit.

Shift the elevation views to the left to make room for an additional view.

Note you see a toposurface in the South elevation view because one was added for the exterior rendering.

6.

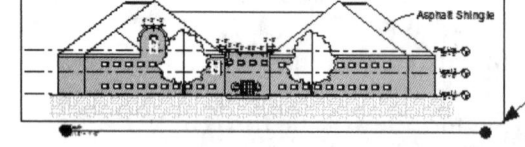

In the browser, locate the **Southeast Perspective** view under *Renderings*.

Drag and drop it onto the sheet.

7.

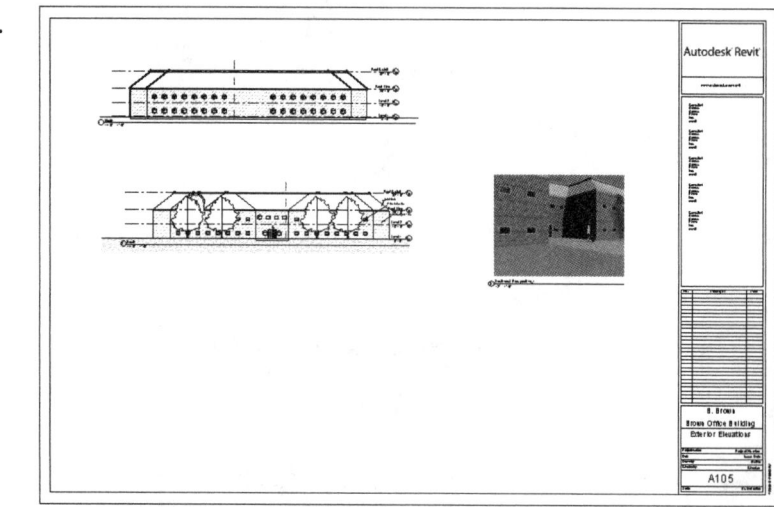

You see how easy it is to add rendered views to your layouts.

8.

To adjust the length of the view title, click on the view. This will activate the grips and allow you to adjust the length and location of the title.

9.

Select the rendering image that was just placed.

10.

In the Properties pane:

Select **Edit Type**.

11.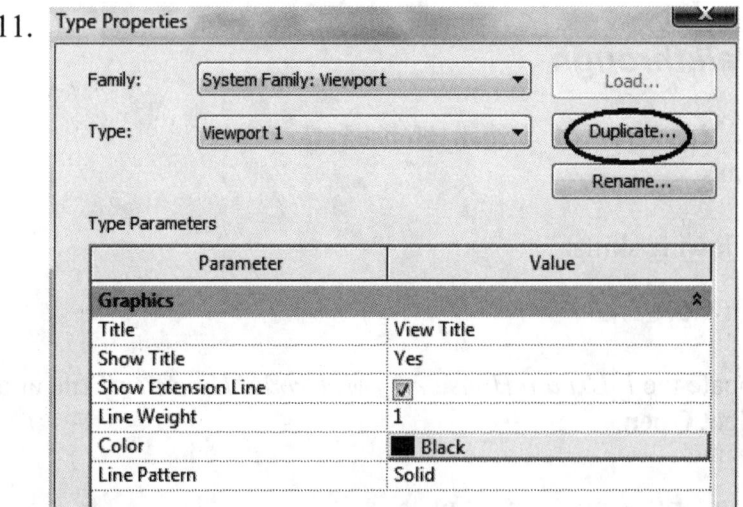

Note that the current type of Viewport shows the title.

Select **Duplicate**.

12.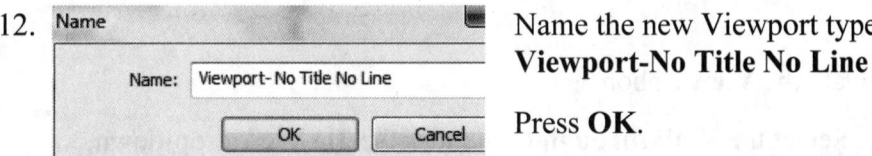

Name the new Viewport type: **Viewport-No Title No Line**

Press **OK**.

13.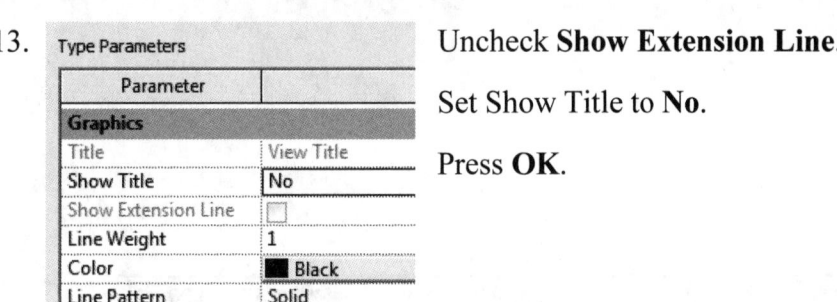

Uncheck **Show Extension Line**.

Set Show Title to **No**.

Press **OK**.

14. Save the file as *ex8-5.rvt*.

TIP: You can free up memory resources for rendering by closing any windows you are not using. Windows with 3D or renderings take up a considerable amount of memory.

Exercise 8-6
Placing a Path for a Walkthrough

Drawing Name: i_Urban_House.rvt [M _Urban_House.rvt]
Estimated Time: 10 minutes

This exercise reinforces the following skills:

- Creating a Walkthrough view

1. File name: i_Urban_House.rvt Locate the *i_Urban_House.rvt [M_Urban_House.rvt]* file and
    File name: m_Urban_House.rvt select **Open**.

2. Floor Plans Activate the **First Floor** Floor Plan view.
    FIRST FLOOR
    GROUND FLOOR

3. View Activate the **View** ribbon.

4. Select the **Walkthrough** tool under the 3D View drop-down.

    3D View | Section | Cal
    Default 3D
    Camera
    Walkthrough

5. Walkthrough | ☑ Perspective Scale: 1/8" = 1'-0" ▼ Offset: 5' 6" From FIRST FLOC ▼

    Verify that **Perspective** is enabled in the Status Bar.

    This indicates that a perspective view will be created.
    The Offset indicates the height of the camera offset from the floor level.

6. 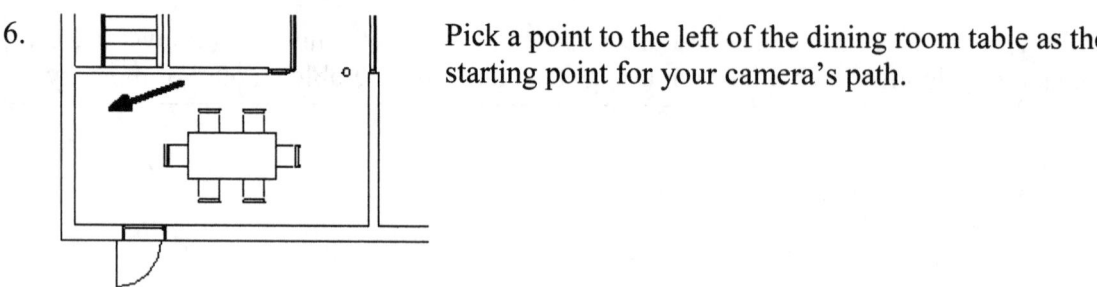 Pick a point to the left of the dining room table as the
    starting point for your camera's path.

7. 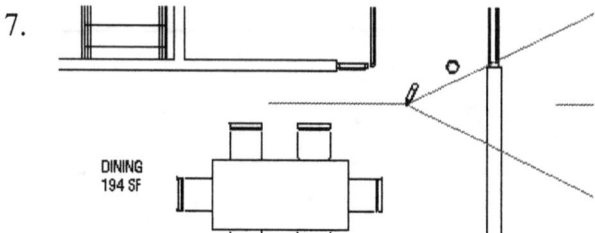 Place a second point at the start of the
    hallway.

    DINING
    194 SF

8.

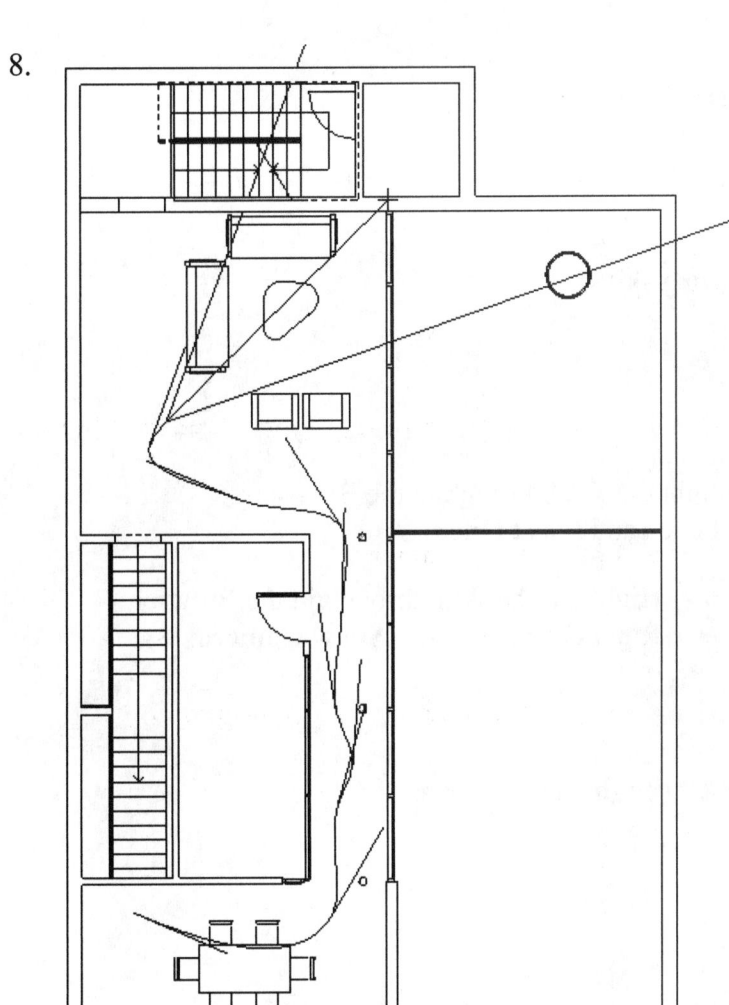

Place points at the locations indicated by the arrows to guide your walkthrough.

9. 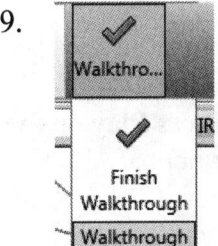   Select **Walkthrough→Finish Walkthrough** from the ribbon.

10. ⊟····Walkthroughs   In the Project Browser, you will now see a Walkthrough listed under
      ····Walkthrough 1   Walkthroughs.

11. Save as *ex8-6.rvt*.

Exercise 8-7
Playing the Walkthrough

Drawing Name: ex8-6.rvt
Estimated Time: 5 minutes

This exercise reinforces the following skills:

- Playing a Walkthrough

1. Open *ex8-6.rvt*.

2. 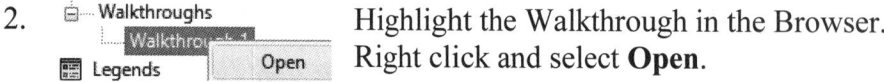 Highlight the Walkthrough in the Browser.
    Right click and select **Open**.

3. 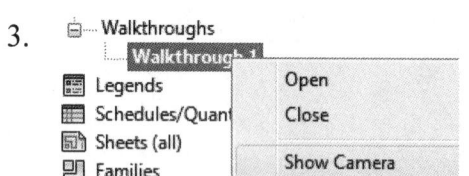 Highlight the Walkthrough in the Browser.
    Right click and select **Show Camera**.

4.  Select **Edit Walkthrough** on the ribbon.

5. Look at the lower left of the screen.

    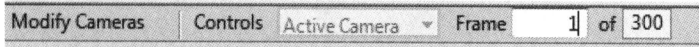

    Set the Frame number to **1.0**.

6. 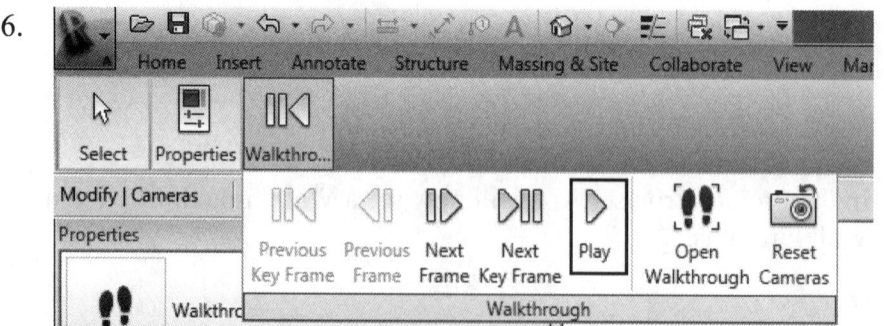 Press **Play** on the ribbon.

7. ☐ 300 ☐   Press the button that displays the total frame number. Your frame number value may be different.

8. Total Frames : ☐ 50 ☐   Change the Total Frames value to **50**.
    Press **Apply** and **OK**.

9. Press **Play**.

10. Save as *ex8-7.rvt*.

TIP: To stop playing the walkthrough, press **ESC** at any frame point.

Exercise 8-8
Editing the Walkthrough Path

Drawing Name: ex8-7.rvt
Estimated Time: 15 minutes

This exercise reinforces the following skills:

- Show Camera
- Editing a Walkthrough
- Modifying a Camera View

1. Open *ex8-7.rvt*.

2. 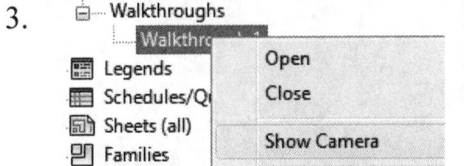 Activate the **First Floor** Floor Plan View.

3. Highlight the Walkthrough 1 in the Project Browser.

   Right click and select **Show Camera**.

4.  Select **Edit Walkthrough** from the ribbon.

5. 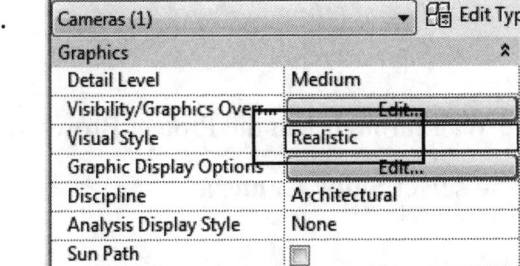 In the Properties pane:

   Set the Visual Style to **Realistic**.

6. Disable **Far Clip Active**.

7. Double left click on **Walkthrough 1** to open the view.

8.  Select **Edit Walkthrough** from the ribbon.

9. Press **Play**.

10. Save as *ex8-8.rvt*.

 TIP: The appearance of shaded objects is controlled in the material definition.

Exercise 8-9
Creating an Animation

Drawing Name: ex8-8.rvt
Estimated Time: 15 minutes

This exercise reinforces the following skills:

* Show Camera
* Editing a Walkthrough
* Modifying a Camera View

1. Open *ex8-8.rvt*.

2. 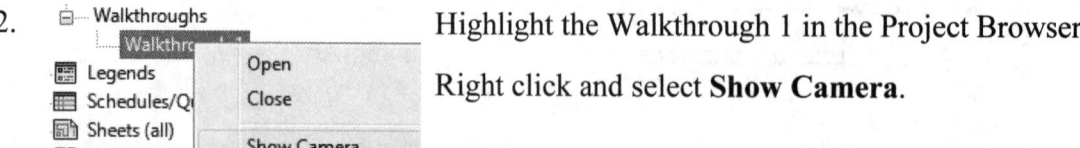 Highlight the Walkthrough 1 in the Project Browser.

Right click and select **Show Camera**.

3.  Select **Edit Walkthrough** on the ribbon.

4. Frame | 1.0 | of | 50 | Set the Frame number to **1.0**.

5. Go to **File→ Export→Images** and **Animations→ Walkthrough**.

   Creates exchange files and sets options.

   CAD Formats
   Creates DWG, DXF, DGN, or SAT files.

   DWF/DWFx
   Creates DWF or DWFx files.

   Building Site
   Exports an ADSK exchange file.

   Images and Animations
   Saves animations or image files.

   Reports
   Saves a schedule or Room/Area report.

   Walkthrough
   Solar Study
   Image

6. Set the Visual Style to **Realistic**.

   Press **OK**.

   Length/Format

   Output Length
   ◉ All frames
   ○ Frame range
   Start: 1   End: 50
   Frames/sec: 15   Total time: 00:00:03

   Format
   Visual Style <Realistic>
   Dimensions 900   675
   Zoom to 100 % of actual size

   OK   Cancel   Help

7. File name: ex8-8 Walkthrough 1
   Files of type: AVI Files (*.avi)

   Locate where you want to store your avi file. You can use the Browse button (…) next to the Name field to locate your file.

8. Name your file *ex8-8 Walkthrough 1.avi*.

9.   Press **Save**.

10. Select **Microsoft Video 1**.

This will allow you to play the avi on RealPlayer or Microsoft Windows Media Player. If you select a different compressor, you may not be able to play your avi file.

11. Press **OK**.

12. A progress bar will appear in the lower right of your screen to keep you apprised of how long it will take.

13. ex8-8 Walkthrough 1.avi
     Video Clip
     21.6 MB

     Locate the file using Explorer.
     Double click on the file to play it.

14. Save as *ex8-9.rvt*.

Exercise 8-10
Walking up Stairs

Drawing Name: ex8-9.rvt
Estimated Time: 15 minutes

This exercise reinforces the following skills:

- Show Camera
- Editing a Walkthrough
- Modifying a Camera View

Every Revit class I teach inevitably there are students who want to be able to go up the stairs with the camera. So, here is how to do that.

1.   Open *ex8-9.rvt*.

2.   Select the **East Elevation** view.

3. Switch to **Wireframe** mode.

4. On the View ribbon, select the **3D→Walkthrough** tool.

5. Place the walkthrough path going through the door, up the stairs, into the next room.

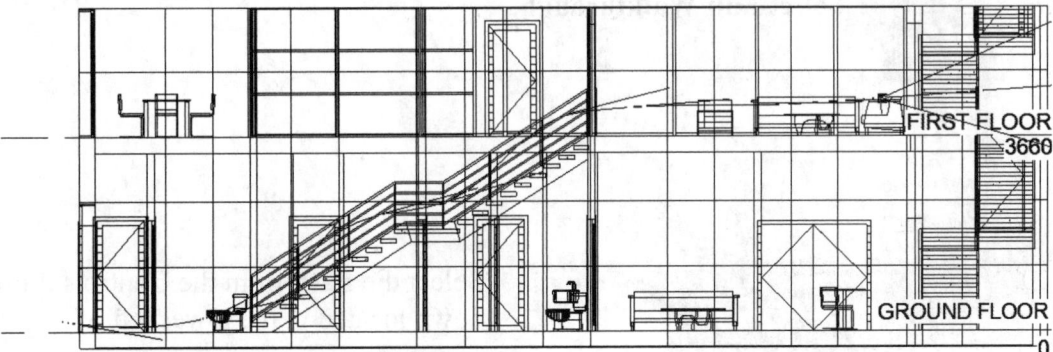

6. Press **Finish Walkthrough**.

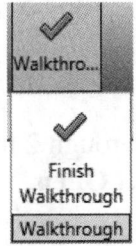

7. Activate the **GROUND FLOOR** floor plan.

Floor Plans
FIRST FLOOR
GROUND FLOOR
ROOF PLAN

8. 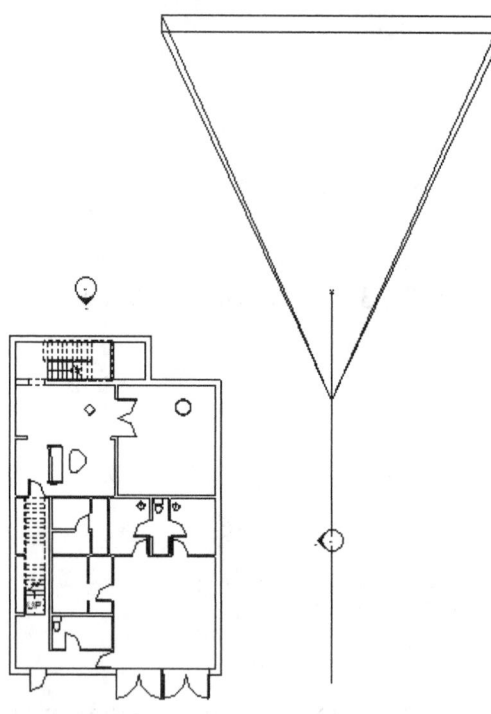 You will see that the walkthrough path was placed outside the building.

Use the **MOVE** tool to move the path over the stairs.

9.  Select **Edit Walkthrough**.

10. Select the **Path** from the Controls drop-down located in the lower left of the screen.

11. Adjust the path as needed.

12.  Highlight the Walkthrough 2 in the browser.
Right click and select **Open**.

13. Reset to Frame 1.

14. Press **Play**.

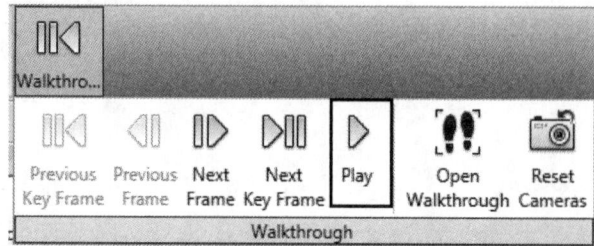

15. Save as *ex8-10.rvt*.

Additional Projects

1)   Create a rendering of the cafeteria area

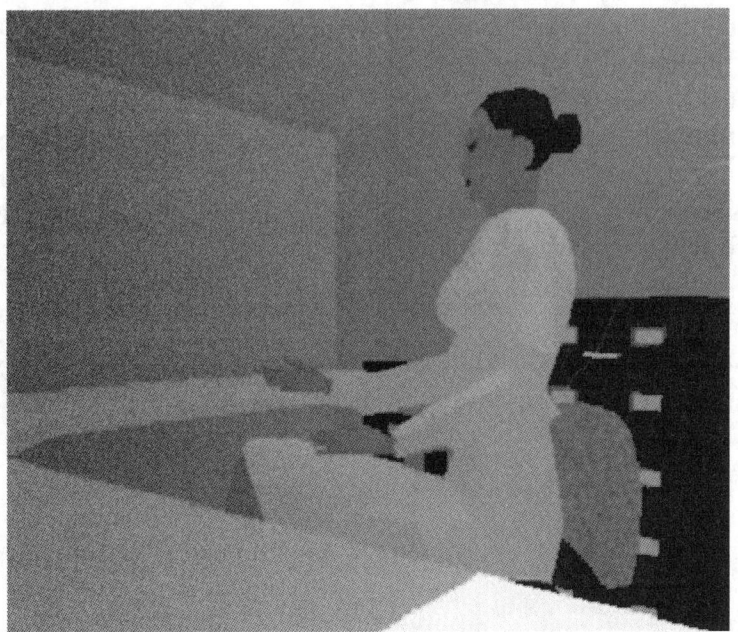

2)   Create a rendering of one of the office cubicles

3)   With one of the interior rendered scenes, adjust the lighting.

4) Add exterior lighting using the bollard lights in the Revit library to both sides of the walkway to the building.
Set up the Southeast Perspective Rendering so that the day is December 11 and the time is 7:30 pm.
Set the Season to Winter.
Set the Lighting so the interior lights are off and the exterior lights are on

This rendering will probably take several hours, so you may want to actually perform the rendering overnight.

5) Create a walkthrough avi of one of your rendered scenes.

Lesson 8 Quiz

True or False

1. The Walkthrough tool on the View ribbon allows you to create an avi.
2. The Environment button on Render Settings dialog allows you to set the time of day.
3. The Sun button on Render Settings dialog allows you to set the time of day.
4. When you create a Rendering, you will be able to see how your people will appear.
5. Rendering is a relatively quick process.
6. Renderings can be added to sheets.
7. You can adjust the number of frames in a walkthrough.
8. You can not create walkthrough animations that go from one level to another.
9. Once a path is placed, it can not be edited.
10. You can not modify the view style of a walkthrough from wireframe to shaded.

Multiple Choice

11. The folder, which contains RPC People, is named:

    A. Site
    B. People
    C. Entourage
    D. Rendering

12. The Camera tool is located on the _____ ribbon.

    A. Rendering
    B. Site
    C. Home
    D. View

13. To see the camera in a view:

    A. Highlight the 3D view in the browser, right click and select Show Camera.
    B. Highlight the view in the browser, right click and select Show Camera.
    C. Go to View→Show Camera.
    D. Mouse over the view, right click and select Show Camera.

14. In order to save your rendering, use:

    A. File→Export
    B. Save to Project
    C. Capture Rendering
    D. Export Image

15. When editing a walkthrough, the user can modify the following:

    A. Camera
    B. Path
    C. Add Key Frame
    D. Remove Key Frame
    E. All of the above

ANSWERS:
  1) F; 2) F; 3) T; 4) T; 5) F; 6) T; 7) T; 8) F; 9) F; 10) F; 11) C; 12) D; 13) B; 14) B; 15) E

Lesson 9
Customizing Revit

Exercise 9-1
Creating an Annotation Symbol

File: north arrow.dwg (located on the Supplemental Files CD)
Estimated Time: 30 minutes

This exercise reinforces the following skills:

- ❑ Import AutoCAD Drawing
- ❑ Full Explode
- ❑ Query
- ❑ Annotation Symbol

Many architects have accumulated hundreds of symbols that they use in their drawings. This exercise shows you how to take your existing AutoCAD symbols and use them in Revit.

1. Locate the north arrow.dwg on the CD included with the text.

2. 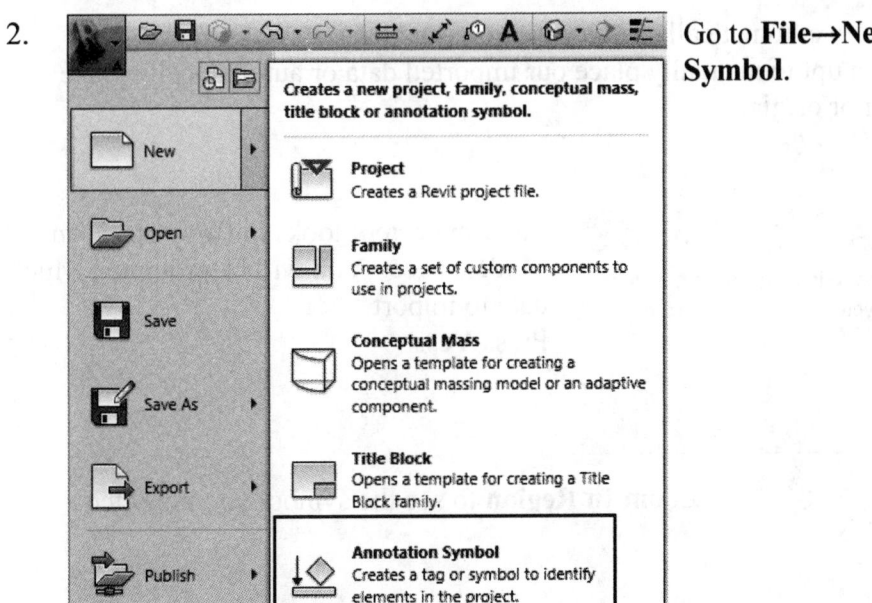 Go to **File→New→ Annotation Symbol**.

3. Highlight the **Generic Annotation.rft** file under Annotations.

    Press **Open**.

4. Activate the Insert ribbon.

Select **Import CAD**.

5. Locate the *north arrow.dwg* file on the Supplemental Files CD.

6.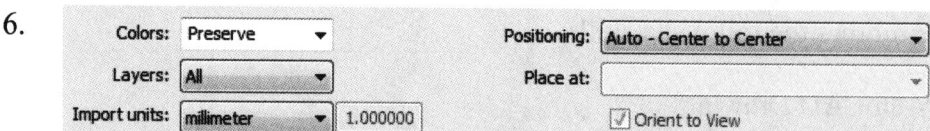

Under Colors:
Enable **Preserve**.
Under Layers:
Select **All**.
Under Import Units:
Select **millimeter**.
Under Positioning:
Select **Auto – Center to Center**.

This allows you to automatically scale your imported data.
Note that we can opt to manually place our imported data or automatically place using the center or origin.

Press **Open**.

7. The Import tool looks in Paper space and Model space. You will be prompted which data to import.
Press **Yes**.

> **Revit**
>
> Import detected no valid elements in the file's Paper space. Do you want to import from the Model space?
>
> Yes   No

8. 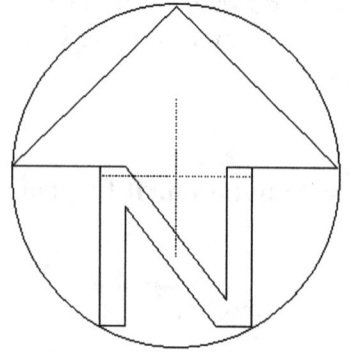 **Zoom In Region** to see the symbol you imported.

9.

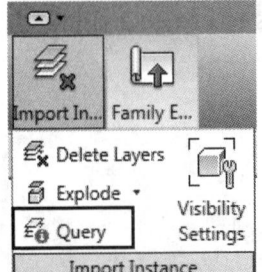

Pick the imported symbol.

Select **Query** from the ribbon.

10.

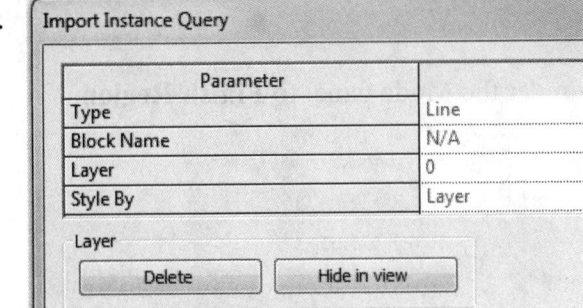

Pick on the line indicated.

11.

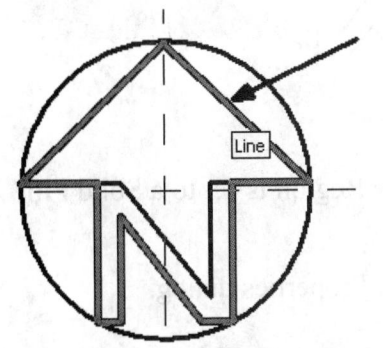

A dialog appears that lists what the selected item is and the layer where it resides.

Press **OK**.

12.

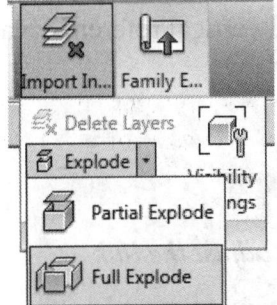

Pick the imported symbol.

Select **Full Explode**.

We can now edit our imported data.

13.

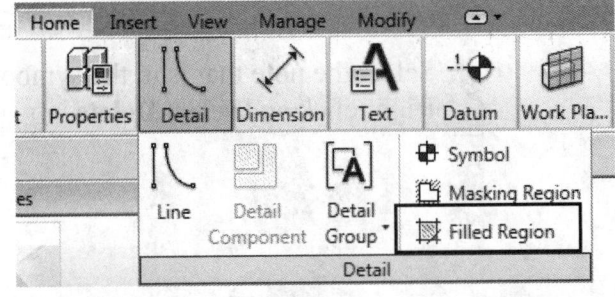

Select the **Filled Region** tool on the Detail panel from the Home ribbon.

14. ☑ Chain   Offset: 0' 0"   ☐ Radius: 1' 0"

Enable **Chain** on the status bar.

15. 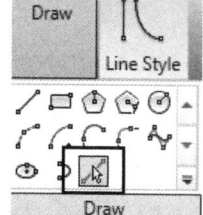 Use the **Pick** tool to select the existing lines to create a filled arrowhead.

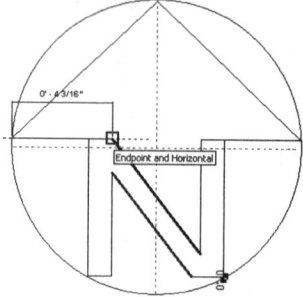

16. ⊞ Edit Type Select **Edit Type** from the Properties pane.

17.

Type Parameters	
Parameter	
Graphics	
Background	Opaque
Line Weight	1
Color	■ Black
Other	
Cut fill pattern	Solid fill

We see that the Region is set to a Solid Fill, Color Black.

Close the Type Properties dialog.

18. ✕ Select the **Green Check** under the Mode panel to **Finish Region**.

19. 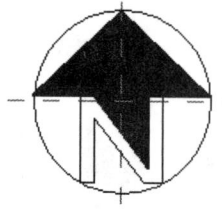 Using grips, shorten the horizontal and vertical reference planes if needed.

You will need to unpin the reference planes before you can adjust the link.

Be sure to pin the reference planes after you have finished any adjustments. Pinning the reference planes ensures they do not move.

20. Delete this note before using

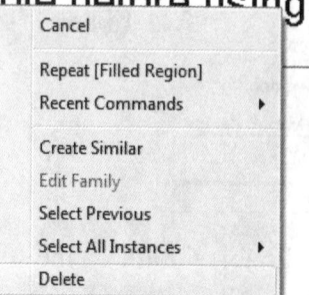

Select the note that is in the symbol.
Right click and select **Delete**.

Cancel

Repeat [Filled Region]
Recent Commands   ▶

Create Similar
Edit Family
Select Previous
Select All Instances   ▶
Delete

21. Select **Category and Parameters** under the Properties panel on the Modify ribbon.

22. Note that **Generic Annotations** is highlighted. Press **OK**.

23. Save the file as a new family.

File name: north arrow

Save as type: Family Files (*.rfa)

24. Open *ex8-5.rvt*.

25. Activate the **First Level Floor Plan** sheet.

26. Activate the **Annotate** ribbon.

27. Select the **Symbol** tool.

28. Select **Load Family**.

29. Load the *north arrow.rfa* file that was saved to your student folder.

File name: north arrow.rfa

Files of type: Family Files (*.rfa)

30. Place the North Arrow symbol in your drawing.

31. Save *ex8-5.rvt* as *ex9-1.rvt*.

Exercise 9-2
Creating a Title Block

Estimated Time: 60 minutes

This exercise reinforces the following skills:

- ❑ Titleblock
- ❑ Import CAD
- ❑ Labels
- ❑ Text
- ❑ Families

1. 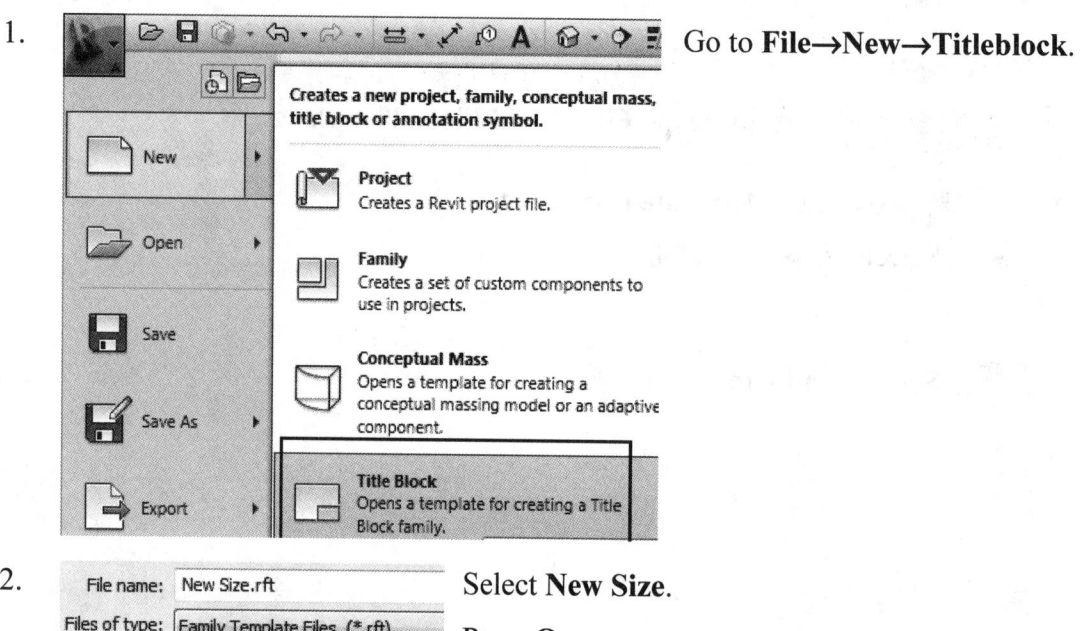 Go to **File→New→Titleblock**.

2. 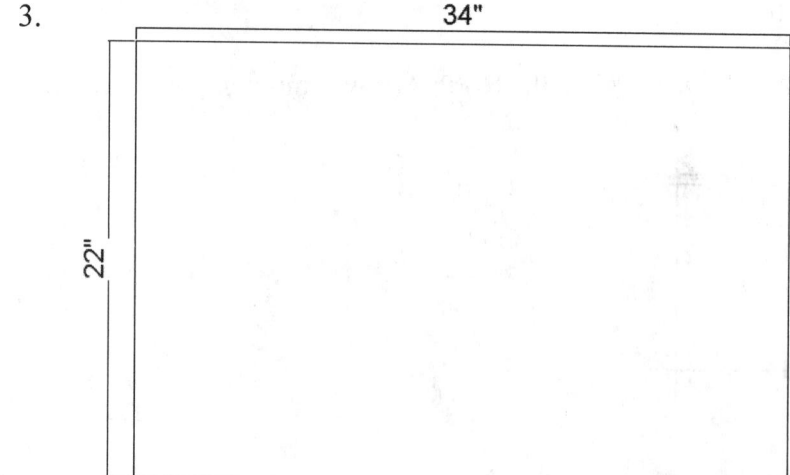 Select **New Size**.

   Press **Open**.

3. Pick the top horizontal line.
   Select the dimension and change it to **22″**.

   Pick the right vertical line.

   Select the dimension and change it to **34″**.

34"

22"

TIP: The title block you define includes the sheet size. If you delete the titleblock, the sheet of paper is also deleted. This means your titleblock is linked to the paper size you define.

You need to define a titleblock for each paper size you use.

4. | Zoom In Region |
    | Zoom Out (2x) |
    | Zoom To Fit |

Right click in the graphics window and select **Zoom to Fit**.

5.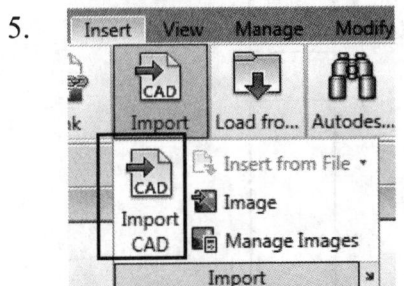

Activate the Insert ribbon.
Select **Import→Import CAD**.

6. | File name: | Aec Arch D |
    | Files of type: | DWG Files (*.dwg) |

Locate the *Aec Arch D* in the exercise files directory.

7.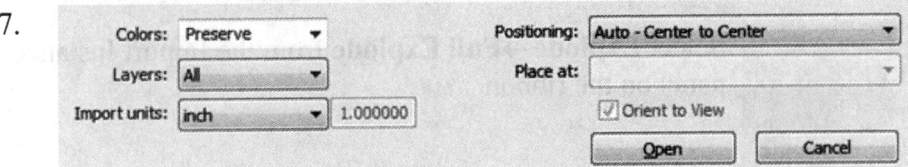

Set Colors to **Preserve**.
Set Layers to **All**.
Set Import Units to **Inch**.
Set Positioning to: **Auto - Center to Center**.

Press **Open**.

8.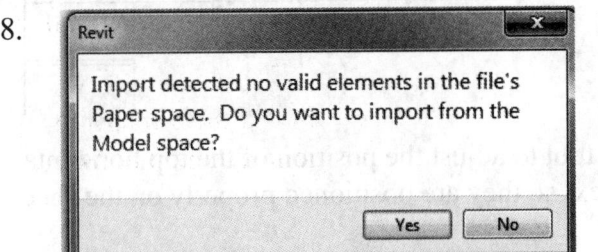

Press **Yes**.

9. 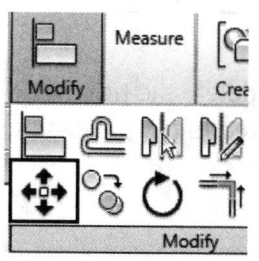 Select the title block.

Use the **Move** tool on the Modify panel to reposition the titleblock so it is aligned with the existing Revit sheet.

10. Select the imported title block so it is highlighted.

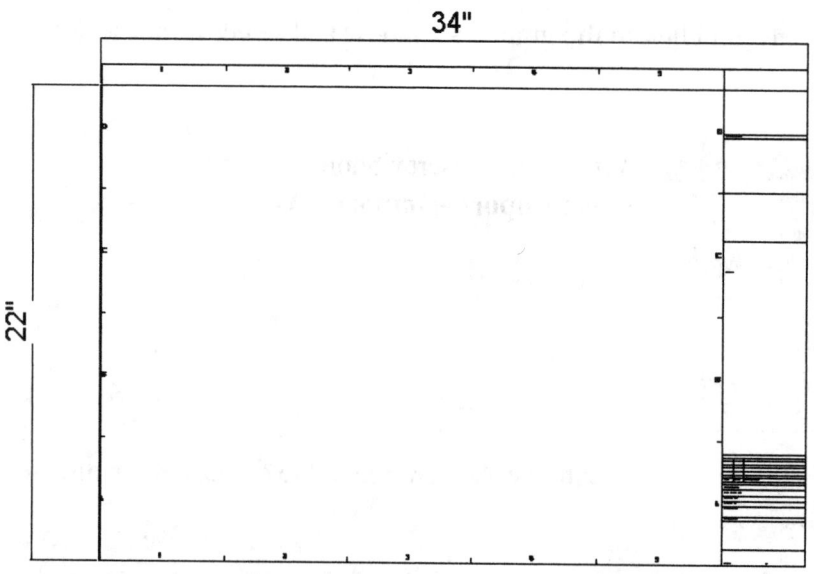

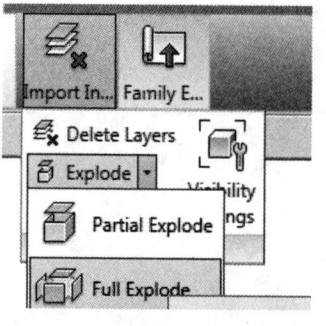 Select **Explode→Full Explode** from the Import Instance panel on the ribbon.

11.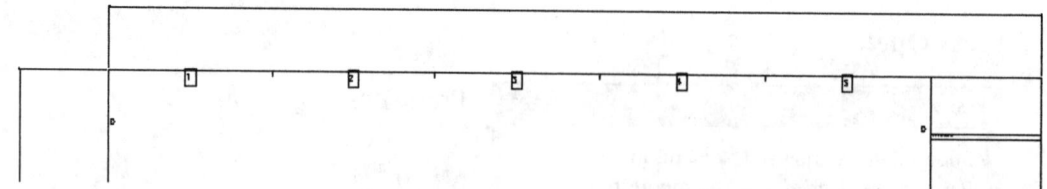

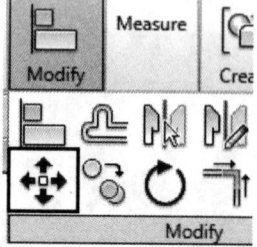 Use the Move tool to adjust the position of the top horizontal lines and the text so they are positioned properly on the sheet.

12.  We will place an image in the top rectangle.

13. Activate the **Insert** ribbon.
Select the **Import→Image** tool.

14. File name: sfsu
Files of type: All Image Files (*.bmp, *.jpg, *.jpeg, *.png, *.tif)

Open the *sfsu.jpg* file from the CD exercise files.

15. 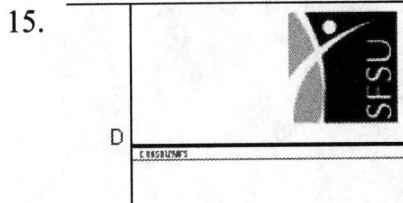 Place the logo in the upper right corner.

 TIP: Revit can import jpg, jpeg, or bmp files. Imported images can be resized, rotated, and flipped using activated grips.

16.  Select the **Text** tool from the **Home** Ribbon.

17. 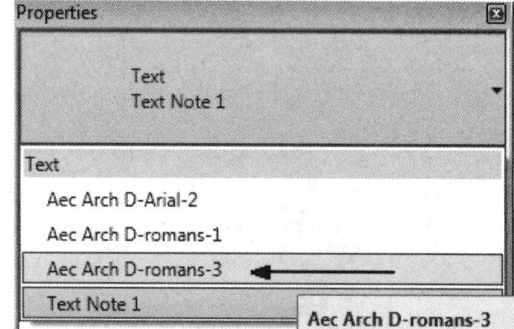 On the Properties pane:

Select the **Aec Arch D-romans-3** text type.

Note that when you imported the CAD file, you also imported any text and dimension styles.

18.  Type in the name of your school or company under the logo.

Select the text.

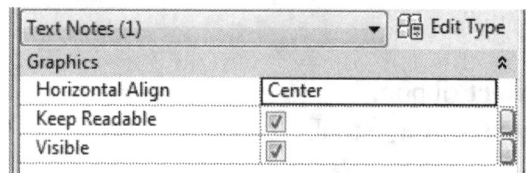 In the Properties pane:
Set the Text Alignment to **Center**.

19.  Place the address and other information under the school name.

TIP: The data entered in the Value field will be the default value used in the title block. To save edit time, enter in the value that you will probably use.

20. 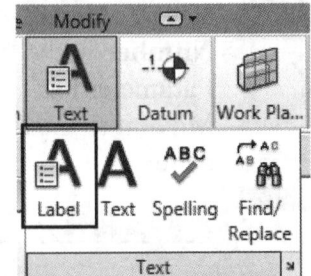 Select the **Label** tool from the Home ribbon.

Labels are similar to attributes. They are linked to file properties.

21. 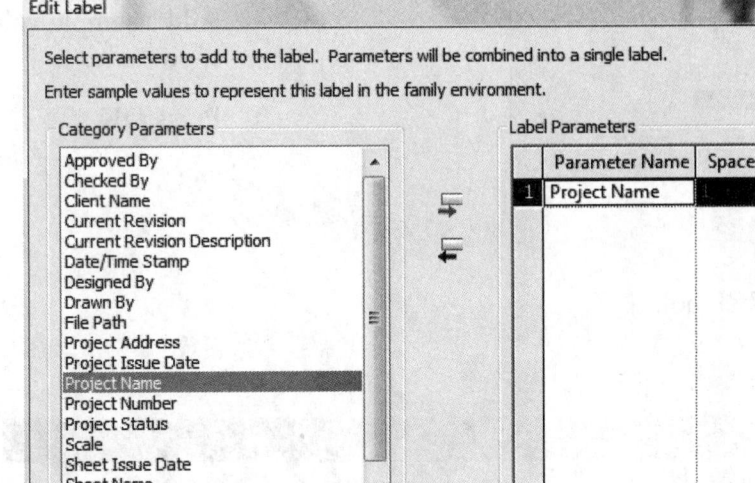 Pick to place when the dashed line appears.

Select **Project Name**. Use the **Add** button to move it into the Label Parameters list and then **OK**.

22.

Wrap between paramete...	☐
Vertical Align	Top
Horizontal Align	Center
Keep Readable	☑
Visible	☑

Select the label.

In the Properties pane:

Set the Horizontal Align to **Center**.

23.  Use Modify→Move to position the project name in the correct location.

24. Select the **Label** tool.

25. 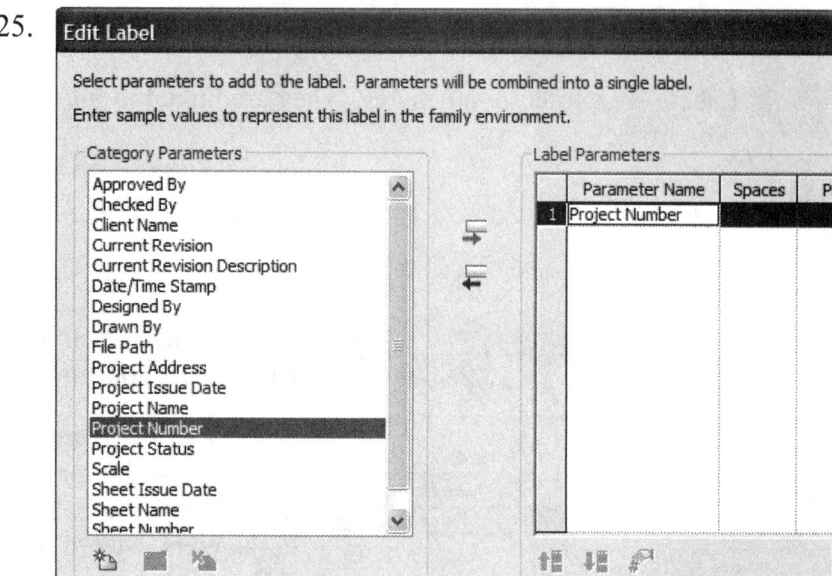 Locate **Project Number** in the Parameter list. Move it to the right pane.

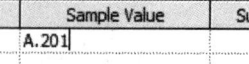

Add a sample value, if you like.

Press **OK**.

26. Select the **Label** tool.

27. Locate **Project Address** in the Parameter list.
Move it into the Label Parameters list.

28.

	Parameter Name	Spaces	Prefix	Sample Value
1	Project Address	1		123 Main Street Los Gatos, CA 59030

Press **OK**.

Enter a Sample Value for the address.

This will help you figure out the proper positioning.

29.

| Project Name |
| 123 Main Street |
| Los Gatos, CA |
| 95030 |

Position the **Address** Label.

30.

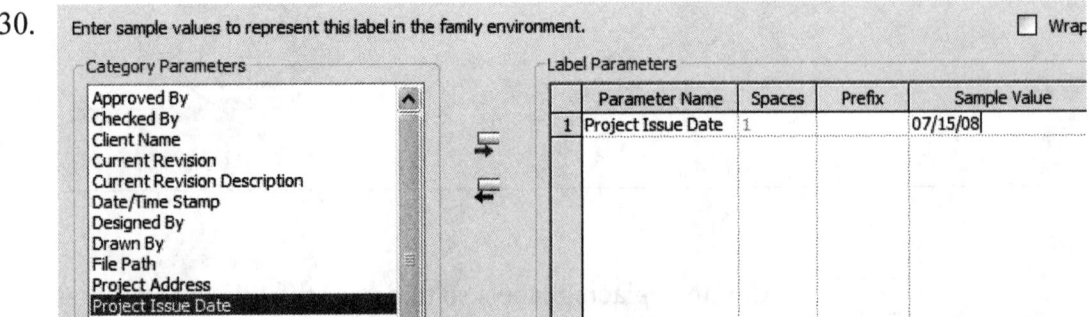

Highlight **Project Issue Date**.

In the Sample Value field, enter the default date to use.

Press **OK**.

31.

Scale	1/8" = 1'-0"
Project Number:	A.201
Project Address:	
	135 Main Street Los Gatos, CA 95033
Project Name:	
	Brown Residence
Date:	07/15/08
Sheet No:	

Position the date in the date field.

32.

Graphics	
Sample Text	Project Number
Label	Edit...
Wrap between paramete...	☐
Vertical Align	Top
Horizontal Align	Left
Keep Readable	☑
Visible	☑

To modify a label, select the label.

On the Properties panel:
Select the **Edit** button next to Label.

This will allow you to select a different parameter, if desired.

TIP: If you select the Add button, you can select Shared Parameters for use in your title block.

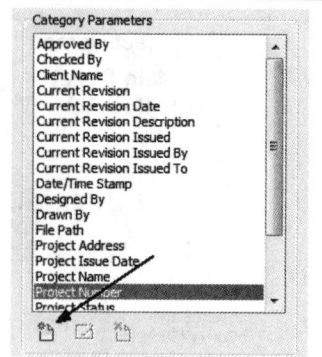

33.

Continue placing labels so that your title block appears as shown.

You do not need to add dimensions to your title block.

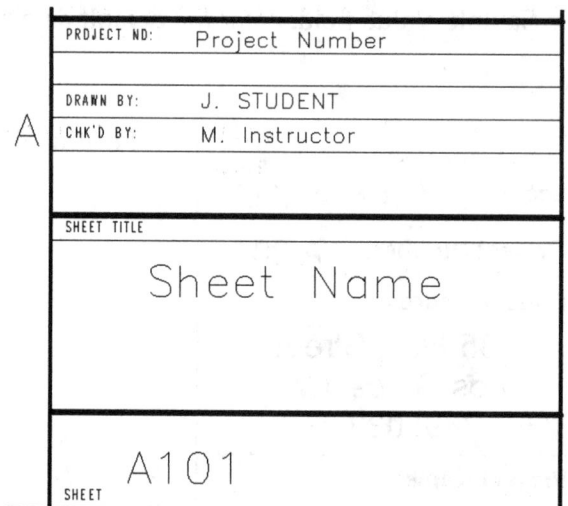

34. Open *ex9-1rvt*, if it is not already open.

35. Activate the View ribbon.

Select **Switch Windows** from the Windows panel.

36. 9 Title Block 22 x 34 - Sheet: -   Select the Title Block from the list.

37. Save the file as *Title block 22 x 34.rfa*.

38. Activate the View ribbon.

Select **Load into Project** on the Family Editor panel.

39. ☑ _ex9-1.rvt   Select *ex9-1.rvt* from the active drawing list.

Press **OK**.

TIP: It is a good idea to save all your custom templates, families, and annotations to a directory on the server where everyone in your team can access them.

40.
```
⊟ 🗐 Sheets (all)
  ⊞— A101 - First Level Floor Plan
  └── A102 - Door Schedule
  └── A103 - Glazing Schedule
  ⊞— A104 - Finish Schedule
  ⊞— A105 - Exterior Elevations
  ⊞— A106 - East Elevation
```
Activate the **First Level Floor Plan** sheet in the Project browser.

41. Select the titleblock.

42.
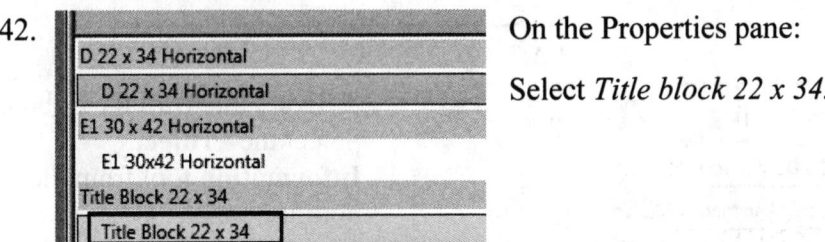
On the Properties pane:

Select *Title block 22 x 34*.

43. The title block is replaced, but you may need to reposition the view.

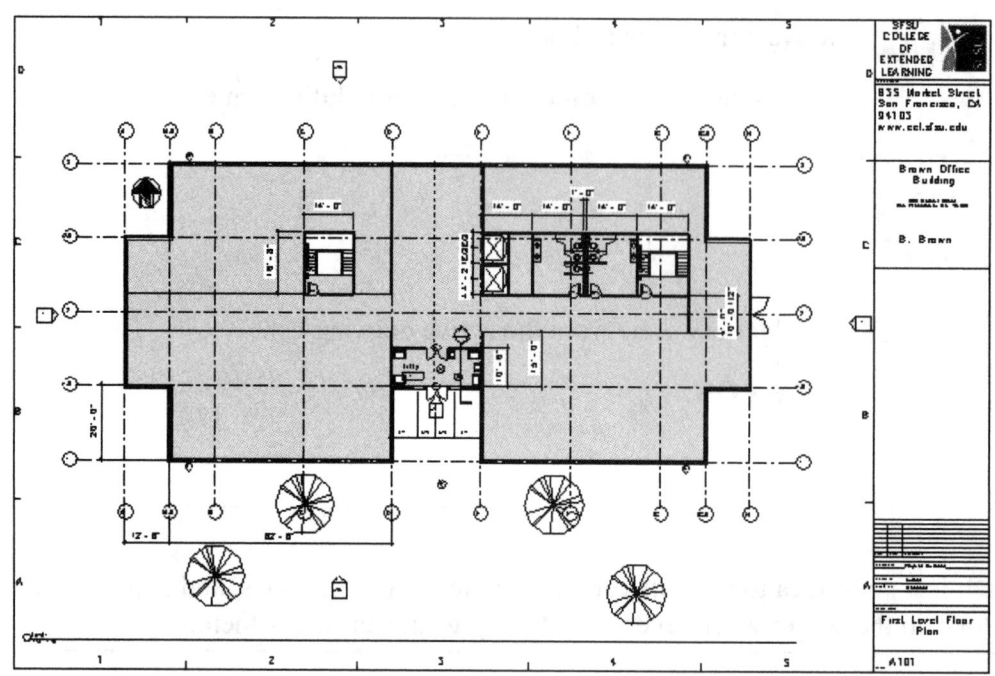

44.

Brown Office
Building

850 Market Street
San Francisco, CA 94105

B. Brown

The title block is replaced. Some of the labels updated, but some of the labels are missing information (Project Number and Author).

PROJECT NO:	Project Number
DRAWN BY:	Author
CHK'D BY:	Checker
SHEET TITLE	

A

45.

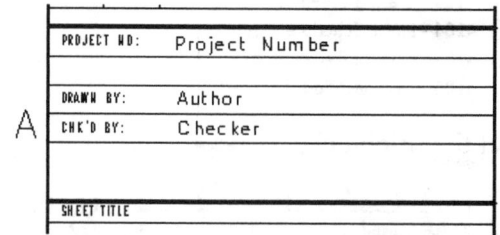

Activate the **Manage** ribbon. Select the **Project Information** tool from the Settings panel.

46.

Parameter	Value
Energy Analysis	
Energy Data	Edit...
Other	
Project Issue Date	04-09-2009
Project Status	Project Status
Client Name	B. Brown
Project Address	Edit...
Project Name	Brown Office Building
Project Number	A2001

Enter **A2001** in the Project Number field.

Press **OK**.

47.

Sheet Issue Date	07/18/10
Checked By	M. Instructor
Designed By	I. Architect
Approved By	Approver
Sheet Width	2' 10"
Sheet Height	1' 10"
Other	
Date/Time Stamp	07/18/10
File Path	
Drawn By	J. Student

With the title block selected, in the Properties pane:

Enter the instructor's name in the Checked By field and the student's name in the Drawn By field.

48.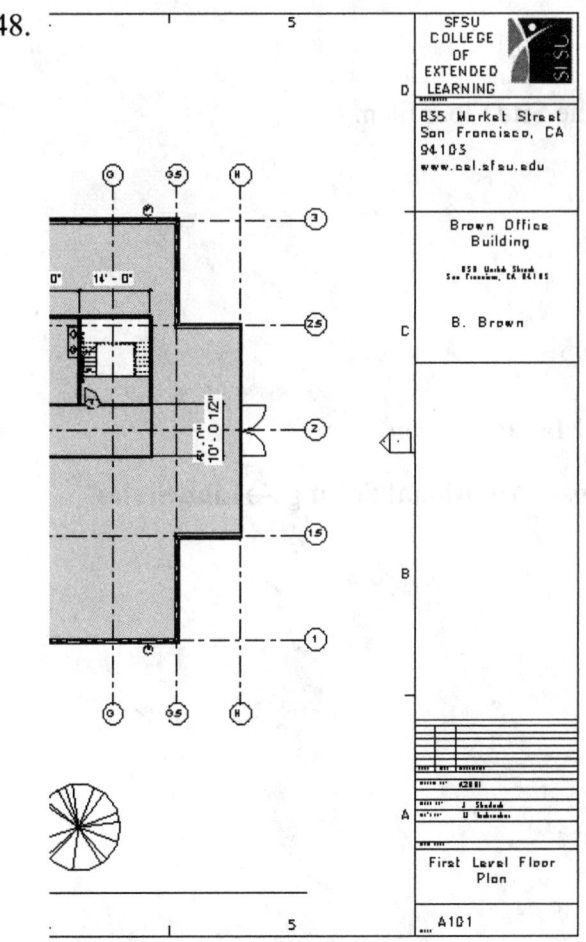

The title block looks good.

49. Save the file as *ex9-2.rvt*.

Exercise 9-3
Creating a Line Style

Drawing Name: 9-2.rvt
Estimated Time: 10 minutes

This exercise reinforces the following skills:

    ❑   Line Styles

1.   Open *ex9-2.rvt*.

2.   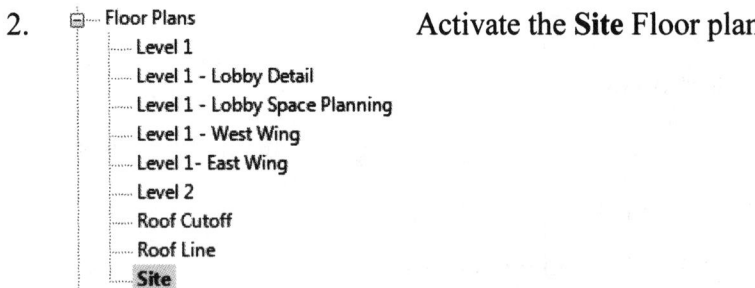   Activate the **Site** Floor plan.

3.   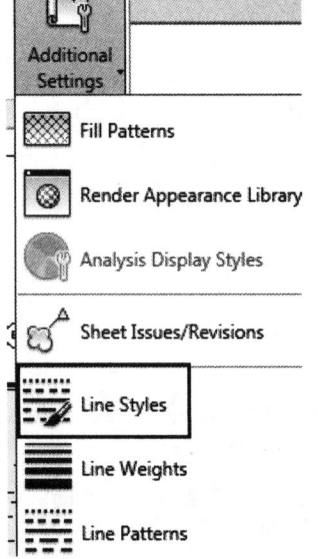   Activate the **Manage** ribbon.

Go to **Settings→Additional Settings→Line Styles**.

4.   Modify Subcategories   Select **New** under Modify Subcategories.
       New

5.   Name: Enter **Sewer** in the Name field.
    Sewer
       Press **OK**.
   Subcategory of:
   Lines

6.

Lines	1	▇ RGB 000-166-000	Solid	
Medium Lines	3	▇ Black	Solid	
Sewer	1	▇ Black	Solid	
Thin Lines	1	▇ Black	Solid	
Wide Lines	12	▇ Black	Solid	

Sewer appears in the list.
Note Revit automatically alphabetizes any new line styles.

7.

Insulation Batting Lines	1	▇ Black	Solid	
Lines	1	▇ RGB 000-166-000	Solid	
Medium Lines	3	▇ Black	Solid	
Sewer	3	▇ Blue	Dash dot dot	✔
Thin Lines	1	▇ Black	Solid	

Set the Line Weight to **3**.
Set the Color to **Blue**.
Set the Line Pattern to **Dash Dot Dot**.

Press **OK**.

8. [Annotate] Activate the **Annotate** ribbon.

9. Select the **Detail Line** tool under Detail.

10. 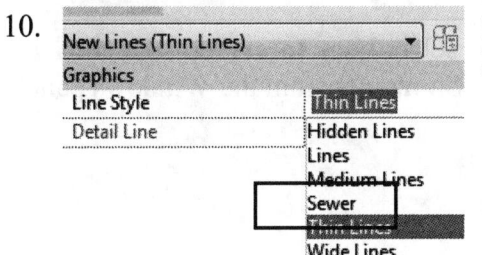 Select **sewer** from the drop-down list in the Properties pane.

11. 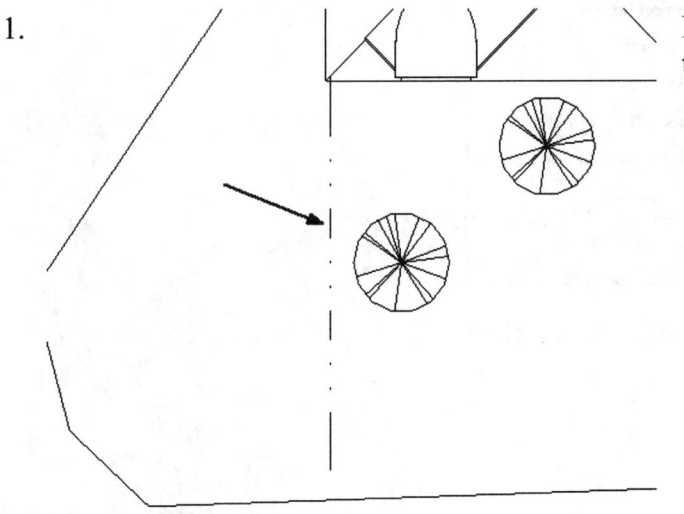 Draw a line from the building to the property line.

12. Save the file as *ex9-3.rvt*.

TIP: Revit has three line tools: *Lines*, *Detail Lines*, and *Linework*. All of them use the same line styles, but for different applications. The *Lines* command draws model lines on a specified plane and can be seen in multiple views (i.e., score joints on an exterior elevation). The *Detail Lines* command draws lines that are view specific and will only appear on the view they were placed (i.e., details). The *Linework* tool is used to change the appearance of model-generated lines in a view.

Exercise 9-4
Defining Keyboard Shortcuts

Estimated Time: 5 minutes
File:

This exercise reinforces the following skills:

❑   Keyboard Shortcuts

1.
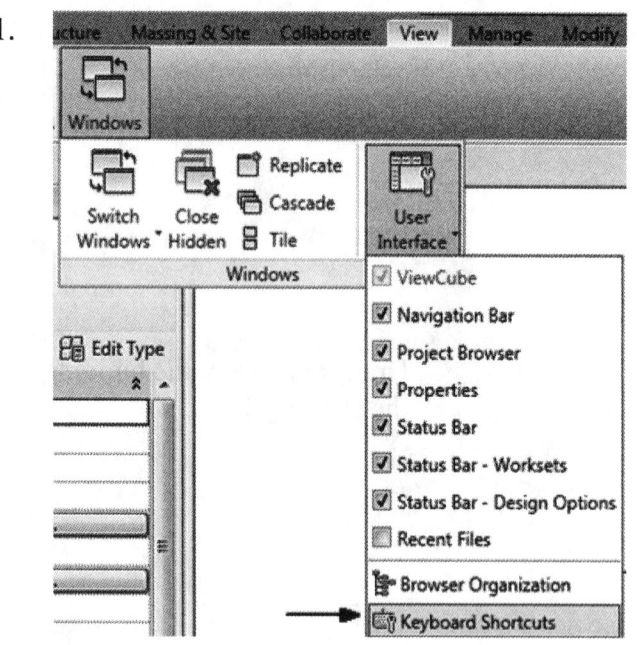

Activate the View ribbon.

Select **User Interface→Keyboard Shortcuts** from the Windows panel.

2.

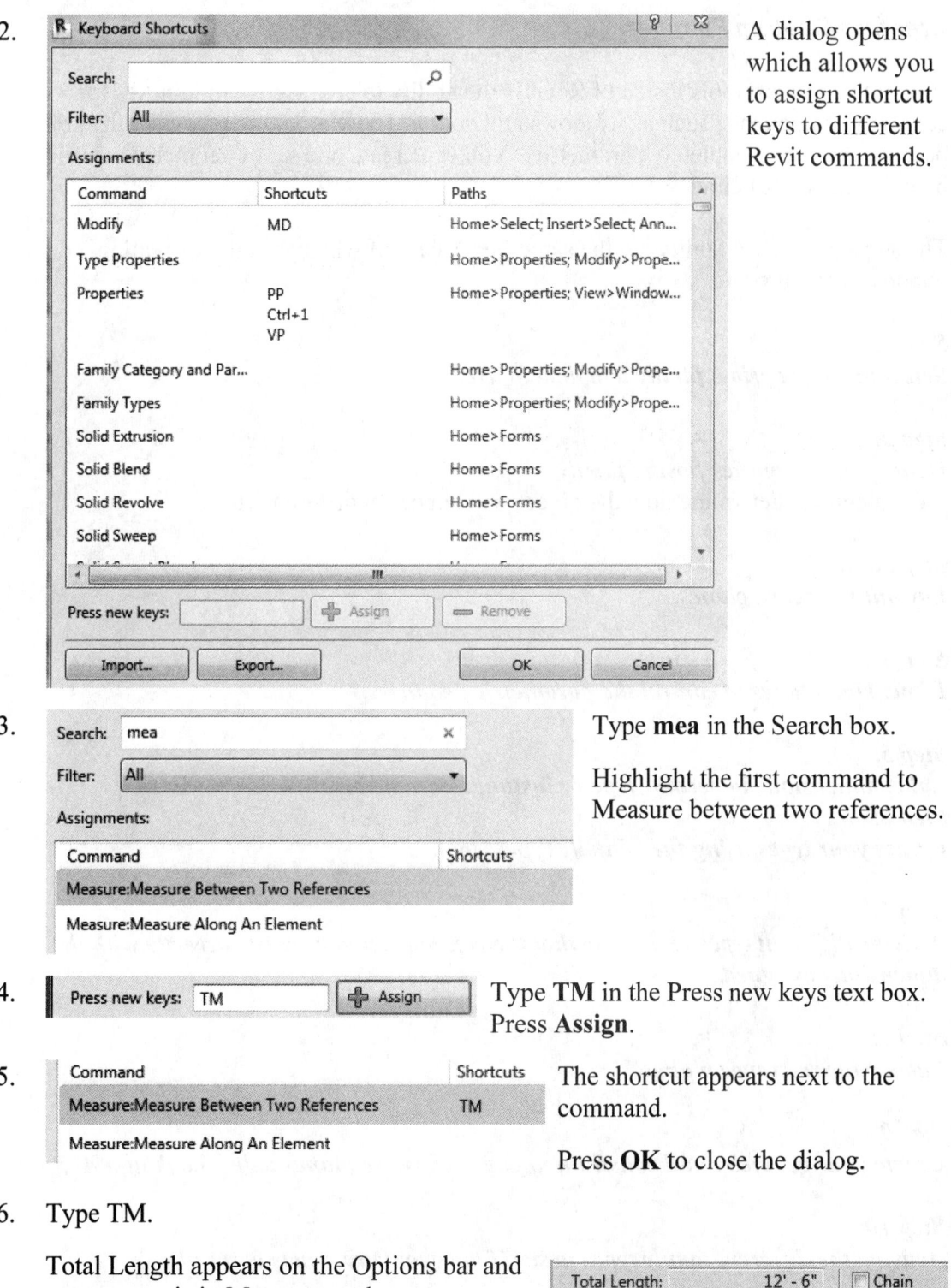

A dialog opens which allows you to assign shortcut keys to different Revit commands.

3. Type **mea** in the Search box.

Highlight the first command to Measure between two references.

4. Type **TM** in the Press new keys text box. Press **Assign**.

5. The shortcut appears next to the command.

Press **OK** to close the dialog.

6. Type TM.

Total Length appears on the Options bar and your cursor is in Measure mode.

Creating Custom Families

One of the greatest tools inside of Revit is the ability to create custom families for common components, such as windows and doors. These are more powerful than blocks because they are completely parametric. You can create one set of geometry controlled by different sets of dimensions.

The steps to create a family are the same, regardless of whether you are creating a door, window, furniture, etc.

Step 1:
Select the appropriate family template to use.

Step 2:
Define sub-categories for the family
Sub-categories determine how the object will appear in different views

Step 3:
Lay out reference planes.

Step 4:
Dimension planes to control the parametric geometry.

Step 5:
Label dimensions to become type or instance parameters.
Step 6:
Create your types using the 'FamilyTypes' tool.

Step 7:
Activate different types and verify that the reference planes shift correctly with the dimensions assigned.

Step 8:
Label your reference planes.

Step 9:
Create your geometry and constrain to your reference planes using Lock and Align.

Step 10:
Activate the different family types to see if the geometry reacts correctly.

Step 11:
Save family and load into a project to see how it performs within the project environment.

Exercise 9-5
Creating a Furniture Family

Estimated Time: 120 minutes
File: generic model.rft

This exercise reinforces the following skills:

- Standard Component Families
- Templates
- Reference Planes
- Align
- Dimensions

- Parameters
- Sketch Tools
- Solid extrusion
- Materials
- Types

1. 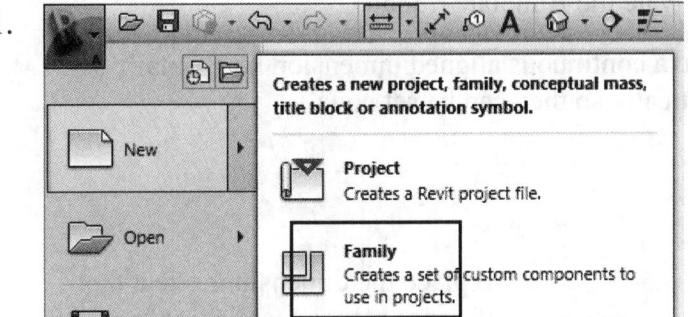 Start a **New** family.

2. 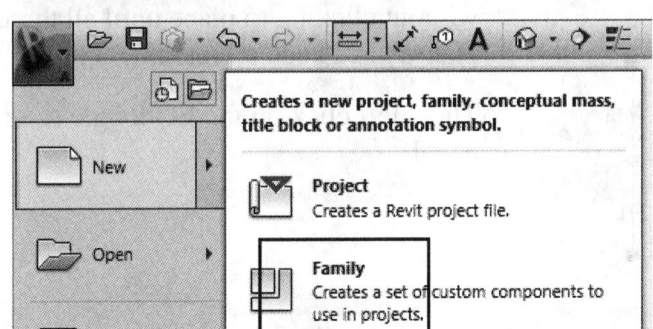 Start a **New** family.

3. File name: Generic Model.rft   Select the *Generic Model* template.

4. Select the **Reference Plane** tool from the Datum panel on the Home ribbon.

5.

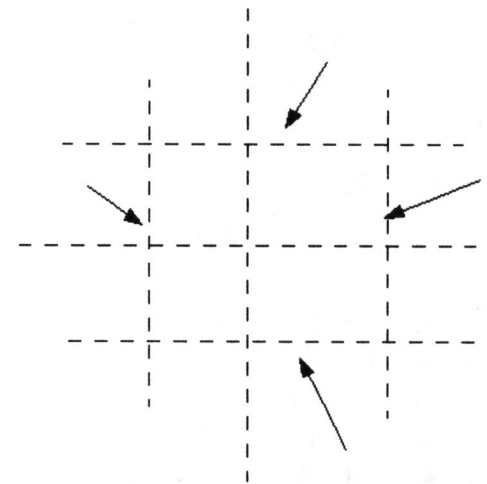

Draw four reference planes: two horizontal and two vertical on each side of the existing reference planes.

These will act as the outside edges of the table top.

6.

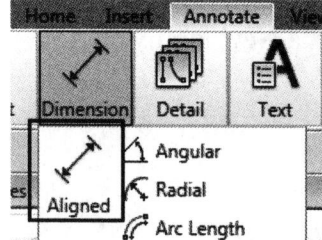

Activate the Annotate ribbon.

Add a continuous aligned dimension horizontally and vertically so they can be set equal.

7.

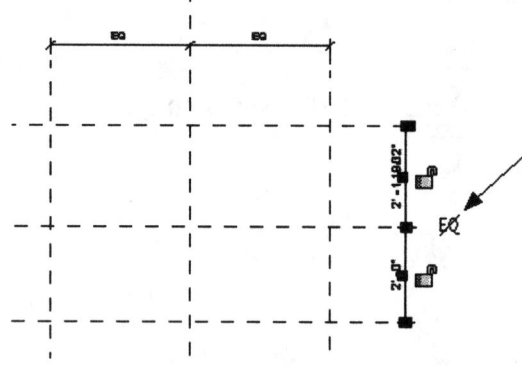

To place the dimension, select the reference planes by clicking in order without clicking to place until all three planes have been selected.

Then, left click on the EQ toggle to set equal.

8.

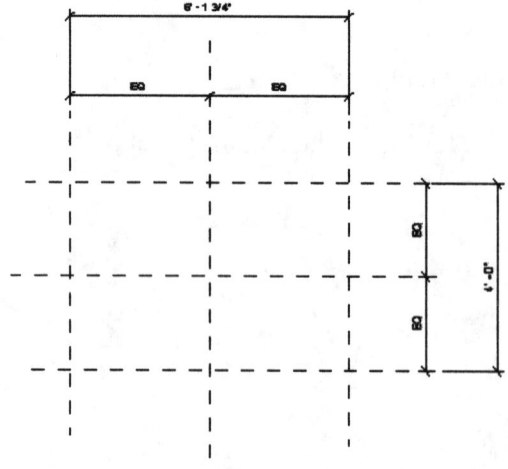

Place an overall horizontal dimension.

Place an overall vertical dimension.

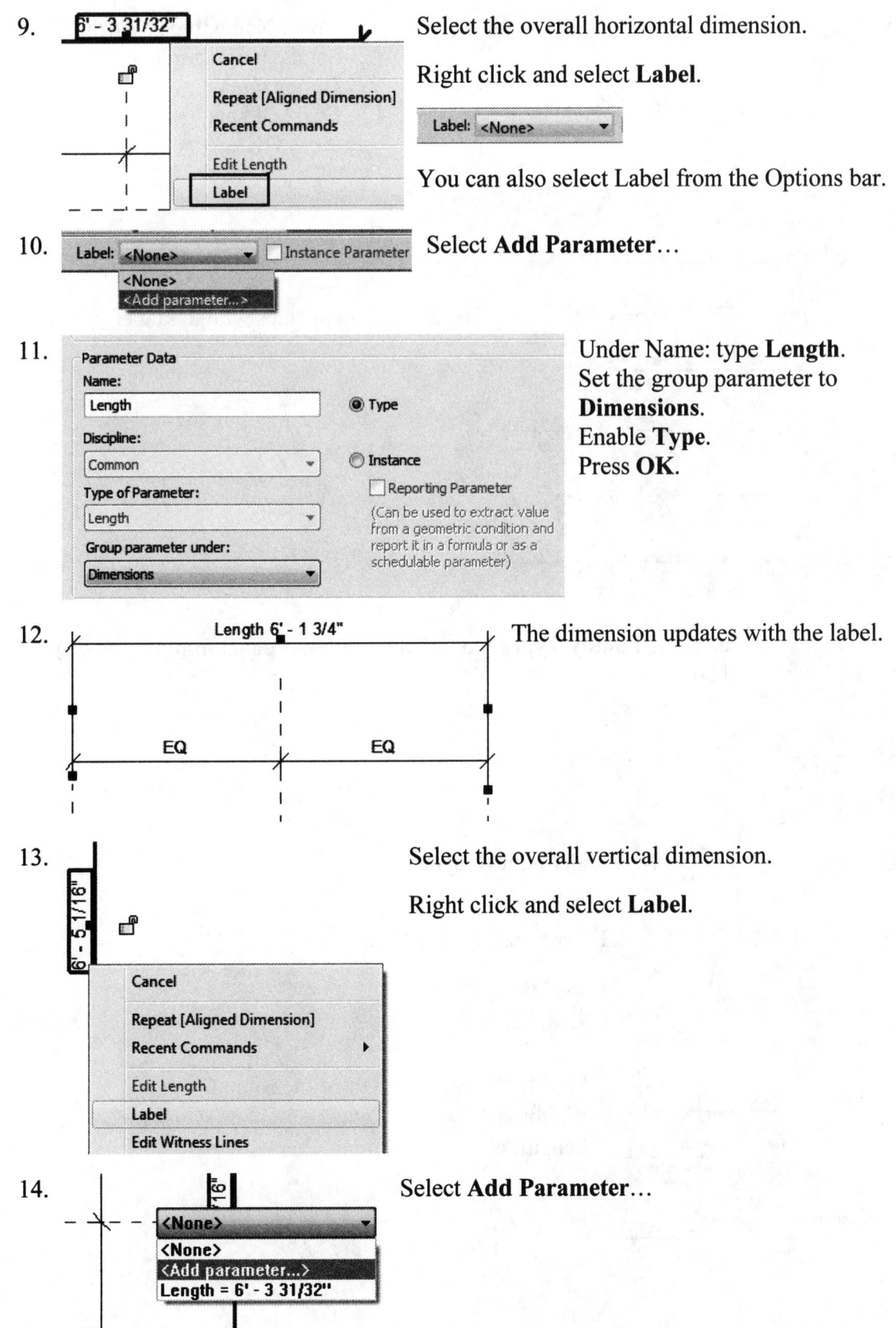

9. Select the overall horizontal dimension.

   Right click and select **Label**.

   You can also select Label from the Options bar.

10. Select **Add Parameter**...

11. Under Name: type **Length**.
    Set the group parameter to
    Dimensions.
    Enable **Type**.
    Press **OK**.

12. The dimension updates with the label.

13. Select the overall vertical dimension.

    Right click and select **Label**.

14. Select **Add Parameter**...

15.

Under Name: type **Width**.
Set the group parameter to **Dimensions**.
Enable **Type**.
Press **OK**.

Parameter Data

Name:

Width|

Discipline:

Common

Type of Parameter:

Length

Group parameter under:

Dimensions

◉ Type

○ Instance

☐ Reporting Parameter

(Can be used to extract value
from a geometric condition and
report it in a formula or as a
schedulable parameter)

16.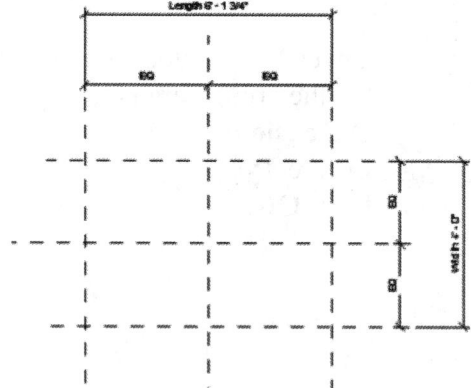

The dimension updates with the label.

17. Select the **Family Types** tool on the Properties panel from the Modify ribbon.

Properties Clip

Properties

18. Family Types

Select **New** under Family Types.

New...

19. Name

Enter **Small** for the Name.

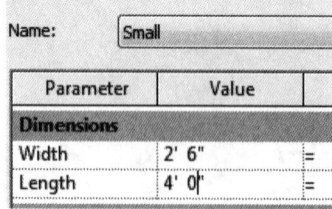

Name: Small

Press **OK**.

OK

20.

Name: Small

Parameter	Value	
Dimensions		
Width	2' 6"	=
Length	4' 0"	=

Modify the values for the dimensions:
Width: **2′6″**
Length: **4′0″**

21.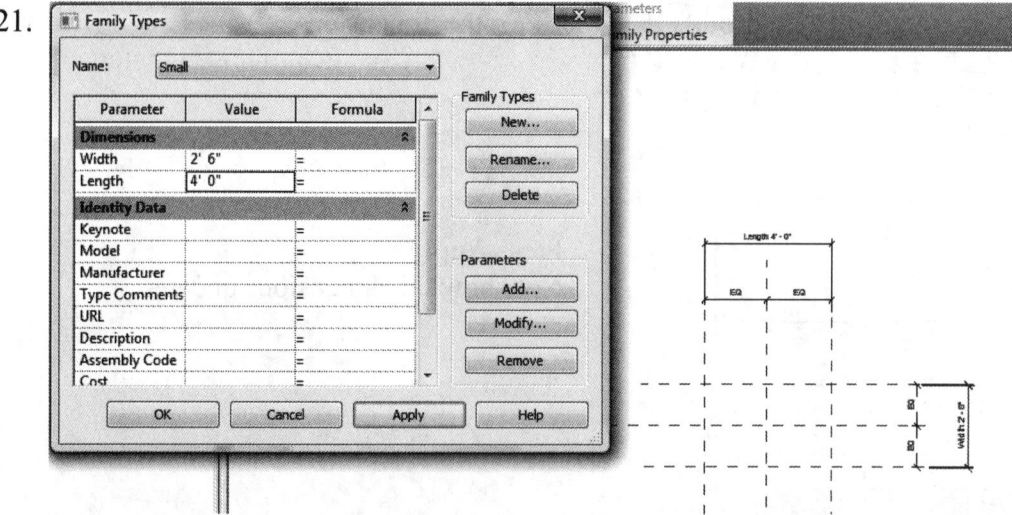

Move the dialog over so you can observe how the reference planes react.
Press **Apply**.
Note how the dimensions update.
This is called *flexing* the model.

22. Family Types
    New...
    Select **New** under Family Types.

23. Name
    Name: Medium
    Enter **Medium** for the Name.
    Press **OK**.

24. Name: Medium

Parameter	Value
Dimensions	
Width	3' 0"
Length	5' 0"

    Modify the values for the dimensions:
    Width: **3'0"**
    Length: **5'0"**

25.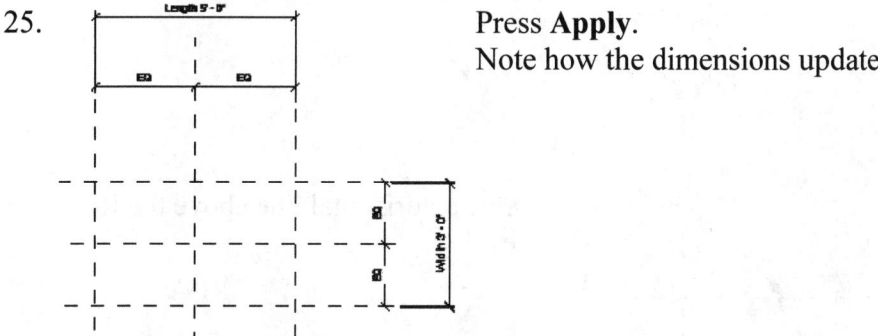

    Press **Apply**.
    Note how the dimensions update.

26. Family Types
    New...
    Select **New** under Family Types.

27. Name
    Name: Large
    Enter **Large** for the Name.
    Press **OK**.

28. 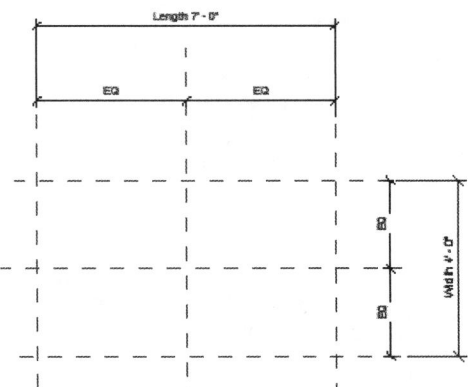 Modify the values for the dimensions:
Width: **4′ 0″**
Length: **7′ 0″**

29. Press **Apply**.
Note how the dimensions update.

30. Left click on the drop-down arrow on the Name bar.
Switch between the different family names and press Apply to see the dimensions change.

Press **OK**.

31. 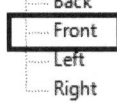 Activate the **Front** elevation.

32. 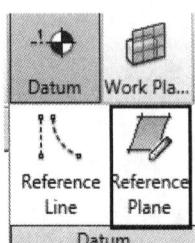 Select the **Reference Plane** tool on the Datum panel from the Home ribbon.

33. 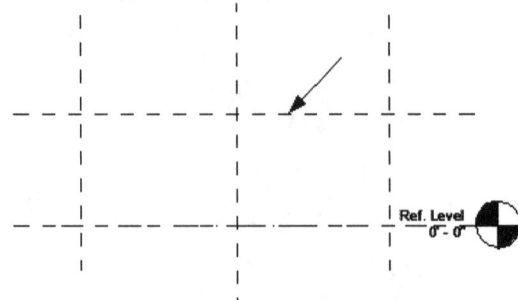 Draw a horizontal line above the Ref Level.

34.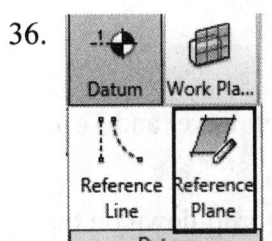

In the Properties pane:

Rename the reference plane **Table Top**.

35.

If you mouse over the reference plane, the name will appear.

Reference Planes : Reference Plane : Table Top

36.

Select the **Reference Plane** tool on the Datum panel from the Home ribbon.

37.

Draw a horizontal line below the TableTop Ref plane.

Ref. Level
0' - 0"

38.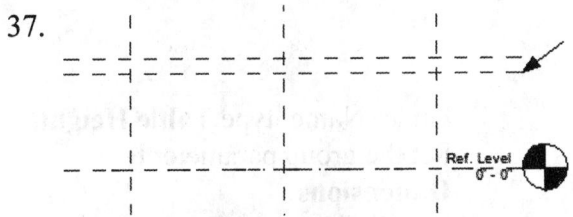

In the Properties pane:

Rename the reference plane **Table Thickness**.

39.

Activate the Annotate ribbon.

Add a continuous aligned dimension horizontally and vertically so they can be set equal.

Dimension   Detail   Text

Aligned   Angular
Radial
Arc Length

40.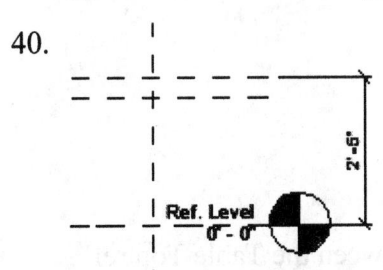

Place a dimension between the Ref. Level and Top ref. plane.

41. 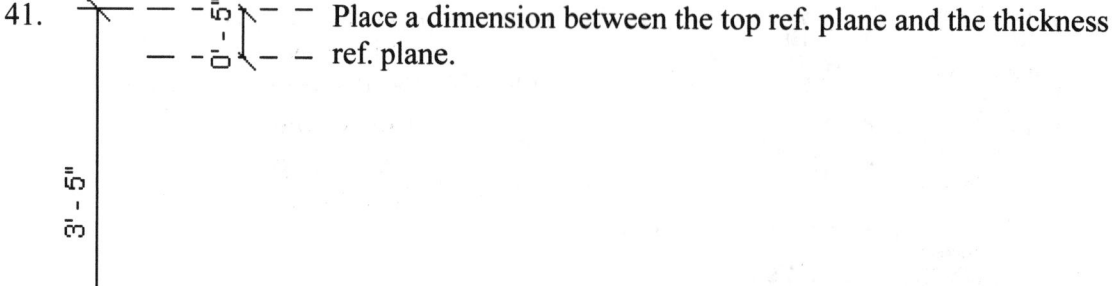 Place a dimension between the top ref. plane and the thickness ref. plane.

42. Select the table height dimension, the dimension between the Ref. Level and Top ref. plane.

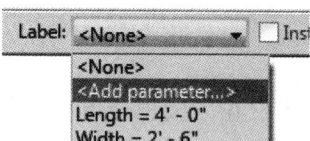 Select *Add Parameter* from the **Label** drop-down on the Option bar.

43. 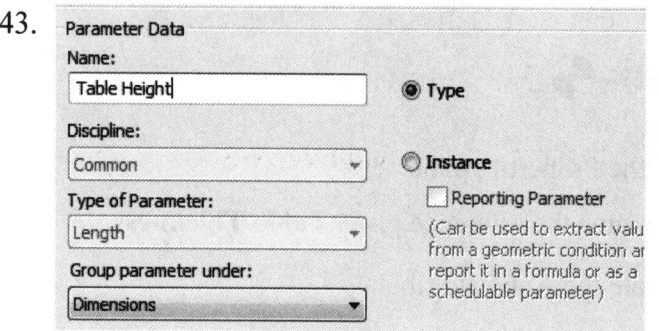 Under Name: type **Table Height**. Set the group parameter to **Dimensions**. Enable **Type**. Press **OK**.

44. 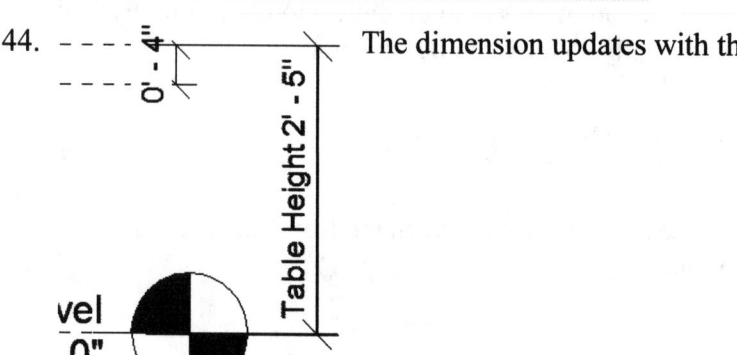 The dimension updates with the label.

45. Select the table thickness dimension, the dimension between the Table Top ref. plane and the ref. plane below it.

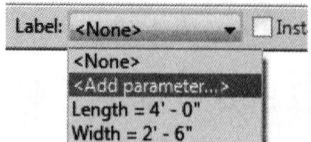 Select *Add Parameter* from the **Label** drop-down on the Option bar.

46. 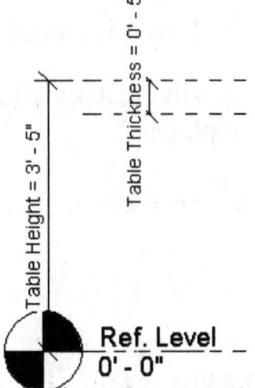 Under Name: type **Table Thickness**.
Set the group parameter to **Dimensions**.
Enable **Type**.
Press **OK**.

47. The dimension updates with the label.

48. Floor Plans
   Ref. Level   Activate the **Ref. Level** under Floor Plans.

49. 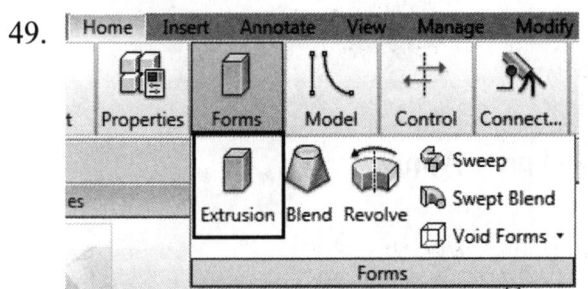 Select the **Solid→Extrusion** tool from the Home ribbon.

50. 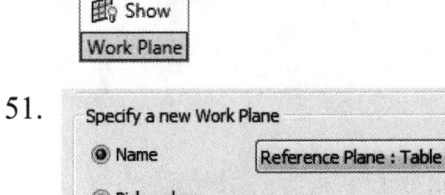 Select **Work Plane→Set**.

51. Enable **Name**.
Select the **Table Thickness** work plane from the drop-down list.
Press **OK**.

52. 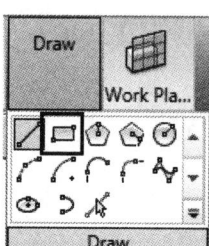 Select the **Rectangle** tool from the Draw panel.

53.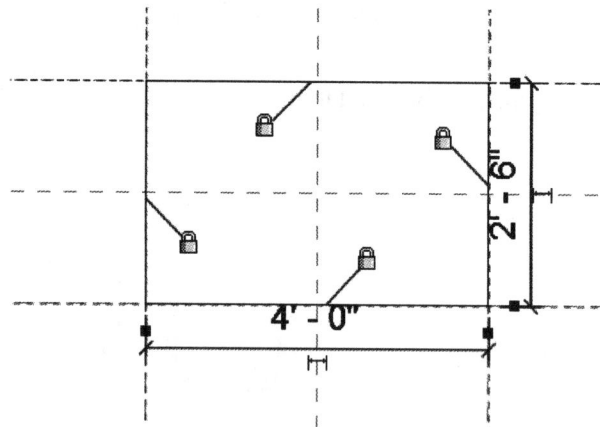

Place the rectangle so it is aligned to the outer reference planes.

Select each lock so it is closed.

This constrains the rectangle to the reference planes.

54.  Select the **Family Types** tool from the Properties pane.

55.  Select each type and press **Apply**.

Verify that the rectangle flexes properly with each size.
If it does not flex properly, check that the side has been locked to the correct reference line using the Align tool.

56.  Select **Properties** from the Properties pane.

57. In the Material field, select the Browse button indicated. For the Browse button to appear, you need to left click in the column where By Category is shown.

58.  Set the Material to **Glass**.

59. Enable **Use Render Appearance for Shading**.

Press **OK**.

60. 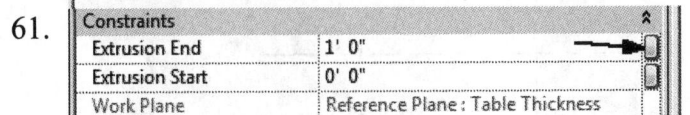 The Material now indicates Glass.

61. Click the button in the Extrusion End row.

62. Select **Table Thickness** from the parameters list.

Press **OK**.

63. 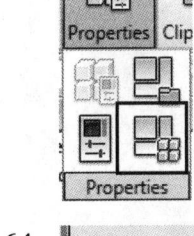 Select the **Family Types** tool from the Properties pane.

64. Table Thickness has now been added as a parameter to the Family Types.

Change the value of the Table Thickness to 2″ for each type.

Press **OK**.

65. 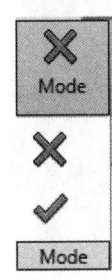 Select the **Green Check** under Mode to **Finish Extrusion**.

66. 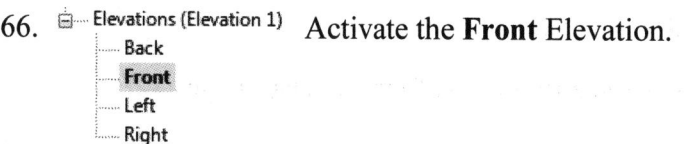 Activate the **Front** Elevation.

67. 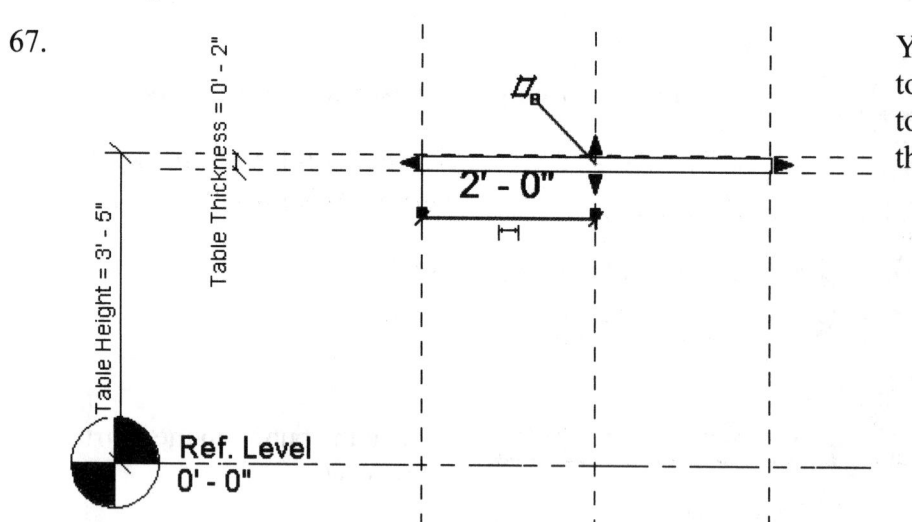 You see the table top which is equal to the table thickness.

68. Switch to a 3D view.

69. 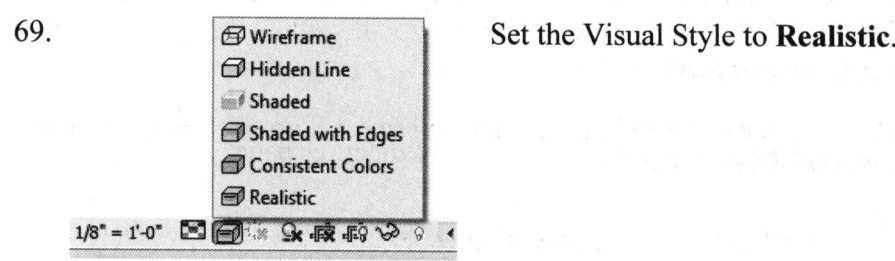 Set the Visual Style to **Realistic**.

70. Select the **Family Types** tool from the Properties pane.

71. 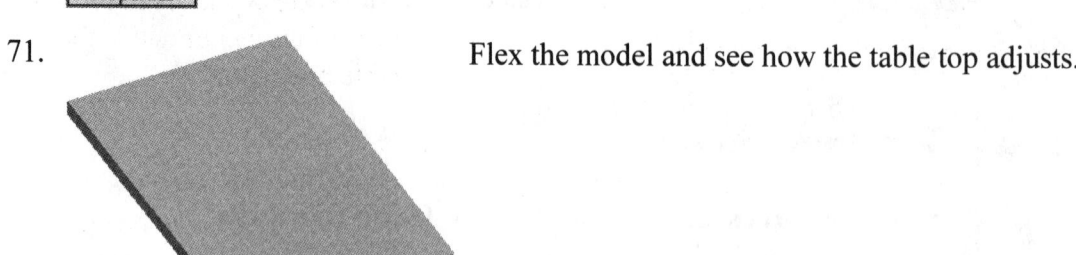 Flex the model and see how the table top adjusts.

72.  Activate the Ref. Level view.

73. 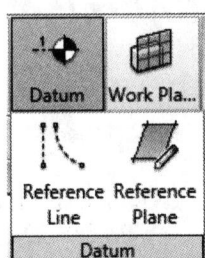 Activate the Home ribbon.

Select the **Reference Plane** tool from the Datum panel.

74. 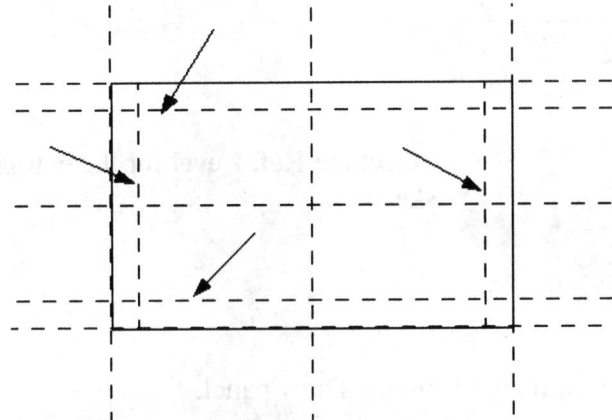 Place four reference planes 4″ offset inside the table.

75. 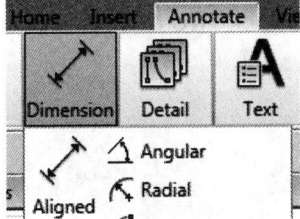 Name the reference planes LV1 and LV2 for the vertical planes and LH1 and LH2 for the horizontal planes. This is to make it easier for selection and identification.

To name the reference plane, select it, right click and select Element Properties and type in the name in the Name field.

76. Select the **Aligned Dimension** tool from the Annotate ribbon.

77. 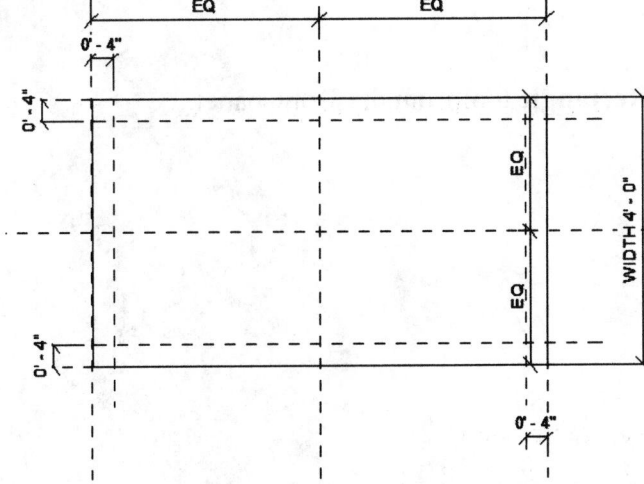 Add dimensions to constrain the reference planes to be offset four inches inside the table boundaries.

Make sure you place the dimensions between the reference planes and NOT between the table extrude edges and the reference planes.

Lock each dimension so it is constrained.

78. Select **Forms→Extrusion** from the Home ribbon.

79. Select the **Set Workplane** tool.

80. 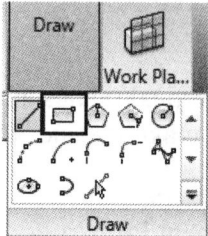 Select the **Ref. Level** for the extrusion sketch.

81. Select the **Rectangle** tool from the Draw panel.

82. 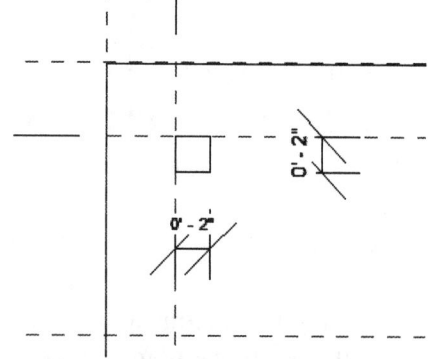 Draw a 2″ x 2″ square.

Use the **ALIGN** tool to lock two of the sides to the reference planes.

83. 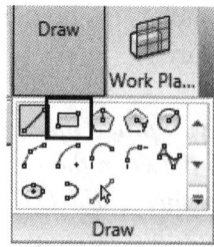 Select the **Rectangle** tool from the Draw panel.

84.

Place a second 2″ square.

Align the sides indicated by the arrows using the reference planes and the right side of the first square.

85. 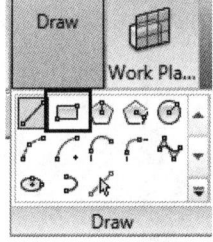 Select the **Rectangle** tool from the Draw panel.

86.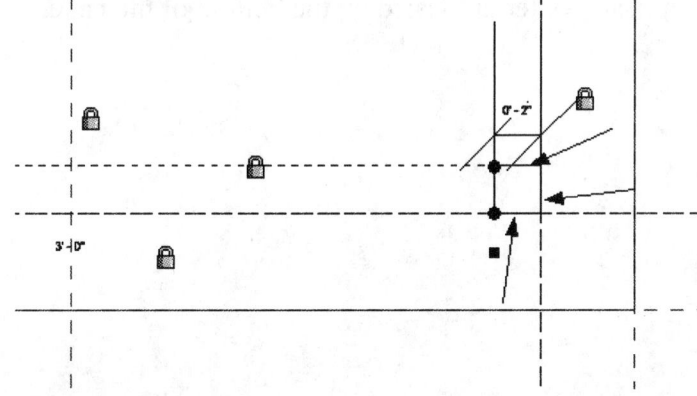

Draw a third 2-inch square.

As you draw, you should see alignment locks to place the square. Arrows indicate the sides to be aligned and locked.

Place one dimension to fully constrain the square.

87. 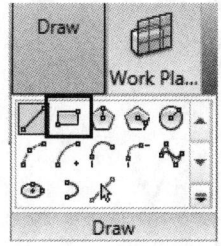 Select the **Rectangle** tool from the Draw panel.

88.

Place the fourth 2-inch square.

Again, you should see alignment locks to constrain the square's size and location.

You should be able to fully constrain the square without placing any dimensions.

89. Select **Properties** from the Properties panel.

90.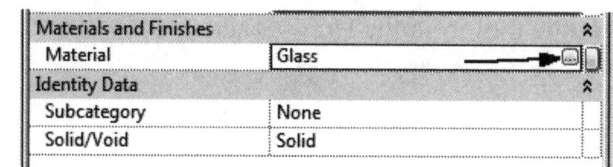

Browse for a material.

91.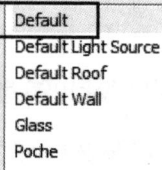

Highlight the Default material.

Select Duplicate Material located on the bottom of the pane.

92. Name the new material **Cherrywood**.

Press OK.

Duplicate Revit Material

Material Class: Miscellaneous
Name: Cherrywood

93. Enable **Use Render Appearance for Shading**.

Shading
☑ Use Render Appearance for Shading

94. Select the Render Appearance tab.
Select the **Replace** button.

Graphics | Render Appearance | Identity | Physical

Render Appearance Based On:
Generic   Replace...

Preview

Scene:
Default

95. Type **cherry** in the search box at the right top of the dialog.

Locate the Wood Solid **Cherry Stained Dark Medium Gloss Material**.

Press **OK**.

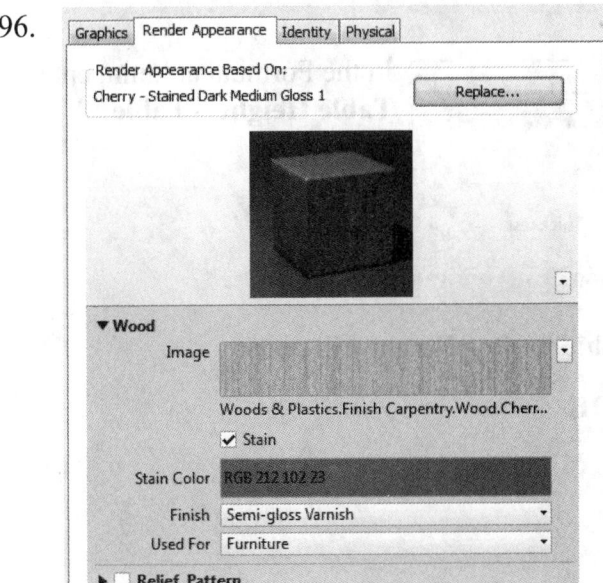

cherry   ✕
                        Sort ▾

Cherry   Cherry - Lig... Cherry - Lig... Cherry - Na... Cherry - Na...

Cherry - Na... Cherry - Sol... Cherry - Sol... Cherry - Sol... Cherry - Sta...

Cherry - Sta... Cherry - Sta... Cherry - Sta... Cherry 2

96. The dialog will update with the cherry wood material properties.

Press **OK**.

Graphics | Render Appearance | Identity | Physical

Render Appearance Based On:
Cherry - Stained Dark Medium Gloss 1   Replace...

▼ Wood
Image
Woods & Plastics.Finish Carpentry.Wood.Cherr...
☑ Stain
Stain Color RGB 212 102 23
Finish Semi-gloss Varnish
Used For Furniture
▶ ☐ **Relief Pattern**

97.

Materials and Finishes	
Material	Cherrywood
Identity Data	

The material is now listed as **Cherrywood**.

98.

Constraints		
Extrusion End	0' 5"	
Extrusion Start	0' 0"	

Select the button on the Extrusion End row.

99. [Add parameter...]   Select **Add parameter** at the bottom of the dialog.

100.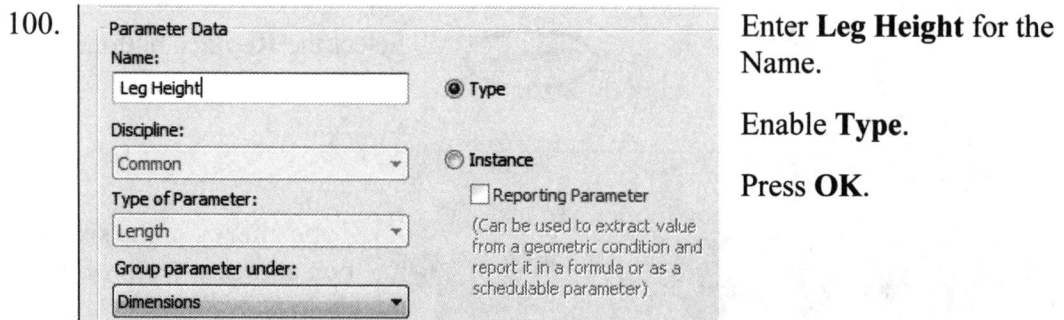

Enter **Leg Height** for the Name.

Enable **Type**.

Press **OK**.

101.

<none>
Leg Height
Length
Table Height
Table Thickness
Width

Highlight **Leg Height** in the parameter list.

Press **OK**.

102.

Properties | Clip

Properties

Select **Family Types** from Properties pane on the Home ribbon.

103.

Parameter	Value	Formula
Dimensions		
WIDTH	2' 6"	=
Table Thickness	0' 4"	=
Table Height	2' 6"	=
Leg Height	0' 0"	= Table Height - Table Thickness
LENGTH	4' 0"	=
Identity Data		

In the Formula column, enter **Table Height – Table Thickness**.

Press **Apply**.

104.

Table Height	2' 6"	=
Leg Height	2' 2"	= Tabl
LENGTH	4' 0"	=

The value for Leg Height will update.

Press **OK**.

105.  Select the **Green Check** on the Mode panel to finish the extrusion.

106.  Activate the **Front** Elevation view.

Elevations (Elevation 1
- Back
- **Front**
- Left
- Right

107. 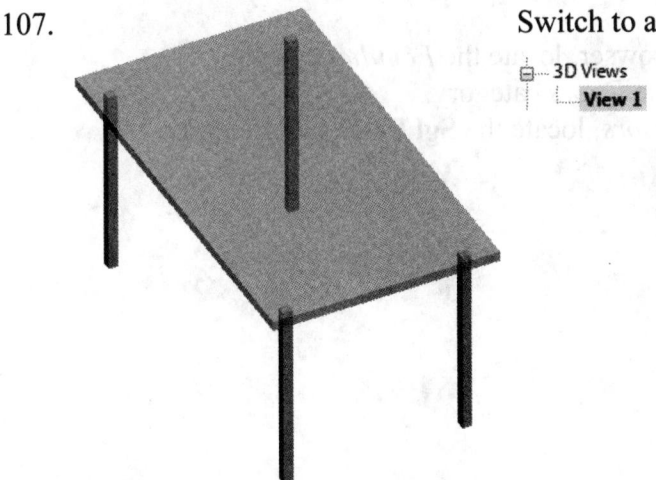 Switch to a 3D View.

3D Views
View 1

108. 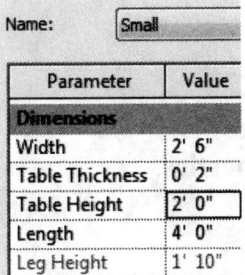 Select **Family Types** from Properties pane on the Home ribbon.

Flex the model to check if the legs adjust position properly.

109. Change the value for the Table Height and Table Thickness for each size to see what happens to the model.

Name:	Small
Parameter	Value
Dimensions	
Width	2' 6"
Table Thickness	0' 2"
Table Height	2' 0"
Length	4' 0"
Leg Height	1' 10"

Name:	Medium
Parameter	Value
Dimensions	
Width	3' 0"
Table Thickness	0' 2"
Table Height	3' 6"
Length	5' 0"
Leg Height	3' 4"

Name:	Large
Parameter	Value
Dimensions	
Width	4' 0"
Table Thickness	0' 2"
Table Height	4' 6"
Length	7' 0"
Leg Height	4' 4"

110. Save the family as *Table.rfa*.

111. Close the file.

Exercise 9-6
Modifying a Family

Estimated Time: 10 minutes
File: i_Office_2.rvt

This exercise reinforces the following skills:

- ❑ Standard Component Families
- ❑ Types

1. 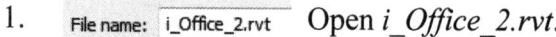 Open *i_Office_2.rvt*.

2. 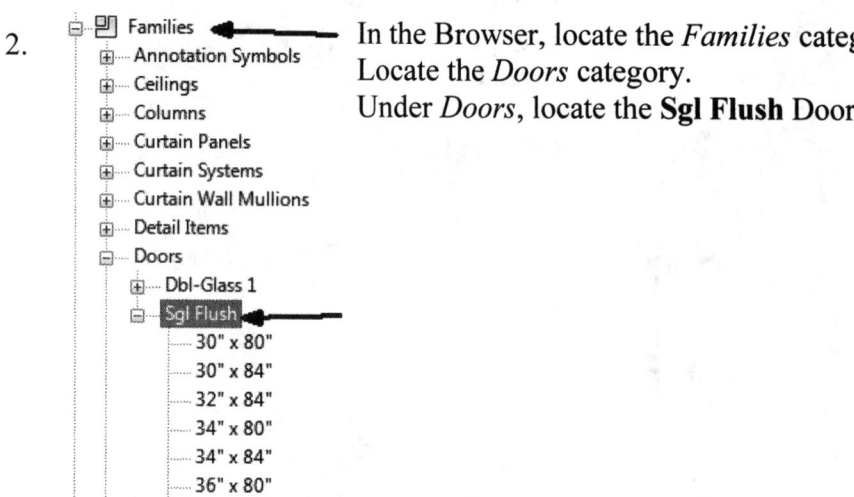 In the Browser, locate the *Families* category.
Locate the *Doors* category.
Under *Doors*, locate the **Sgl Flush** Door Family.

3. 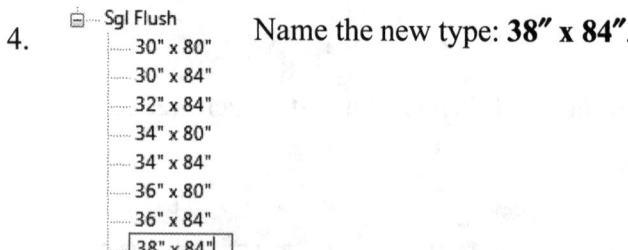 Right click and select **New Type**.

4. Name the new type: **38″ x 84″**.

5. Highlight the **38″ x 84″** door type.
Right click and select **Type Properties**.

6. Change the Width to **3′ 2″**.
Press **Apply** and **OK**.

Dimensions	
Height	7' 0"
Thickness	0' 2"
Width	3' 2"
Rough Width	
Rough Height	

7. 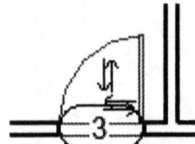 Select a door in the graphics window.

8. 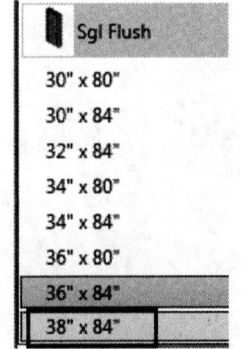 In the Properties pane:
Select **38″ x 84″** from the drop-down list.

Note that the door updates.

9. Close without saving.

Notes:

Revit Hot Keys

AL	Align		RP	Reference Plane
AR	Array		RR	Raytrace
CC	Copy		RT	Room Tag
CM	Component		RW	Reload Latest Worksets
CO	Copy		S	Split Walls and Lines
CS	Create Similar		SC	Snap to Center
DE	Delete		SD	Shading with Edges On
DI	Dimension		SE	Snap to Endpoint
DL	Detail Lines		SF	Split Face
DR	Door		SH	Snap to horizontal/vertical
EL	Spot Elevation		SI	Snap to Intersection
ER	Editing Requests		SL	Split Lines and Walls
F	Move		SM	Snap to Midpoint
G	Group		SN	Snap to Nearest
GP	Group		SO	Snaps OFF
GR	Grid		SP	Snap to Perpendicular
HC	Hide/Isolate Category		SQ	Snap to Quandrants
HH	Hide/Isolate Objects		SR	Snap to Remote Objects
HI	Hide/Isolate Objects		SS	Standard Snap Mode
HL	Hidden Line		ST	Snap to Tangent
HR	Reset Temporary Hide/Isolate		SW	Snap to Workplane Grid
IC	Isolate Category		SX	Snap to Points
LC	Lose Changes		TG	Tag
LI	Lines		TR	Trim/Extend
LL	Level		TX	Text
LO	Lock Objects		UN	Project Units
LW	Linework		UP	Unpin Position
MD	Modify		VH	Category Invisible
MM	Mirror		VI	View Invisible Categories
MV	Move		VG	Visibility/Graphics
OF	Offset		VP	View Properties
P	Properties		VV	Visibility/Graphics
PP	Pin Position		WA	Wall
PR	Properties		WC	Window Cascade
PT	Paint		WF	Wire Frame
R	Rotate		WN	Window
RE	Resize		WT	Window Tile
RO	Rotate		ZA	Zoom to Fit

ZC	Previous Zoom
ZE	Zoom to Fit
ZF	Zoom to Fit
ZN	Zoom Next
ZO	Zoom Out (2X)
ZP	Zoom Previous
ZR	Zoom in region (window)
ZS	Zoom to Sheet Size (limits)
ZV	Zoom Out (2X)
ZX	Zoom to fit
ZZ	Zoom in region (window)
Ctl-Y	Redo
Ctl-Z	Undo
F1	Revit Help
F5	Refresh Screen
F7	Spelling
F8	Dynamic View

About the Author

Elise Moss has worked for the past thirty years as a mechanical designer in Silicon Valley, primarily creating sheet metal designs. She has written articles for Autodesk's Toplines magazine, AUGI's PaperSpace, DigitalCAD.com and Tenlinks.com. She is President of Moss Designs, creating custom applications and designs for corporate clients. She has taught CAD classes at DeAnza College, Silicon Valley College, and for Autodesk resellers. She is currently teaching CAD at SFSU, in the College for Extended Learning campus and at Laney College in Oakland. Autodesk has named her as a Faculty of Distinction for the curriculum she has developed for Autodesk products. She holds a baccalaureate degree in Mechanical Engineering from San Jose State.

She is married with three sons. Her older son, Benjamin, is an electrical engineer. Her middle son, Daniel, works with AutoCAD Architecture in the construction industry. His designs have been featured in architectural journals. Her youngest son, Isaiah, is starting high school, but shows signs of being a budding engineer. Her husband, Ari, has a distinguished career in software development.

Elise is a third generation engineer. Her father, Robert Moss, was a metallurgical engineer in the aerospace industry. Her grandfather, Solomon Kupperman, was a civil engineer for the City of Chicago.

She can be contacted via email at elise_moss@mossdesigns.com.

More information about the author and her work can be found on her website at www.mossdesigns.com.

Other books by Elise Moss
AutoCAD Architecture 2011 Fundamentals
Autodesk Revit Architecture 2011 Basics

Notes:

Notes:

Notes:

Notes:

Notes:

Notes:

Notes: